SURVIVING
Paradise

The Perils and Pleasures
of the Caribbean

This is an auto-fiction novel. Many of the characters' names have been changed, and some of the details, to protect the not-so-innocent, and extremely private. While the characters may be real, and the locations accurate to the best of my memory, the novel genre has been chosen to permit storytelling in the best way possible.

Published by Novacom Press, Silver Spring, MD

Library of Congress Control Number: 2024905005

For more information and permissions, go to www.bryanmbyrd.com
Paperback ISBN: 979-8-9897987-1-1
Hardcover ISBN: 979-8-9897987-0-4
E-book 979-8-9897987-2-8

emtippettsbookdesigns.com

SURVIVING
Paradise

✳

THE PERILS AND PLEASURES
OF THE CARIBBEAN

BRYAN M. BYRD

In the world there is nothing more submissive and weak than water.
Yet for attacking that which is hard and strong,
nothing can surpass it.
—Lao-Tzu

NOVACOM PRESS

Acknowledgments

Writing a good book can be difficult, and it is a blessing that, among the doubters, there are angels willing to help make it happen. At different times during the long journey, they will both seem to be right. A very early advocate for this project was Ronald, an excellent tenant and a very wise man: "No one else could say it the way you will." In my own words, no one can describe the joy or the beating better than the one who received it. The downside of his confidence was, with a story so unique, I could take my own good time in writing it. That I did.

Without further delay, I must thank Brad Fisher and Carole Ford, who separately got together with me to do the winnowing of a manuscript three times the size of this version, though it covered more Caribbean territory, ergo more stories to come. Following that, Mary Lou Williamson has been the longest surviving helper, a relentless and reluctant editing (and life) partner whom I encouraged to think more about the readers than my feelings in order for her to persevere. Alas, there were times she took that encouragement too muchly, for which many will benefit. In keeping with his British heritage, competitive sailor Doug Newman was more delicate when questioning expressions of sailing, teaching me the Kings English in word choice, dotting the eyes, breaking ties, or letting me know how the writing might be perceived.

Tracy Williamson, and Rochelle Foster—a budding sailor herself—were outstanding among my beta readers, giving the manuscript a vigorous flogging, detailing where I could apply resuscitative love. Both ranked its potential as five stars.

The Olney Writers Group was steadfast in going through the manuscript five pages at a time over my membership of six years. Thorough if not fast, the group would give eight to twelve opinions on each segment, seldom unanimous, while teaching me how to write better. Members come and go, but I want to recognize Jerri, Linda, William, Liza, Andrew, Mark, Emily, Patrick, DJ, Bhavesh, Michele, Mitch, Amy, Kaitlyn, Bob and Sue, Bohdan, Francine, Maria, Caroline, and many others to whom I am grateful for your insistence it be published, and your contributions, each of your opinions likely to represent millions of readers like yourself. I recommend aspiring writers join a writers group and engage in the technical and emotional support, in friendship.

I interviewed many editors before selecting Stacy Carlson, with the request she reduce the number of words without changing the voice or tone. I thought her touch was excellent (lost a few good jokes, bon mots; c'est la vie). Note that many authors change their manuscript after the last edit, as I have, so she is not responsible for changes she did not see (e.g., this page). Kelly Byrd (no relation) did the proofreading; the same applies. Katie Dentino, a graphic designer and a whiz at what she does, created a cover better than I imagined. E.M. Tippetts' staff performed the interior design and formatting. I am grateful to all for their outstanding work.

To the many only temporarily, inadvertently unidentified, thank you for your wisdom, guidance and encouragement along the way. And I thank Captain Walt for the opportunity of a lifetime.

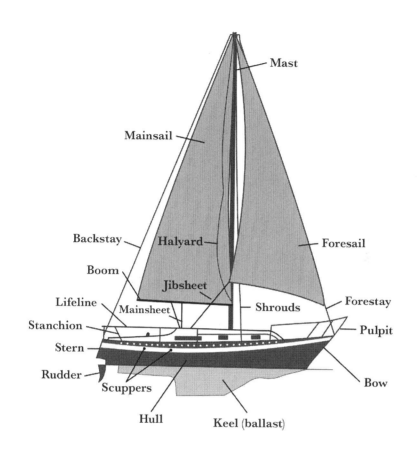

Mast

Mainsail

Backstay

Halyard

Foresail

Boom

Jibsheet

Lifeline

Mainsheet

Shrouds

Forestay

Stanchion

Pulpit

Stern

Rudder

Scuppers

Bow

Hull

Keel (ballast)

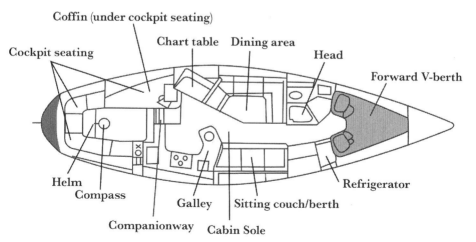

Coffin (under cockpit seating)

Chart table

Dining area

Head

Cockpit seating

Forward V-berth

Helm

Compass

Galley

Sitting couch/berth

Refrigerator

Companionway

Cabin Sole

Turks and Caicos Islands U.K.
Caicos
Provo
S.Caicos
Grand Turk
North Atlantic Ocean
Tortuga
Luperón
Puerto Plata
Santiago
Samaná
DOMINICAN REPUBLIC
Punta Cana
Santo Domingo
Mona Passage
Isla Mona
San Juan
Isla Palominos
Puerto Rico
Fajardo
Boquerón
Ponce
Salinas
Palmas del Mar
British Virgin Is. U.K.
Virgin Is. U.S.
St.Croix
Caribbean Sea
72
70
68
66
22
20
18
16
14

Contents

Dedication

To all the mentors—parents, siblings and volunteers, who help us on our
journey to live life to its fullest, by smoothing bumps in the road with your
love, guidance, and wisdom, leading by example, providing good books and a
vision we might otherwise never see—thank you.
Your expressions of love are priceless.

Blessed is the man
who uses knowledge and experience
to improve the well-being of others,
who guides with respect,
and encourages with love."
—Unknown

CHAPTER *One*

The End is Near:
Latitude: Don't cry for me!
Longitude: Aren't you Tina?

I didn't trust Rocco, but had no choice.

When I awoke that fateful morning in paradise, expecting to see the sunrise through the passageway, the sun was, unfortunately, rising over the bow, meaning the wind was not from the southwest, as forecast, but from the east, where we were headed. As a passenger whose role was like that of a spare tire, ferried around in case of emergencies, only deflated, I knew nothing about sailing other than you cannot sail upwind.

Captain Walt had to convince me to join the voyage. I didn't expect to be sailing alone with Rocco—he hated humanity, or maybe just me, and he rarely spoke. A little eye contact would have helped. He was first mate until Captain Walt left suddenly two days ago from Great Exuma, the nearest airport, and Rocco became my captain.

We were anchored in the Bahamas off unknown Rum Cay, headed east to Mayaguana. Rocco had waited one more day for the weather window he didn't get. Knowing he had been eager to sail on, I hurried to the cockpit, anxious to know what he was thinking.

"Rocco, looks like we didn't get the wind shift we were promised. Where's it coming from?"

"East-northeast."

"Damn! It didn't move at all last night! Where's Mayaguana?"

"East-southeast."

"Uhh . . . that's almost head-on into the wind. We can't sail that course, Rocco. We'll have to wait another day . . . right?"

"Nope. We're leaving. Make things tight and get that anchor up."

"What?" I stood in the cockpit, stunned and perplexed, and looked toward Rum Cay, not sure of my next move. The island was almost deserted, having fewer people than when Columbus went ashore, and no place to stay if I abandoned ship. We'd seen no other boats since Great Exuma. Did we pass a natural frontier, where others knew not to go? I was concerned. We were in a 34-foot boat during the hurricane season, the wind in our face, heading into the Bermuda Triangle, a million square miles of unforgiving water that swallows boats as large as freighters in one sudden gulp.

Between Rocco and the Bermuda Triangle, I feared Rocco more. He was choosing to ignore the unfavorable conditions and set sail. What could I do other than stay with the boat? Whether I was brave, cowardly, or loyal didn't matter. My choices were nil.

I weighed the anchor and we were moving by 0950. Our 25- to 30-hour passage to Mayaguana became rough before lunch, when battering winds had the boat perilously heeled over. Going below for food was dangerous, requiring me to walk on the boat furniture and cabin sides while they bounced up and down; the cabin floor was almost vertical, no longer a viable walkway. It was the closest thing to space travel imaginable other than the gravity of the situation.

Outside, we used the autohelm as much as possible until after dark, when the bucking of the bow became upright and repetitive, like a trained dolphin doing non-stop tail-walking. As a result, the autohelm's gyrocompass was constantly pointing at the sky, unable to find the North Pole, an earthly feature and a requirement for following a relative course. The autohelm motor made high-pitched whining noises as it drove the belt that controlled the rudder, rapidly alternating from one direction to the other, trying to find the preset course. Only taking manual control of the helm stopped our zigzagging.

Sailing in the dark was hell, with a lot more water and no light but the stars. We could see as far as the next wave, maybe 25 feet from trough to peak, coming at us obliquely, tossing us around like tennis shoes in a clothes dryer. While the boat would usually rise on the next wave, if one of those waves broke on top of us, we'd likely not survive.

Fearing our fate was all but sealed, my thoughts drifted off to our relatives, who would wonder for years what happened. I hoped we would be able to tell our families we survived a night of hell in the Devil's Triangle, and imagine their surprise, since their concept of paradise was probably like mine—sunshine 24/7. Nowhere in the Bahamian marketing brochures was any of this mayhem revealed. Is this why we'd not seen another boat for several days? What did we not know?

"Take down the damn jib!" Rocco barked, snapping me out of my tragic reverie.

We were making no headway while getting the stuffing kicked out of us. Our best indicated speed toward our destination, 144 miles away, was an arduous two knots (2.3 mph), often less. Water could be passing under us at that pace and our speed over ground could be zero or worse (like a slow southbound boat in the 4–5 mph northbound Gulf Stream). We could be here this time tomorrow, or back at Rum Cay. At least we weren't going off-course or in circles, because the wind was always on our nose, unless we were counter-spinning a huge waterspout, not irrational from my viewpoint.

I frequently checked the GPS receiver, which was mounted on the inside wall of the bulkhead in a dark corner. I could read it from the cockpit by craning my neck, but I was reading it upside down, which didn't help my nausea. Throughout the night, the receiver continued to herald the bad news: *No Position Found.* The compass spun as the bow heaved up and down, requiring we guess whether we were headed in the right direction. To me, turning around would set us in the right direction, but in those waves, it could be deadly.

Rocco yelled again; "Get that damn jib down and tied to the damn rail before we lose it!"

I stuffed two red sail ties in my pocket, two in my mouth, stepped outside the cockpit while holding on to the lifelines and the grab rail on the cabin top, and crept forward. Gripping the shroud, I stepped up on the cabin top, released the forestay halyard from its cleat, and let it run free. Stepping back on the deck, I crouched and resumed moving toward the heaving bow, turning aside in a futile effort to shield myself from the drenching salt spray of every wave. I knelt on the deck and pulled the sail down, leaving it attached to the forestay while gathering and bundling the sail in my arms, then spit out a sail tie to wrap around the sail and lash it to the toe rail.

BOOM! . . . A monstrous wave broke head-on over the bow while standing the boat on its stern, knocking me flat from my crouched position, my legs swept out from under me, sliding on the wave, my arms wrapped around the sail slipping through my grasp, falling feet first down the near-vertical deck, hitting several stanchions. The lifelines and toe rail restrained my fall as I held tight to the sail.

Downed but not out, I quickly got to my knees, crawled back to the bow to finish tying down the sail through still more punishing waves, then groped my way back to the cockpit.

Good God, that was close! That can't be the only wave out there with that kind of power. We are so screwed.

Soaking wet and shaking from chills, approaching shock, I huddled against the bulkhead and reflected on my near-death event. If I hadn't pulled the sail down when I did, we might be bottoms up. And had I not been on my knees hugging the sail, I might have fallen headfirst and been seriously injured. Had I gone overboard, Rocco would have never found me; not in the dark, or in those waves. With him being hard of hearing and the diesel engine running, there was no chance he'd hear my screams if I didn't drown instantly. He was fully occupied holding on to the backstay, like riding a rodeo bull, trying to stay aboard with one hand while struggling at the helm with the other. Every wave had to be answered with a course correction, a constant physical challenge to stay on track or lose control. He was countering forces similar to what we, as teenagers, used to call "fishtailing" when the rear wheels of the car lost traction while drag racing on the street. But Rocco couldn't stop, and there'd be no leaving the helm to look for me.

Thoughts of what could have happened made me feel queasy, not to mention stupid, then lucky. Queasy stayed the night. The rest of my mental dwarfisms, other than Dopey for wearing no safety equipment, were no-shows. There was still time to freak out; it was not over. I'd cheated death several times, was still alive, and had no choice but to shake it off and keep going.

Rocco may have done a little ocean sailing in and around his home state of Maine, but probably in good weather and not overnight. I doubt anything compared to this. If he would speak, he'd say he was as scared as I was, possibly more so, sailing another man's boat, angry he had the responsibility and couldn't quit or put it on me. He should have been angry about his decision to set sail. I was.

The movement of the boat made it impossible to sleep. Every time a wave struck, the boat shuddered and creaked like it was breaking apart. I frequently looked below to see if the cabin was filling with water. The constant pounding had cans rolling in the lockers, banging when they stopped, reversing course on every wave. The baskets on the bookrack had emptied their fruits and vegetables onto the cabin sole, and the bookrack was coming loose. I didn't want to be under it when it fell, so I stayed in the cockpit as Poseidon ruled the night.

After being beaten up in 15- to 25-foot seas for twelve hours, only the break of dawn, hours away, offered us hope. The Triangle was living up to its reputation of equipment failures, Godforsaken wind, and unruly water, while I imagined sea monsters appearing at any minute. Whatever it could throw at us, it seemed we got—on the bow or over the side. Only the mermaids were a no-show.

At 0700, we saw the light on the NW point of Mayaguana through the fog, a welcome first sighting of land since leaving Rum Cay on our longest and roughest passage. Around 0930, still miles out, we were nearing Betsy Bay on the west coast, where Sun Seeker, who monitors Channel 16, advised us to anchor. But Rocco was set on Abraham Bay, so we headed southeast, then east, at a point when I would have taken any port in a storm for the mental harbor. I got neither.

"Take down the mainsail," Rocco barked.

On the southwest side of the island, we turned directly into the wind toward a shallower sea of evenly spaced rollers, like corduroy on Earth's surface, causing the boat to pitch up and down on short frequencies. I carefully picked my time for each advance, cautiously stepping out of the cockpit and up to the mast base. Holding tightly to the mast, I quickly dropped the sail, tied it to the boom, secured the halyard, and returned to the cockpit.

A tortured hour or two later, Rocco barked again. "Get that damn jib in the bag so we can anchor!"

I stared at him and shook my head.

"WHAT?" he roared.

He could read my lips: "No. Way. In. Hell. IF YOU WANT IT BAGGED, YOU DO IT!" *You jerk!*

The diesel engine was running; I had to shout to be heard, though we were just a few feet apart. I knew what space was needed to anchor and had secured the sail to the lifelines and rail; it was adequate. I made no move toward the bow. I'd almost died there last night, and I wasn't about to return prior to us stopping. Or the stern catching fire.

"If you won't bag the fucking sail, then steer the goddamn boat while I do it," Rocco yelled, as he headed toward the foredeck.

Fine with me. It was my turn anyway. For one or more reasons, I wasn't asked to steer all night. I slid and pulled my way toward the wheel, steadied it, stood up, and took the helm, wondering how he would get along handling the sail, having only one good hand.

We continued to pitch up and down like a bucking bronco. It was a sickening, wet, slow trip to the bow of crouching and balancing, suffering the percussive waves and drenching salt spray. Was this the time to get the sail out of the way and into a bag? Not by me! He'd have to kick my ass before I would go forward anytime soon! Or set the stern on fire.

He returned from the bow without bagging the jib, scowling and growling. "Why the hell didn't you say it wasn't in the way of the anchor?"

"You didn't ask! And you wouldn't have believed me if I had," I yelled back. I wasn't in any shape to stuff a sail in a sack just to look good approaching a deserted island. We could have dead bodies hanging from the spreaders and no one would notice. Or they'd understand: *Bit of a rough crossing ye had, eh mate? Drying out the crew, are ye?*

That exchange constituted my first mutiny: Disobedience of the captain's orders. How dare I? The old British Navy used to flog impudent sailors for such contumacy, often until they died. The sail could wait and, ultimately, Rocco agreed. What was he going to do? Flog me? Throw me overboard? Not likely. Though my options were limited, I possessed many of the requirements for making this trip; I just needed to capitalize on my strengths.

We approached the entrance to Abraham Bay around 1400 after four and a half grueling hours of riding that bronco, physically demanding whether steering or sitting. Once inside the bay, the winds diminished, the water flattened, and the constant onslaught of saltwater stopped.

A twenty-eight hour crossing, the last twenty hours without food, water, or bathroom breaks, and we were now looking for a calm area to throw down an anchor and collapse. Victory was in sight and should afford time to reconsider how I got here and whether to continue. Dropping and setting the anchor wouldn't be a problem. Or would it?

CHAPTER *Two*

The Beginning:
Dear Sailor, Adventurer, Gambler, Loser

On a near-picture-perfect afternoon in the summer of '93, while driving across the Severn River Bridge in Annapolis, Maryland, I found myself enjoying the view of the river. To the west, it glistened blindingly in the sunlight, like a field of diamonds. To the east, boats danced around the Naval Academy regattas and the V-shaped wakes of motorized crafts. The large, white sails imposed against the water and the deep-blue sky evoked colorful memories of happy times on the Severn and nearby Chesapeake Bay.

Later that day, I impulsively called Walt, a sailor friend who lived in Annapolis, thinking if I was unemployed, he surely would be also. We hadn't spoken for thirteen years since working together at the telephone company.

Walt answered my call on the veritable eve of his planning a major sailing adventure to the Caribbean. Incredulous, he asked several times, "Whatever prompted you to call?"

I explained the memories stimulated while crossing the Severn. Walt, who must have looked everywhere for crew, was amazed he missed a logical prospect, since my first time spending more than one day on the water was with him in the spring of 1972, when his father, a boat captain, asked us to help deliver a 42-foot cabin cruiser from West Palm Beach, Florida, to Annapolis, Maryland. Afterward, Walt loved to tease me about how I searched, without any light, on coastal islands so dark I had to scuff my shoes to know if I was still on the road or at an intersection, trying to find elusive convenience stores with film for my hyperactive camera. Walt never understood the need for so much film, or how I found my way. I felt every odyssey had to be remembered and shared via pictures, and was willing to risk crossing paths with snakes and alligators to do it.

Back at the boat, Walt's father, lacking any patience for filing a missing persons report, would grumble, "Where in the darkest hell did he go?" Even I didn't know.

Still, they both appreciated help with repairs, and I savored the opportunity for the nautical adventure.

Had Walt not answered my call, there might have been no Caribbean sailing adventure for either of us.

We decided to get together for dinner that night. I threw on a silk tropical shirt and a Panama hat suggestive of a rendezvous in paradise, and met him in the historic boating town of Annapolis, a nice respite and an hour's drive from my home in the nation's capital.

Sea lore has it that once you've sailed with someone, a special bond is created between you. Over a dinner of broiled shrimp and scallops, Walt expounded on his planned voyage and suggested I might want to consider it. I found his plan audacious, though intriguing.

"Walt, your trip sounds like a big deal—the ocean is no pond or Chesapeake Bay. Have you sailed the Atlantic?"

"Sure, been to Bermuda several times."

"How'd that go?"

"Well, to be honest, it varied, between holy crap and Heaven."

"Ever lose anybody?"

"No . . . well, lost a few to the airlines. One time we had to wire for help on the return trip since a few friends jumped ship." He rubbed his thinning hair and looked away, then admitted, "In bad weather, it gets a little rough and the crew gets sick, especially if the boat is crowded."

"Who's going on this trip?"

"Rocco, a guy I met in the Bahamas. Probably done more sailing than me."

"Any of it blue water?"

"He was in the Bahamas."

"Oh. That's blue water? Shows how much I know. I think of it as being, like, right there, not too far from Florida. Well, you know my experience, a few day-sails on the Chesapeake with you, years ago. I'm probably not the guy you need. I can windsurf, but probably couldn't sail a tiny Sunfish with any proficiency."

"Well, you might want to think about it. You know more than you think, and you survived that boat trip with my dad."

"What I remember most was being with you in Albemarle Sound in waves so high the boat's propellers spun free before every next wave broke over the cabin top. I was puking my guts out because your dad was smoking like a chimney and I couldn't go outside for fresh air."

"I think this one has your name on it, B-Byrd."

"Byrd connotes flying, not sailing. I'll commit right now to fly there and meet you so you don't have to luxuriate in paradise without feeling bad about not sharing it."

"You're welcome to do that, but it's not where I need you most. We have to get there first."

"I think I'd be dead weight, like feeding a dog that can't bark. . . . When are you leaving, and how long will it take?"

"Mid-October, it'll take six to ten weeks, including time in the Virgin Islands after we get there."

"Mid-October? There'd still be six weeks of hurricane season left. They come right through the Caribbean. You've thought about that?"

He looked at me like a hooked trout, not knowing that, after building a house on the ocean, I kept track of and respected hurricanes.

"If it looks like a stormy season we'll adjust the schedule, but I'd like to be home for Christmas."

Walt was a stoic, capable man with many skills, able to set a path and follow it. Both a gruff and gregarious fellow, he was direct, and less animated and charming with the guys than he was the ladies. I'd seen him through two marriages and several work projects. A ferociously competitive tennis player, he was loathe to lose, and to beat him it had to be earned. He was slow to ask for advice, and slower to follow it, if at all, but I knew he was levelheaded and not subject to risk-taking—or so I thought.

During our working years, Walt came to my department for logical, fact-based data analysis and system design; his trip seemed antithetical. Would I sail a boat across the ocean, through the night? I'd worked long and hard, forsaking much frivolity and irresponsible behavior to achieve a schedule of my own choosing (almost everyone's dream), with a home and income that was comfortable and adequate, while I was still young enough to enjoy it. Would I put it all at risk on a sailing trip into a dangerous, vast unknown? Who did he think I was? Danger? The unknown?

He could be right.

His plan was to sail from Florida to the Virgin Islands, either directly or through the Bahamas, stopping at several islands along the way. Our "home" would be 34 feet, from bow to stern, 10 feet wide at the beam. It seemed I could anticipate adventure, if not comfort. Not knowing boats well nor having seen his current boat, I could not envision the living conditions.

After the waiter cleared the table, I leaned in and asked, "Do you seriously think I'm the person for such a complicated, potentially dangerous event?"

"Here, take a look at this. It's a personal invitation with the qualifications you'll need. You'd fit right in."

I read the checklist. Walt had not checked any of the four, leaving me in suspense:

Dear Sailor__Adventurer__Gambler__Loser__(Choose one)

Receiving this letter indicates qualification under one or more of the following circumstances:

- Have sailed with me before; *well, yes, for long enough to eat lunch, but why is the position still open?*
- Have expressed an interest in sailing; *nothing this big.*
- Had a relative in the Navy; *a son was a Marine (a Dept. of the Navy).*

- Played in your bath water as a child; *and as an adult.*
- Discussed a Caribbean cruise with a friend; *no, not for me.*
- Watched Gilligan's Island for 5 straight nights; *cannot remember, but if Ginger and Mary Ann are going, I'm up for it.*
  (After a few more whimsical non-qualifiers, he finished.)
- Have the time, are gullible, and could be talked into going sailing.

In late October of this year ('93), I plan to sail *Godspeed . . .*"

No mention of sailing skills; I had none. By his slack criteria, I qualified, and had quit work to pursue uncommon opportunities. Walt knew I could swab decks, cook, and make repairs. What more could he ask for and expect to get? People marry for less.

In the balance of the invitation, Walt posited two ways of getting to the islands. I nixed straight-ocean sailing right away; that was just a boat delivery job. Walt agreed.

His second option was a more civilized, feature-laden, romantic route of several countries, the only option I would consider. After all, isn't life all about the journey?

There was no need to rush into a significant commitment; it was still summer, and finding someone willing and able to sail away for ten weeks hadn't been easy. Having visited several of the islands by plane, for business and pleasure, I knew the allure of the area. Sailing from one beautiful island to another appealed to my aesthetic sense as well as my love for sport and adventure.

I suspected a whole new world was waiting, and the learning and experiences would be non-stop. The Bahamas offers diversity galore, and has a long and complex history of settlement by English Bermudans in the 1600s, then Loyalists and Brits from the time of the American Revolution with their slaves, primarily West Africans, and by various others. In the 1700s, there were more pirates than settlers. During the Civil War, many were involved in blockade running between the North and the South.

Many islands are unknown to the average person. The island of Andros, for example, has one of the deepest blue holes in the world, the third largest barrier reef in the world (100 miles long), and its own Loch Ness monster, called Lusca. One of the westernmost islands in the chain, it is regarded as the bonefish capital of the world and sits at the Tongue of the Ocean, 6,000 feet deep on the north end.

Andros is just one of twenty-three (and growing) inhabited islands among thousands of unpopulated land outcroppings. Several islands have tiny villages seemingly transplanted from the Massachusetts coast, set among white sandy beaches and palm trees, most accessible only by boat. Beyond the Bahamas are the Turks & Caicos Islands, Dominican Republic, and Puerto Rico.

The trip sounded intriguing and could be my type of adventure—if reality was anywhere near the dream. In sharp contrast, Walt envisioned we would be sailing all the time and, when we arrived, we would sit in an isolated lagoon and improve life by reading books. He saw the boat as his home. I saw it as transportation, with no better path to an improved life than tying up at a luxury resort. Of course, I was single; he was married. Could we see our way to a mutually satisfying compromise?

Being a high-need-for-achievement type, I found the challenge enticing: to embrace the conditions and survive the unpredictability of the sea, a chance to escape the ordinary, discover new people, places, and things. To not read the story but *create* the story. Perhaps I was ignoring what could be a serious conflict of interests, cloaked by a dusting of Peter Pan-like youthful immortality, but can I fly?

Walt wants me to sail.

CHAPTER
Three

To Sea or Not to Sea:
Bring everything you need, and don't need much

Two months later, though the decision seemed to have been made, I was still racked by uncertainty. I loved adventure, not necessarily sailing. But when Megan, with whom I had a tempestuous on-again off-again relationship, asked a disparaging, thought-provoking "Who would want to spend six weeks bobbing around in a boat that small?" our differing values influenced my decision.

In his book about sailing across the Atlantic, William Buckley wrote that after telling his wife he was going to make the sail, she said: "If you do, I will leave you." His response: "So far, so good." Perhaps I needed a long stint at sea to clear my head and my front porch. I was tired of being the fall guy in unsuccessful relationships. Maybe a break, relaxing without complications, even behaving wildly with the boys while lending someone a hand, would be restorative and might reinvigorate my desire to find Miss Right. If I never returned, problem solved.

Being on the move had always been in my blood. My early years included all manner of ways to use the wheel, my favorite invention: a tricycle, clamp-on roller skates, a bike, then a sedan, a convertible, a motorcycle, and a tent on wheels—I tried them all. Hook the tent camper to the convertible, put down the top, and hit the open road. A cheap high. When personal finances allowed, flying expanded my boundaries. The urge always was to look over the horizon to see what was out of sight, around the block, across the country, and eventually around the world. Having visited 48 of the 50 states and a large part of the rest of the world, I was figuratively standing at the water's edge, contemplating the use of a vehicle without wheels, to explore a spectacular area of Earth in the 70% covered by water.

Previously, to get out on the water, I learned how to windsurf—how to catch the wind, how to tack, and mostly how to fall off. I read about sailing concepts like center of effort, center of lateral resistance, but not what to do with them. It was exhilarating to be hooked in on harness lines, no hands, leaning back against the wind's pressure on the balanced sail, flying over the waves at high speeds, yelling gleeful expressions of joy—until you got catapulted into your own sail, with the boom or mast breaking your fall and perhaps your body parts. Not a dangerous pastime, really, if you are careful not to get stranded far from shore, or in the shipping channel (a freighter is *enormous* when viewed from the waterline, and getting out of the way is your job). Would my windsurfing experience be useful when sailing? The two vessels are so vastly different, I never gave it a thought.

Walt's strict instructions were to use no hard suitcases—soft duffel bags only. Use Ziploc bags or soft plastic storage cases to keep clothes dry when water seeped into the storage lockers. Not if, but when. A ten-week trip at sea required extras of everything and thoughtful consideration of the needs that might arise. Space was limited. "Bring everything you will need, and don't need much."

By Monday, October 18, 1993, the day of departure, I'd been preparing for weeks. After several days of final packing and imagining a vastly different life, I was offered a ride to Annapolis by Megan. We were in the waning days of our relationship, had not been together recently, only occasionally in telephone contact, so the offer was unexpected. It did solve the problem of what to do with my vehicle for such a long period of time.

When we arrived at Walt's house, I met his first mate, Rocco, who owned a boat similar to Walt's 34' Irwin monohull sloop, *Godspeed*. Walt had seen Rocco's boat in the Bahamas one winter and they became friends while discussing boat similarities and maintenance. I was going to spend the next 8 weeks in close quarters with this stranger, so I needed to like him, though he met me with a cold stare, a quick, less-than-gripping handshake, then glanced away. My first impression, based on his lack of interest, was he had little use for me. I suspected, *if this were chess, he's Kasparov, several moves ahead of me; I'm* Hogan's Heroes' *Sergeant Schultz—I know nothing.*

Something wasn't quite right. I'd never met someone so aloof whom I was teaming up with to tackle a daring adventure for months, but I'd never been in this situation. Perhaps this was de rigueur for sailor introductions, and I had to earn his civility. The guy had hard edges and appeared hard throughout. He was bald with a fringe of white hair, had a trim, strong build, and stood a little taller than a post box on a New England stone fence, maybe 5'2". Stoic, laconic, and monotone, with the personality of a floor mop, he didn't seem like a man who would become my next best friend. I had to give it time.

We spent the night at Walt's in anticipation of an early morning departure for the drive to the boat in Stuart, Florida. Choosing to stay, Megan and I pushed sofa pillows together on the basement floor, then spent the night there, our last for a long time, probably forever—a bittersweet occasion. The boat trip was a blessing because our relationship had suffered due to differing communication styles, dreams, and long-term objectives that would seriously "altar" my life. Wrestling with the sofa cushions while Rocco slept six feet away was the first instance of a long period of unconventional and uncomfortable sleeping arrangements.

The next morning, though it felt and looked like night, we crammed our equipment into Walt's car. Megan and I said goodbye, as controlled and muted as the night before. One car followed the other through the neighborhoods and out onto the highway, where each went their separate way, taillights fading in the distance. This scene was somberly familiar. I didn't know if this was the end for us, but it felt like it.

After a 17-hour drive, when one drove while the others slept, luggage packed around us, we arrived in Stuart, Florida, at 9:45 p.m. to verify the presence of *Godspeed*. The boat's sobriquet suggested success, prosperity, glamour, a sleek Hinckley or a Broward yacht, multiple decks, space fore and aft for chaise lounges, air-conditioned ballroom with strobe lights, and . . . I must have fantasized the 34 feet as 34 meters. The dim lighting added to the mystique, but it appeared to be like a bad blind date—not as good as imagined, someone you would describe as "interesting," and may not stay with for long.

Fantasizing only takes you so far before you are left with reality. *Oh my! It's tiny! Though it's bigger than mine.* In the dark, there may not be much showing, but . . . *can you get three people in that?* My legs were cramping up in anticipation. I supposed there was no turning back at this point, not with any honor. We had reserved a room at the marina motel, which Rocco and I would share for the next two nights while we prepared the boat. Walt and Felicity, his wife, had their own room. Exhausted from the long drive, we were soon fast asleep.

After eating breakfast alone in the motel restaurant, I made my way onto the pier to assess my new home. It was not a small yacht. It was not a yacht. In fact, there wasn't any deck space, other than a small patch on the bow. Any deck space along the side was only space for one foot at a time. Aft, there was a small cockpit, big enough for the wheel. The boat was safe from pirates, and unfortunately was not a babe magnet either. I feared I was walking through the gates of a monastery. *Oh my! What have I done?*

Mounted on the transom was a tall, custom-made aluminum rack stretching across the stern holding solar panels on top and a taller pole on the left/port side with a wind generator mounted on it. Hearing that term for the first time, I thought the machine generated wind, a logical invention for a sailboat, were it practical. It was hard to imagine why that wouldn't work— sounds perfect—but this device uses the wind as the power to turn two blades attached to a generator of electricity. On the right/starboard side was a taller upright with an antenna attached, so we had, if it worked, communications capability.

The two real sailors soon joined me, and we spent the day prepping the boat. I gave the dinghy a wash and wax, a skill I had honed as a teenager working on cars. On *Godspeed*, the coaxial connections to the Loran—a radio device providing location information—needed repairs and contacts cleaned, as did most electrical components after eighteen months in dry storage.

Getting ready for bed after a full day of work, I was alone with Rocco in our motel room. Struggling to interact and make conversation, I asked, "Well, Rocco, what'd you do for a career?"

"Just a mail carrier."

Uh-oh. "Just a mail carrier? Seems like an honorable enough job. Mail delivery is important to everyone, defying rain, sleet, or snow, as I recall. Were you offered other jobs?"

"Yeah, coulda been management, but I hate those sonsabitches. Hate 'em."

"I'm thinking you might be retired?"

"You bet your ass." He stormed into the bathroom, slamming the door.

Well, sumbitch! I had other questions but took the hint our getting-to-know-you session was getting-done, giving me a deep concern this voyage might be uncomfortable based on the personal baggage Rocco was carrying. Walt had said there wasn't room for hard cases; Rocco was showing signs of violating it. While I didn't rise to the top in my career, I never used a diminutive "just" in its description. Worse, I had been one of those "sonsabitches" for many years, though possibly best not mentioned now, if ever.

Would he engage in one-upmanship in sailing to get back at me for not having a "just" career? Based on my perception of his body and verbal language, it seemed a near certainty! Maybe we'd give conversation another try tomorrow. Finding the right pillow, I slid into the great white biscuit, putting the day behind me.

We spent the next day repairing and provisioning the boat. Rocco and Walt were tighter than I was with either of them, understandably so. My only chance of breaking into the conversations would be to announce lunch was ready, or the propane tank was about to blow. Instead, I volunteered to take the car to get the diving tanks filled before Walt's wife returned to Maryland. If the day had been dark and rainy instead of sunny and temperate, I might have considered helping her drive home. Her health was not good, and it was a long journey. If I was going to bail on this adventure, it needed to be soon. My presence was unexpected in the planning of the trip—they were going with or without me—and ignored by Rocco. This trip, at five knots per hour, could be my longest 1,500 miles.

However, Walt's desire that I be on the trip became more obvious as time went on and kept me moving forward. I called his recommended dive shop. An alluring voice answered the phone. "Hello, Dixie Dive and Jog, how may I help you?"

"Hello; do you fill dive tanks?"

"We sure do. Who wants to know?"

"I do." *Wow, what a great voice.* "But the tanks belong to someone else, Walt. Do I need a card or license to get them filled?"

"Maybe a credit card, or cash, will get them filled."

"Oh, it's that easy? Can you fill two tanks?"

"I think so. We've got some air stashed somewhere that we can shove in there."

"I've really come to the right place, haven't I?"

"You're not here yet, but we've compressed air, just waiting for you. Your name?"

"Uhhh, my name is Bryan."

"Oh . . . okay. Bring them on over and we will see what we can do. When do you need them?"

"Tomorrow would work; we are leaving port soon, within a day or two."

"Hmmm, that's quick. Bring them in and ask for me, Nikki. When can you get here?"

"As soon as I can drive there, maybe fifteen minutes or less?"

"Okay, I'll still be here, but get a move on. We may need to do a hydrostatic test on them, should be done every five years."

"What is that? Is it tough to do?"

"I'll explain it when you get here; let's see if you need it. A visual is easier, done yearly."

Wow, what a sweet voice, and crisp as a Granny Smith apple. There's a lot of spunk in that gal. Pushy? Couldn't tell with her peaches and cream voice. And she's playful, can't possibly match my imagination. Maybe someone else should go, so I can keep the dream alive. Betcha twenty bucks she's a monster. I've had these dreams crushed before.

I jumped in the car, already loaded with the tanks, and took off. At the store, I went to the counter in the middle of the shop where a young, slim brunette was busy with paperwork. She looked up briefly and, without really giving me her attention, asked what she could do for me.

"I called and asked if you could fill two tanks, talked to Nikki. Is she here?"

"That would be me; you're Bryan?"

"That would be me."

"Well, hello there, Mr. Bryan. Where's your equipment?"

"If you mean my diving tanks . . . they're in the car. I didn't know—"

"We'll go with that for now," she said smartly. "Go ahead and bring them in while I get the paperwork started."

I jumped to and did as I was told. She wasn't intimidating, more so comfortably efficient, probably owned a stake in the business. And gorgeous. I take back the monster comment; you'll have to trust me for the twenty bucks, but you didn't take the bet, anyway.

When I came back with the two tanks, she started asking questions from a form.

"Name?" I gave her the whole thing.

"Address?"

"Here, or at home?"

"Home first."

I gave it to her.

"And here?"

"*Godspeed*, down by the marina motel."

"What's your age, and diving experience?"

"Actually, I won't be the one using them. The boat owner is the diver in the group. I don't know how to dive . . . maybe you can teach me?"

"You bet I can; don't let anyone else do it," she said, looking me in the eyes. "So what is your age?"

"Well, I'm over eighteen, and I'm under fifty. What's yours?"

"Just right." She looked down at the form: "Sex?"

"Not what I came for but sounds like the better idea. Your place or my mom's?"

She stopped her ritual, and slowly looked up grinning. "Hey, it's on the form; I had to ask. I'll just check the Male box."

"You're welcome to keep doing that. There may be a letter in it someday."

" . . . I like your sense of humor, and your voice on the phone was . . . hmmm . . . pretty nice. You don't make late-night calls, do you?"

"It's a possibility. Calling rates are cheaper. And your voice is . . . let's say it's Goldilocks-three-bears-porridge just right. You surprised me. My experience has been the really sexy phone voices cannot back it up, if you know what I mean." By now I was bending over the counter on my elbows, pretty much eye-to-eye, being bolder than I can ever remember. She had ushered me in.

"Yeah, life can dish out disappointments; things aren't always what's first imagined," she sighed.

"Whoa, that didn't sound as playful as the rest of your banter. What's going on? Does your ring mean you're engaged or married? Problems?" We had danced from comedy to tragedy in one swift two-step.

"Plenty! Or at least a small number of big ones. You may not want to hear it."

"Oh no. . . . I'd be glad to listen. Want to start someone on the tanks, in case any need to be hydro'ed? We can talk while they work, if you don't get busy?"

"A minute ago, that was my line, got distracted. That's how it's been. I'll be right back."

She picked up the two heavy tanks as if they were nothing, and sashayed to the back of the shop, issued a couple of quick commands, then returned to her desk. I did not mind watching her go and come. The bare waist beneath the shortened top, and the trim, brief shorts revealed enough to start a guy dreaming. Probably gets to be like a sports bar in here on weekends, guys watching what's game. If she's a monster, I'm in the monster business.

She returned and took a few moments to check me out. After a deep breath, she poured out a story of her partner in the business who was her boyfriend, then fiancé, but the relationship had become unbearable. The wooing had stopped when he thought marriage to her was a done deal and they became business partners. He was intolerably selfish, the Big Boss type, and she realized he had a mean and angry nature when drinking. She was not going to hook her wagon to that for life, especially when a few of her observations had been reluctantly verified by his family—easily forgiving of him since his father had also been an abusive drinker.

The more she revealed, the closer I felt to her, sensing I was privy to a story few had heard.

"When you go diving, or you're in a business together, especially a diving business, you have to be able to trust your partner," she said.

I was intimately drawn into her dilemma, knowing a very private and deeply troubling piece of her life story. Obviously, she had felt a dire need to vent to someone—even, or preferably, a stranger, particularly one planning to sail off the edge of the planet, had she known. Any secrets she confided in me were potentially forever secure.

I was smitten. A person who looks you in the eye and tells you their concerns and fears from deep within has the potential to be a close, possibly intimate, friend. I'd found this to be rare, and totally missing from my last relationship. The only incident when it did occur is blazed indelibly and favorably in my mind, but once in four years wasn't captivating; once in twenty minutes was. "Love is blind . . . but so is lust. It's hard to tell the difference," I said.

"Yeah, well, my eyes are wide open now. At least wider open."

"They are, and as beautiful a blue as the Caribbean."

(Exhales.) "Thanks."

"So, what's to be done about the business?"

"Well, that's what makes this so sticky, and keeps me from doing what I want outside of work, if you catch my drift," she said, staring me in the eye. "I have to watch what I do if I want to get my share out of this business, or get a reasonable deal if I decide to buy him out. I've done most of the work and provided most of the cash to keep the doors open. Since he knows he can depend on me, he thinks he can play around, play the big man without doing any work. Mean people are hard and unreasonable to deal with and, until this thing is settled . . ." she looked around, leaving me to assume what she meant.

"How long has it been?"

"You mean without sex?"

"Okay," I replied, thinking if that's where she wanted to go, I wouldn't insist on what I was really asking, which wasn't about sex. What was on her mind was certain to be more interesting.

"Six months and three days, but who's counting? Actually, I don't really know. Who knows when was the last time? But that's close," she said despondently.

"Oh, my God!" I said. That would be near impossible at my age, even more difficult were I her age. "Are you still sharing a place?"

"Yep, which adds to the problem. I'm stuck, and not enjoying it at all. I'm wasting my life, in some respects, probably affecting my sanity. I feel like I'm going crazy, trying to build a business, but to what effect? I'm stopped when I want to go."

At this point, she looked up from the counter she had been focusing on when not looking at me, raising her eyes without moving her head, almost with a question mark on her face, forehead furrowed. Was this an unrequited angel asking for help? If there was a time to demonstrate compassion, this had to be it.

"Any way I can help?"

"Good God, I wish! But don't know how. Being an owner, I'm stuck here at the shop."

After a respectful pause, "You know, if you don't mind me being perhaps crude, would you consider that?"

Unruffled by any possible risk of crudity, she asked, "What do you mean?"

"Well, to play off your words, could you get stuck here at the shop, if that would help? Do you have a dressing room, an office or a private place? Could release some tension . . . or make things worse."

"You mean sex! That'd be risky. If anyone caught on or suspected me, I . . . let me think about that. You're . . . well, certainly adventurous. And not married?"

"I am—both. Was married, but single now for about twenty years."

"Should I assume we're talking you and me?"

"Well, wouldn't someone more local, more convenient, better serve your needs, more than once? Suppose you fell in love? I'm just here for another day. I was—"

"Why don't you speak for yourself, John Alden. Did I just get rejected?"

"No way! Who was it . . . Priscilla? Mullins? It'd be my highest honor, a dream come true. I just thought—"

"Anyone local would become a problem. Or it'd be like hiring someone; I can't date yet, can't take the risk. Already thought about that; been living with it. You, on the other hand . . . are . . . here . . . nowwww, and . . ." her eyebrows went up as if to ask for concurrence.

"Hmmm" accompanied my involuntary tight nod of collusion.

After a little thought, she said: "I've an idea. We have Speedo bathing trunks on sale, 50% off, over there near the window. What are you, a 32 or 34?"

"One of those, depending on how generous the cut and the size of my last meal, but I need tennis shorts more. You sell them, too, don't you?"

"Yeah, if you wish. I'd rather see you in Speedos. The dressing room is made of curtains all the way around. In the middle of our storeroom area, turn left and go all the way back. There're signs. Get a pair, try 'em on. Wait for me. I'll check the fit," she said coolly, glancing around the empty store.

Well, alright! Beats a slap in the face. She seemed determined to settle a score. Women who have repeatedly been mistreated by an unfaithful husband, once past the tipping point, cut out the preliminaries and head straight for their sweet revenge. They don't date; they copulate.

"Jerry, this gentleman is waiting for those tanks to be filled. I'm going to go back to doing inventory. Will you handle the customers, watch the floor?" she said to a hippie-like clerk further back in the shop.

"No problem. Take your time, do the numbers!"

She disappeared into the storage area. I casually looked around—forget the tennis shorts; how stupid is that?—then found a pair of Speedos that would work. I grabbed a few more to justify additional time, then asked Jerry how to get to the dressing room, hoping to make it seem like we were two individuals on separate missions. He pointed me through the curtain, past the third row of shelves, then turn left.

Things were moving too fast to question whether this was really happening. We had come this far on quick-witted wise-guy conversation fueled by the adrenaline created by a mutual attraction with someone who worked with me on a bantering tit-for-tat. At this point, I usually screw up something so promising, but if she remains in control? *Forget Mom's place; we're going to yours, darling. And you can drive.*

I found and settled in the dressing area, dropped my shorts, and slid into the trunks. To get the full effect, I took off my shirt to ensure the trunks did not squeeze too hard on my love handles, making them seem larger, faux cleavage I didn't want. I checked the scene in the free-standing mirror, much like the one at home. Hmmm! Not bad, not bad at all. Yeah, that works. No muffin-top here.

A whisper: "Bryan?"

"Yeah."

She lifted and ducked under the curtain. She looked at me, then put down her inventory materials and portable phone, saying, "I'm having second thoughts about whether this is right." She stood back, "Nice fit. They look really good on you." She came closer, wrapped her arms around my neck, and quickly pulled me to her. Her kiss was searchingly delicate until she found her fit and knew she was welcome, then poured on the pent-up passion. I wasn't in control, tried to get it back, but it was a fondling love-fest. She paused, stepped back and, with a glint of mischief in her eyes, said, "Let me check out the fit. You seem to already be outgrowing these little 'ole trunks."

"It may be your fault; a couple minutes ago, they fit just fine. I hope you can fix it." That brought her smiling face back to mine, and we kissed with a tender hunger.

"Is it too soon?"

"Possibly," I replied. "Want to date a bit longer?"

"That's the problem. . . . Hey, wait, we've already had two dates."

"We have?"

"Yeah . . . our telephone date and at the counter. This is our third."

"I overlooked the telephone date. Anyway, it's now or never."

She had been scraping her fingernails softly across me while talking, stimulating me, which was easy, instantaneous.

"Wow! Okay, I can't stop now. Father, please forgive me, but we've spoken about my needs, and you've sent me him."

With that, whatever it was (dispensation?) she pulled the trunks down, shimmied out of her shorts, and took a position on the low, free-standing, padded bench, reminding me of my weight-lifting bench, a multi-functional asset, excellent for getting close. She laid back and pulled her T-shirt above her breasts, having her own ideas of what she wanted from this high-risk encounter, a sense that she had limited time for catching up.

If Jerry walked into the storage area looking for her, how would she reappear from checking inventory in the dressing room? *I count one hugely aroused customer in room 69?* The biggest challenge was to not get caught. But who would break into the fitting room while someone is being fitted? That wouldn't be fitting.

What a gift to walk in on: a beautiful, passionate, physical woman with a desperate need for intimacy and fulfillment, delightful from every angle. Her diving, along with her youth, had her in great physical shape, and she was not shy about sharing it. Whether from experience or innovation, she knew how to use that bench in several positions to near exhaustion.

Eventually, as she sat on the bench to recover, I dropped to my knees to be eye to eye and lips to lips. We shared the tenderness of a long hug surrounded by light, gentle kisses.

She broke the silence. "Hmmm, I needed that. Life's been hell."

"You gonna be alright?"

"Oh yeah. Life has never been a bed of roses, as they say."

"I'm sorry I can't be around to give you more support."

"You've given me what I needed. A taste, a push . . . a clarion and rare, unforgettable moment."

"Wow. I hope it will always seem as positive."

"It will. I can see things could get worse before they get better . . . a lot of strings to untangle. But my feelings of desperation are leaving. I now know what has to be done. Thank you, thank you."

"Well, feel free to call me; leave a message and I'll call you when I can. There's a recorder on my home phone. Don't know anything about phone service in the islands. Maybe you do; you dive there."

"It's poor quality, sparse to non-existent."

"Oh!"

"Nikki! Call from Glenn," Jerry yelled into the storage area.

Nikki directed her voice away from Jerry, "I'll take it. Thanks."

"You got it!"

She picked up her phone: "Hi Glenn, I've got my hands full. I'll call you back in a few minutes . . . no, we need them tomorrow. . . . I'll call you back. Thanks."

Turning back to me, she said, "We'd better wrap things up. I may be needed any moment."

"Makes sense. We've been lucky. I like the shorts, and they did fit, for a while. I'll take them. The price is right, and the memories are priceless."

"They're a gift, for being a friend. Besides, I can't sell these. Suppose they were found at a crime scene with your DNA on them?" We shared a lingering kiss.

"You have the makings of a lawyer if the shop doesn't work out."

"I might consider it; may need a new job."

While we made ourselves presentable, I asked, "Did you really have to do inventory?"

"Other than checking you out? Yes. I'll do it after hours. They say criminals like to revisit the scene of their crime, so, we'll see."

Another kiss, then she turned to leave, paused, and turned back toward me, a concern creasing her brow.

"Wait. I may know what you're thinking," I said. "Try something with me; press your heart against mine, relax and breathe deeply, together, see if you feel anything."

After a moment of warm embrace, she whispered, "I do, I really do. That's . . . amazing! Never have . . . that's a real hug."

"Thought it was worth a try. Take what you can; plenty where that comes from."

Pulling back was tough—not knowing would there be a next time—but the risk level was rising. How long does it take a person to try on four skimpy swimsuits?

She left the same way she arrived. I waited until she'd had time to leave the storeroom, then headed toward the sales racks to put the other suits back. When we were at the desk together, I took her business card from its holder and put it with the "too small" shorts, "May I call you?"

"Of course, I hope you will . . . you'd better! But don't be offended if I sound like I hardly know you, depending on who else might be listening."

"I understand that. So, you really want to get together again? Not just a one—"

"Hell no! I mean yes. Wait . . . yes, I want to see you again."

"Good. Count on it. But don't worry, and wonder why I don't call. I'll be at sea, you know."

"Yeah, that's good and bad news! But please call; you give me hope, which I can use right now; feels good."

"There is hope. I've never met anyone quite like you: sexy, cerebral, pretty, daring, a sense of humor, and you must like sports. What more could a guy want?"

"Some don't want what they want when they get it. And I'd better get back to work. You wouldn't want a job in a dive shop, would you?"

"Wouldn't want it if I got it. Hey, before I go, are you serious about teaching me to dive?"

"Absolutely, if you're up for it. That'd boost my spirits."

"Great. Hope all is not dire 'til then."

"Not here; we're in the business of fun, stay pretty busy, and now I'm good for . . . 'til you return . . . right?"

"Yep."

One of the tanks had to be hydro'ed, but they had the ability and both were filled and ready to go. This had been a fortuitous errand. I paid for the tank servicing, then we shook hands. I wanted more, but dared not. We exchanged glances so frequently, I was practically backing out of the store, feeling like I was seventeen. I didn't get to know her well, but it was a good start. I took her business card from the bag and put it in my wallet.

The tanks knocked around on their way into the car's trunk. No damage, but it was obvious my mind was not on clearing the lip of the trunk. I sat still in the driver's seat, not yet ready or able to get out on the highway. If I'd left immediately, I'd have been driving while intoxicated, my mind racing too fast to drive within limits.

I wondered if she was looking outside, or if she went back to work. Less than 50 yards separated us. I had to be going before her partner came back and saw that smile on her face, then came looking for me with a gun: "Did you put that smile on her face, boy? Did ya? Huh? Did ya?" Felicity would almost certainly look askance at me if her car was returned perforated with bullet holes. It is reasonable that questions might be asked, but it was just a piercing of the heart that may heal over time.

Though under the control of nature's most influential hormonal flood and still not ready for prime time, I nonetheless headed out into the flow of traffic on U.S. Route 1. I mused about whether my out-of-character actions were really that, or were they in-character actions that surface infrequently when disregarding the social screening polite society expects of us? It was my perennial question of who are we—the person we know, or the person our friends perceive? Psychoanalysts boil it down to "you are what you do." Well then, was it an act more male conquest or feminine sensitivity? Selfish, or generous and compassionate? Oh, wait just a minute! Aristotle is more lenient (probably Episcopalian) and informs me we are what we repeatedly do. Excellent! The key is to research until you get results you can use. Sounds like a "Get Out of Jail Free at Least Once" card. Unlikely that more would be needed. My most concerning musing: was I acting out of character like a person who only had thirty days to live?

The relationship with Megan had been over. It was the formality of declaring it over that neither of us had undertaken. Until now. It felt good to be free, even if adrift.

Back at the boat, I mounted the tanks in the cradle on deck, then went below and wrote her number in my diary, not wanting to lose it. Eventually, my heart stopped thumping and I was able to resume my duties on the boat. The memories would forever linger, and evolve into something, hopefully, but who knows? For now, we're fast friends—very fast.

We put the outboard motor on the dinghy, *Speedy*, and took a ride around the St. Lucie River. Zipping across the water in Florida in the wintertime, knowing it is cold at home, is invigorating. The brilliant, sparkling water, fresh air, blue skies, pelicans, palm trees, white boats and bridges were picturesque and lifted my spirits, though I was already floating on a cloud.

That evening, Walt took Rocco and me to dinner at Olive Garden, where he presented us with white polo shirts monogrammed with the *Godspeed* moniker. At this point, we took on a professional look, indiscernible from the staff of the 200' yachts of West Palm Beach, except I had a more functional

Tilley hat. The staff had the starched white uniforms, and most likely derived great advantage from knowing what they were doing and receiving a paycheck. This was our small start to becoming a professional, cohesive team. Unfortunately, it would take more than matching shirts to keep us afloat; we would always be short by 166 feet and the paycheck, at a minimum. And I still knew nothing about sailing, though life seemed great so far.

Rocco had not warmed up to me yet. He was not conversational, but terse and gruff when he did speak. My guess was he didn't want to be there or he didn't want me there. Walt must have leaned on him to help with the endeavor when there were no other takers. How many people could and would disappear for six to ten weeks? Rocco was acting like he was fulfilling an obligation, not pursuing his love of sailing. Maybe he didn't have support at home for this trip, and he felt he was in Buckley's bind. If I was his problem, I could address that during our journey, but I figured it was really him, this early in the game, since he didn't know me yet. I tried to shrug it off. Hell, the only thing I had done that he knew of was to show up; maybe that was enough.

Curious about what Walt might have already told him from our history together, I wondered if Rocco were to learn that I grew up as poor as, or poorer than he did, in a rent-subsidized government housing project, would he feel a kinship? This was during the period of integration in the '50s and '60s, when the upheaval of the time caused tension between the races. Gangs would follow me on my paper routes and collections, then ambush me when I had money in my pocket. Should I tell him about standing to fight small groups, and in order to hold onto my collections, outrunning the larger gangs, or "wolf packs" as my mom used to call them, running like a gazelle and hand-springing four-foot fences without breaking stride? I would have excelled in this Olympic sport, frequently training on the streets, rushing into the house with guys so close behind that my mom, sitting close by the door, could identify them to the police by the shirt cuffs she saw extending through the front door into the living room.

There were several ways to filter into the project from better adjoining neighborhoods. When I tired of the *Chariots of Fire* approach, I would take the much longer route home by heading in the wrong direction, then circling back and sneaking through the woods. This route required a shorter sprint through the project. Would Rocco appreciate even though I'm here on the dock with discretionary time at an early age, I wasn't born into privilege, and my career track started at the bottom where his may have? Rocco's desire or curiosity to talk seemed negligible, so I feared that conversation would never happen, and I'd feel strange suggesting he needed to know more about me, me, me.

Many weeks at sea, on a cramped boat with few facilities and an unpleasant crew could be a recipe for a painfully long, possibly disastrous trip. The boat looked even more crowded with the diving tanks mounted on the foredeck (although they held a special place in my heart), with Jerry cans of extra fuel lashed to the same mounting brackets.

If I were to bolt, sooner would be better. Possessing the official *Godspeed* shirt made the abandon-ship decision more difficult. If I abandoned her husband, I doubted Felicity would give me a ride home. Just how would that seventeen-hour conversation flow? Maybe I could make a telephone call, then return and announce my last close friend was being admitted to the hospital for an unpainted toenail, a tragedy, and I had to be there for moral support. That might work. Or try open heart surgery to repair a broken heart. No, not likely.

To further sharpen my perspective about this cruise, after dinner Walt held a briefing on the boat to review the house rules: "Okay, guys, listen up. First, the portholes have to be closed whenever we're moving. Sometimes, I'll leave the one in the head open to disperse odors if we're on a port tack. Otherwise, they all have to be secured."

"Uhh, what's a port tack?" I asked.

"When the wind is crossing the boat from the left side. In that case, the port side will be higher above the water than the starboard side."

"Okay. Let me try securing a porthole," I suggested, then twisted a few screws over flanges. "Is that tight enough?"

"That'll do. Now, here in the head—if you use the sink, wipe it out with a towel when you're finished. As for the toilet, this is the pump handle, and this is the valve control. Pump water into the toilet before you sit down. After you're done," and he mentioned other steps to do with the valve and pump. Somewhere in his demonstration, he added something about it being unpleasant, but that you'd eventually become a realist and accept bodily functions as facts.

"Walt, if we want to take a pee, can we just go over the rail without being sent home? Going below while underway can be nauseating."

"Well you can, but be careful you're peeing downwind and that you don't fall overboard. It gets a little rough out there; make sure you hold onto the boat. Sailors have been known to literally piss their life away, especially in the middle of the night, when you'll be on your own to get home."

"Do you have a bottle, a cup, something simple?"

"Since no ladies will be aboard, we'll use a yellow cup, kept in the cup holder on the port side of the binnacle/compass, nowhere else. Don't drink out of it."

Then he got into the need to conserve potable water and how to make water (using the reverse osmosis water maker) by opening and closing certain valves in the right sequence, testing for reduced salinity, then throwing another valve when it was potable. Since Rocco had a twin ship, only the water maker was new to him. For me, this much information was sensory overload, and I'd seek assistance before taking on the water maker, confident they'd want to help before drinking salt water.

Sleeping locations were assigned without any explanation. Rocco was given the aptly named "coffin," where you had to boost yourself up and stick your legs into a short, flat, boxlike space with your head out in the open. Was it because he was considerably shorter than me? Taller people would have to sleep on their side with their legs bent; in order to sleep on their other side, they'd partially emerge, turn, and re-coffin themselves.

Rocco would have been sleeping in the master bedroom if he were on his boat. Here he got the dregs, treated like a hired hand. Not good for team spirit. I had the settee in the saloon, a better berth than Rocco by several stars—short, but not as short as the coffin. If he resented my being there, after drawing that berth, his resentment must have soared. Or he saw it coming.

Back at the motel, getting to bed was quick. I wasn't ready to share my dive-shop experience with Rocco or seek his counsel on whether I should stay ashore with Nikki or go to sea with him and Walt. I needed to hear another ten or twenty words or grunts from him before we could bond, but he acted like he'd donated his vocal cords to science, unable to even say goodnight.

Conversely, William Shakespeare, though dead, was a better source of counsel than the man sleeping several feet away. So I looked to Shakespeare's lines from *Julius Caesar* for inspiration:

> *There is a tide in the affairs of men,*
> *Which, taken at the flood, leads on to fortune...*

Should I interpret tide literally, and sail away, or choose the *femme d' affaires*, buy out her partner, and see if that's where the fortune lies? William, the wordsmith, continued:

> *Omitted, all the voyage of their life*
> *Is bound in shallows and in miseries.*

Is this the possible consequence of passing her up, or the frequent destiny of men hunkering down with the female instead of taking on the risks and challenges of life's more daunting journeys? Unfortunately, William cannot answer me. Bards have an annoying habit of writing in riddles to avoid accountability, leaving experts and students to discuss ad infinitum.

For several years, I'd nurtured the concept of boundlessness found in psychobabble books during my search for the meaning and purpose of life. In a robust life, we possess boundless love and compassion for others, and have unlimited capacity for personal growth and achievement. Here, it seemed that we were competing with one another when we should be acting as a team. There was no boundless appreciation of others, only silence and a withholding of information. I asked many questions Rocco could answer, but only Walt responded—briefly.

Nikki offered at least a chance to share boundless passion and appreciation. Where was the prize, the reward for winning, if it was a competition? I felt I'd already won. Natural law imbues most men with a desire for women. I had three choices: go home, stay with Nikki, or sail with two grumpy goats, and Nikki may not have been an option. I thought the task of getting us and the boat to the target destination was competition enough—us against the elements. Was the team concept and spirit unknown to these guys? First one to fall overboard would find out.

After three days together, it appeared Rocco was renting space in my mind. Discovering whether he was competing with me— hard to imagine— or something more complex was beyond the scope of my psychological training. There are people you cannot understand, but can walk away from. To my knowledge, there was nothing Walt could have told him to make him feel competitive and provoke one-upmanship. His being a quarter century older complicated my analysis. What did another twenty-five years do for and to a person?

This was too complicated for what was supposed to be a straightforward sailing trip with the guys. On the other hand, if my recent luck held, it could be very stimulating. The difficulty was I didn't know, and the unknown was of concern. It was also why I was there.

On Friday morning, October 22, with the laundry finished, the water and fuel tanks filled, and the food stored, we set sail at 1115 military time. (Since we were headed southeast into the prevailing wind, in many instances the term "set sail" really meant "motored.")

It was a delightful day. Rocco, surely an old salt and more experienced even than Walt, was at the helm, no doubt to ensure a propitious start. After going under our first of many drawbridges on the Intracoastal Waterway (ICW), Rocco immediately ran us aground while holding his cup of coffee (he had his priorities, above all). We were still within sight of the traffic we had just delayed, now becoming our jeer-leaders while we were delayed, as the drawbridge was lowered and traffic resumed its endless pace on U.S. Route 1. We could have walked to the bridge we sailed under moments ago using the new land Rocco had discovered. Was he a descendant of Columbus? He looked Italian.

Walt: "What the hell?"

Rocco: "What the fuck?"

Me: "Are we there yet? Is this our stop? That was quick. I over-packed."

Rocco: "The damn marker is dead ahead."

Me, looking around: "There's another marker just like it to the left, looks to be closer. Does that matter to us?"

Walt: "Quick, put it in reverse. The channel goes to the left here."

Rocco: "Well, Jesus H."

Inauspicious beginning, but better him than me, and it looked like missing a channel marker would be easy to do. This was one time it was good for me to start at the bottom, though we needn't be stuck on it. This soft grounding was no problem, put there by fate to remind us of our fallibility early in the journey, and set a dirge-like tone for the cruise. If the old pro was going to show me a thing or two, he was half finished. Lesson number one of connect-the-dots: you had to clear the nearest channel marker first, no going out of turn or there'd be no going.

Reversing the engine soon had us afloat and motoring south on the picturesque waterway toward North Palm Beach: beautiful homes, boats, and no stoplights. We encountered a brief, refreshing shower in the afternoon, providing the first test of our ability to find our rain gear and don it quickly.

Blue herons and pelicans were the wildlife of the day. Walt kept Rocco company in his gray funk. I was alone in being inexplicably cheerful. Apparently, I didn't have a proper appreciation for the sport of sailing. To fix that, they let me steer as early as 1430, including navigating a drawbridge around 1545. Circling wide and slowly to avoid the other boats awaiting the bridge opening, which in this part of the waterway occurs on the half-hour at best, I ran aground where the channel narrowed due to silt accumulation. There was water there, but not enough. How was I supposed to see underwater? (That's what charts were for, but no one thought it necessary to look at them.) By that time, Walt had also run us aground, probably why I was given the helm. It was hard to do as bad as my partners until given a chance.

Being another soft grounding, a quick reverse of the engine lifted us off in time to clear the drawbridge. We eventually stopped on purpose, to get fuel, then anchored at Peanut Island near the inlet at North Palm Beach to prepare dinner.

After dark, we motored out of the inlet into oncoming rough seas pushed by the wind. A mile out, we hoisted and set the sails, turning south on a port tack. The wind was from the east at 6 to 10 knots, which made for an easy sail under a clear sky, the moon's soft light reflecting off the white sails. The feeling was peaceful and enchanting, with the excitement of a high-risk adventure. I took the watch from 2100 to midnight and thoroughly enjoyed the quiet beauty of it. If the whole trip were this ideal, it would be wonderful. I imagined the boat had a happy spirit, doing what it was made to do. The autohelm handled much of my work while I supervised, thinking through the highs of yesterday and enjoying the lights of the Florida coastline, trying to guess which city was coming, which was being left behind, with no idea whatsoever after North Palm Beach. The maps I understood were in the car, there being no visible roads out here.

No issues existed between the boat and me and, before long, the other humans were in their bunks. How soundly could they possibly sleep knowing I was on watch after no more than a few minutes of training? Sailing must be easy, prior groundings notwithstanding. Life was good.

When relieved of my watch, I went below. My bunk was on the starboard side, we were on a port tack, so I was secure in my bunk by the list to starboard. Sleep eventually came, but I was jolted awake at sunrise as Walt stomped around in the cockpit to start the engine, saying we had drifted too close to the Gulf Stream. We could have drifted all the way back to Maine, Rocco's home, in short order—a subliminal error, perhaps? It was eerie to clearly overhear the conversation in the cockpit, there being no other sounds but a few slapping waves on a listless boat, no feeling of forward motion. The wind had diminished, the heat was building, and we were drifting out to sea. Walt started the engine, put it in gear, and motored on.

I didn't presume it would be well received for me, the junior seaman, to ask who was on watch while we were drifting. Based on Walt's tone, it was someone else. If this was what we got in safe, open water, what lay ahead when it got complicated? Falling asleep makes it difficult to see the compass, or a freighter in your path. In the Gulf Stream, there are a lot of freighters. I was in more danger with them on watch than they were with me. I was green and challenged enough to stay bug-eyed awake.

There would be other mornings of sudden scrambling, excited comments, and cussing. You could count on cussing. It was possible we had a crew of four, because Jesus Christ seemed to be involved with everything that went wrong, and God was occasionally called upon to bless or, more frequently, damn this or that. I had a formative church grounding when my marching orders came from my parents, though my attendance lately hadn't been Rock-of-Ages solid. Perhaps that's why I thought we only had a crew of three; I wasn't attuned to perceive the fourth crew member, and He was apparently the only one on watch when the helmsman drifted off. That was scary—or maybe not; He didn't hit anything. I did wonder what Walt thought, if at all, about his new acquaintance other than he had no alternative crew.

I threw together a familiar breakfast of shredded wheat, bananas, and orange juice. New to me was that the table and bowl moved while I was trying to crumble the biscuits, which makes a mess in the best of circumstances, and it was not easy to pour liquids while on the move, better done over the sink. In the future, it would be smart to use a cereal already sweetened and in bite-sized granularity, reducing the challenge and number of steps. Already having milk on it may be too much to ask.

To see such a blazing sunrise while on the water after having traveled all night was a memorable first, absent the abrupt awakening. This adventure was so new, I was frequently impressed. There were a lot of boats about, starting early on Saturday morning. A few were dive boats; many were fishermen, a few using kites. Kite fishing got the pelagic fish to bite when they were otherwise not so inclined. The live bait strung from the kite attracted fish, and the vertical line kept the stringer out of the water, so that stringer-shy fish would take the bait. And, as in all of life, you need a hook.

The day was clear and hot, until we hit heavy showers outside of Miami Beach in the early afternoon that cooled us off quickly. We went in at Miami and anchored at the Coconut Grove Sailing Club. It was only five bucks for a mooring, as Rocco was a member of a sailing club that had a reciprocal agreement for benefits at other clubs. At least that's what he said. Showers were free, hot, and with plenty of water. It felt great after missing a day. I did not know yet what a luxury this would later be, or the number of months before my next warm shower. Walt fixed a great meal of ham, pineapple, sweet potatoes, raisins, and cooked carrots. My beta-carotene needs were being met, though the orange tint revealed in the shower was due to intense sun exposure.

After we had our dinner, the mosquitoes started on theirs. We were busy learning the Global Positioning System (GPS) displayed on a new Garmin GPS receiver before our trek across the Gulf Stream, which would take us out of sight of land for the first time. We couldn't track the glide path of a mosquito and compute our azimuth at the same time, whatever that is, and we needed to figure it out. Without mosquito screening, it was open season.

Technology that reduces the humdrum activities of life and leaves human beings free to challenge the impossible, discover the unexplored, appealed to me. GPS was originally installed by the Department of Defense as NAVSTAR (Navigation System with Timing and Ranging) for military purposes, and is made up of twenty-four satellites traveling 12,000 miles above the earth in a Medium Earth Orbit (MEO), making two complete trips around the earth every twenty-four hours. Our brick-sized receiver receives digital signals from those satellites, which are constantly sending information including the time (accurate to a billionth of a second, according to my tests) and the location of the satellites. Through the process of triangulation (requiring three satellites within view), and the timing of how long it takes to receive a signal, it can tell you where you are on the planet, expressed by latitude and longitude.

The receiver can compute navigational information by knowing the user's location and the longitude and latitude of the destination, which we derived from the navigational charts. Each combination of longitude and latitude constitutes a waypoint. Since you cannot always sail straight to your ultimate destination, it is necessary to devise a route of interim destinations, a series of waypoints, that may, in toto, be an arc, but consists of a lot of straight lines, akin to connecting the dots. Sailing waypoints must be locations in the water. Never make a sailing waypoint on land thinking you will eventually arrive there by boat. You won't, and it could be a disaster. Technically, you would be stuck at the border of sea and land, in however many pieces.

Typically, sailors have to keep logs of their progress and make calculations for compass error, tides, the current and drift, slippage or leeway, and steering errors, frequently taking readings to ascertain how far off course they might be. When approaching land, they have to speculate as to where the destination is on a shore that gives no clue, has no lighted signs with arrows, and has absolutely no resemblance to an Interstate exit. By the time you can tell an inlet from the shoreline, you could be hard aground. It gives me great respect for the pre-GPS navigators—that survived.

Given the right information, our GPS unit will display the appropriate compass course to follow, current speed, course deviation, location, and a lot of other amazing data. This unit will not get us there by itself, but we should know where we are at any time. GPS removes a lot of risk, labor, and guesswork, if the batteries stay charged and the operators know how to use it.

The technology had my attention. It was also new to both Rocco and Walt. Since they would rather learn it later, I decided to make it my forte, to ensure we progressed safely. It was also a skill that, unlike sailing, would not take me long to learn, making me of value in the uncontested field of navigation.

I suffered a jarring, head-slapping night with several relentless mosquitoes and awoke to a gray, still morning in our lagoon-like mooring, ears ringing; I blew the hailing bugle to call the courtesy water-borne jitney for a ride ashore to purchase milk, yogurt, bananas, and bagels at the Easy Shop. Upon my return, we topped off the water tanks and cast off for Angel Fish Creek, 20 miles south, to await a suitable weather forecast and set up a better angle for crossing the Gulf Stream to Gun Cay (pronounced "key") on the typically southeast wind.

While motoring out of the lagoon, the wind was so light, I suggested we try the weather channel on the VHF radio. Forecast was for wind five to ten knots, seas one to two feet . . . perfect! We immediately decided to head for the Bahamas. We revved up the engine and pointed the boat east. Our chain of command had so few working links, decisions could be made and implemented instantly.

We passed abandoned and ghostly looking homes built on pilings in Biscayne Bay, called Stiltsville. There were only seven homes remaining after

Hurricane Andrew the previous year. We saluted the Cape Florida lighthouse on Key Biscayne to our north, our last view of the U.S. for a while, and were soon into the Atlantic Ocean.

This was it. Game on.

The seas were reassuringly calm. As we left the mainland behind, the seas resembled waves of windblown grain fields, starting me to singing. That should boost the spirits! Or get me thrown overboard. Rain showers were all around us, easily spotted at sea as dense columns of gray reaching from the sky to the ocean, but none falling on us. Tankers were occasionally seen in the north-south shipping channels of the Gulf Stream and nearby. The current of the Gulf Stream gives northbound ships a free two to three knots per hour, and I would expect the south-bounders would stay out of the strongest current. A lone bird sat on the water (possibly flotsam) in an area that resembled the Sargasso Sea, and I experienced my first sunset at sea. By this time the Miami skyline had disappeared and we had a water horizon for 360 degrees, a brilliant golden sunset surrounding us with nothing to block the view. It was either sky or smooth water, and the golden sky set the water ablaze, like living on top of a mirror, unlike anything possibly experienced on land—headshakingly resplendent.

We had departed Biscayne Bay around 1200 and would arrive at Gun Cay Pass (our first sighting of landfall) around 2200, where there is a lighthouse. Gun Cay is fifty miles from the Florida coast, the closest Bahamian island to the U.S. along with Bimini, ten miles to the north, either one an easy trip in the high-powered motor boats of the day, assuming good weather and you can afford the fuel.

CHAPTER
Four

The Perilous and Beautiful Bahamas:
Was Christopher Columbus on drugs?

C losely related to the United States both currently and historically, the Bahamas is an archipelago of about 700 islands and islets and nearly 2,400 cays and rocks, extending about 800 km (almost 500 miles) from a point southeast of Palm Beach, Florida, to a point off the eastern tip of Cuba. Few, maybe 30, islands are inhabited, and the number is increasing. Grand Bahama, home of Freeport, is the most northwesterly island; Great Inagua is the most southern, on the eastern end of the chain, where flamingos outnumber humans 50 to 1.

In the 18th century, the American Revolution left disgruntled colonists (Loyalists) living in America who may have had relatives and contacts in Britain, and had been content to live under the rule of King George. Many decided to eventually return to Britain, including slaves offered their freedom. Others settled elsewhere, many in Canada, and about 10,000 Loyalists from the Carolinas—tobacco and cotton farmers who wanted to maintain trade with Great Britain—took an interest in the Bahamas. Cotton plantations bloomed throughout the Bahamas, farmers bringing their slaves with them. As one crop failed to be profitable, the islanders tried others, such as pineapples, sisal, salt farming, sponge diving, and fishing. Though a beautiful locale, it was tough eking out a living, and many original settlements are now abandoned and overgrown.

The Bahamas have been used as a resource for slave traders, a refuge or base for buccaneers and pirates, notably Blackbeard, for the blockade runners of the Civil War as well as rum runners of Prohibition. More recently, members of the drug trade have plied the air and waters in their pursuit of a lucrative vocation. In fact, the Bahamas, with all its islands and waterways, is so perfect for drug runners it was called the Cocaine Islands when the drug trade was running rampant.

In the 1970s, cocaine was the drug of choice, signifying power and panache; it was clean, white, pretty, and expensive. The high didn't last long, so drug makers tried to jack up its potency by free-basing. Adding ammonia and ethyl ether to cocaine hydrochloride improved the hit, but it was dangerous. Users, including Richard Pryor, were seriously burned. It was safer when distilled by cooking it in saucepans with baking soda and water, producing tiny rocks which could be smoked. Bahamians are credited with inventing this "crack" form of cocaine, named for the crackling sound made during the cooking process. Several affectionate names followed, such as rock, kryptonite, kibbles and bits, scrabble, and appropriately, love. By the late 70s, the Colombians produced a glut of cocaine, the price fell, more people could then afford it, and the market took off. Crack moved to New York City, perhaps because the U.S. drug enforcement agencies significantly reduced the Bahamian drug trade after a long and difficult struggle. However, drug seizures still occur among drug traffickers (and Hollywood personalities) in the Bahamas, making this a lively place, unless a seizure killed you first.

There are desirable alternatives available, and it is my highly recommended belief that, when choosing a mind-altering substance, choose education, for lifetime highs and fewer lows. Of all the mind-altering substances in the world, education provides the longest, most satisfying high, and a desirable death rate of zero, in stark contrast to the others.

Was Christopher Columbus on drugs when he made his first landing on San Salvador, a Bahamian island? There is no way of knowing. But volunteering to sail off the edge of what was then considered to be a flat earth seems foolhardy and raises questions about his sobriety. Historians properly credit him with being in pursuit of the mind-altering substance called knowledge. And conquest. Those who followed Chris's daring did so in search of plundered gold and other minerals. Many have also fought over control and use of Bahamian real estate and waterways, including the epic battles between the French and British, followed by more recent action during World War II.

Burdened but undeterred by the knowledge of the unrest that has existed in these islands, and the pirates and drug traffickers who still called the Bahamas home, we negotiated our way in the dark through a narrow channel between Gun Cay and North Cat Cay, thankful Walt had been here before. Being new to this, I didn't know what to look for or when I had found it. (Cat Cay is not to be confused with Cat Island, further east, home of the largest known accumulation of oceanic whitetip sharks, at the edge of the continental shelf where the slope provides deeper waters for whitetips, marlin, and tuna.) We continued our thrust into the dark, empty night, set on a course of 99 degrees magnetic toward Russel, a symbol on the charts representing a light six meters high, flashing every 5 seconds. If true, it should not be hard to spot in a world devoid of all other light.

The moon came up, making the night wonderfully romantic. The noise of the engine seemed comfortingly strong and sure to a neophyte sailor so far away from land for the first time, in the middle of the ocean concealed in the pervasive black of night. I did not question what I was thinking and why I was there.

Sitting propped against the bulkhead in the cockpit, I was facing the vast emptiness behind us. The bioluminescence of the phytoplankton alongside our boat lit up our wake like tiny Christmas lights on a hassock of snow. The illuminated wake and the stern light on the transom belied the glacial six to seven knots we were actually moving. Our progress was smooth, the temperature and the breeze were perfect, and the autopilot was doing the steering. I had determined what number of degrees the compass must read from my back-of-the-compass vantage point to ensure we remained on course, but got up to look around occasionally to verify we weren't on target to collide with another vessel. If it wasn't my watch, it was still my life. At the moment, life was good. I felt insignificant and alone, but still in control of my world—as long as I stayed in the boat.

Suddenly, I noticed a break in the darkness. "Hey, guys, anyone else see that light on the horizon south of us? What's over there?"

"There shouldn't be anything," Walt replied. "Andros is in that direction, but not that close."

"It's a pretty bright light, getting brighter. Do pirates announce themselves in such a way?"

"Dunno," said Walt. "Could be pirates, could be the Coast Guard. Either one is bad news. Coast Guard can tear your boat up if they search it for drugs."

"Au contraire, moi capitan. Coast Guard will probably let you live, pirates not so much, is my guess."

"Hmmmphh! Sonova bitch," muttered Rocco.

"Keep an eye on it," said Walt.

"How 'bout we turn off our lights so they can't find us, in case it might be trouble. Right now, they aren't heading straight for us. Why make it easy?" I said.

"Rocco, you know where the switch is. Let's go dark awhile."

In this remote stretch of nothingness, if those were pirates, we would never see our families again. Was that a real possibility? Where else could that boat be going at this hour? If you had a body to hide, this might be the place.

We waited, and we watched, trying to make out the course of the vessel. My pulse quickened. When it is just you and pirates, alone on the water, and they are fast and armed and you are neither, you're at the mercy of the merciless. Many sailors have disappeared, and the ocean makes for a readily available and boundless grave; fish will clean up the remains. As we headed more southeast, the boat continued to the northwest, falling away with no apparent interest in us. Cautiously, we began to relax.

I watched a few shooting stars and let my gaze drift out across the wake of the boat into a vast nothingness. We were a mere speck afloat on the Grand Bahamas Bank, wrapped in nature, feeling minuscule and vulnerable.

Waking before dawn, I realized it had rained briefly, and the mate on watch had closed the hatches, which eventually made it too hot to sleep. Even though the showers stopped, Rocco left the hatches closed. It seemed insensitive to let those sleeping suffocate. Should I complain, or shut up, swallow hard, and write in my diary to relieve the frustration? We'd been jammed together on this boat for seventy-two hours, and already I was looking for ways to survive the closeness. I wondered if being single made me more allergic to all this togetherness?

In retrospect, it would have taken a considerate person to reopen the hatches with the possibility they might need to be closed again, twice disturbing his sleep while at the wheel. Plus, Rocco was not feeling the heat inside while in the cockpit. Unaware, I may have done the same. What the heck, he wasn't running a Bed and Breakfast, turning down the bed and placing quality chocolates on the pillow at night (although it would be very well received). Once I conceded that fact, I was over it. If I hadn't found him so anti-social before, I would have thought nothing of it. *Hmmm, will this be a sailing trip or a psychodrama? If my mind can do these contortions, what are they thinking? I suspect nothing at all.*

With only a couple hours' sleep, but needing oxygen more, I sat in the cockpit and watched for shooting stars. There were plenty. Celestial fireworks! At home, if you saw a meteor, you thought it was a big deal. But seeing one every place you look in the sky makes Chicken Little seem ahead of her time, or perhaps she also was at sea in October, where the sky is always falling. The Orionids meteor shower runs October 2nd through November 7th, peaking around October 21–22. The moon had not yet risen, so the light created as the meteors entered the atmosphere was easily visible. These are fragments from the famous comet Halley—a trail of dust behind the comet as it travels its elliptical path through the solar system—each one blazing a brief trail in the upper atmosphere as Earth intersects the path. From midnight to dawn is the best time, and the middle of the ocean the best place to see meteors. My pupils must have been dilated to the size of dimes.

Rocco had passed Russel during his time at the helm and was progressing toward the Northwest Channel. We had to follow our course closely to avoid running aground. There was a vast amount of water to look at, but it was dangerously shallow in many places. Still less than impressed with the sailing skills of my skippers, I did not want to be awakened by water slapping on the side of my bunk as the boat settled to the bottom, the professionals powering off in *Speedy* to safety, leaving me forgotten and left behind. So, I stayed awake and kept watch.

Eventually, ever so gradually, sunlight appeared. I didn't know why it picked that morning to come up more slowly than usual. Many mornings it jumps up in the sky like the most eager new worker. When there are no obstructions on the eastern horizon, and you are at sea level, sunrise starts early and ever so slightly. There is a lot of low-light time before that blaze of a fireball peeks over the horizon, during which we were looking for a buoy we had to pass to the south, then a mile later, pass a lighthouse within 50 yards on the north. If we traversed this short maze, we would not run aground, something we'd proven we could easily do. Out here, there were no tow trucks. In fact, there was nothing, just water—water and sky.

And that's all we saw, no buoy and no lighthouse. According to the charts, the lighthouse was visible from eight miles away. Based on our reckoning, we were too close for that to be true, unless we were way off course. But that couldn't be; we had a GPS unit.

A light appeared! Then where the hell was the buoy? I spun around—it's not there! When these things don't come in the right sequence, you fear you will go aground in the next second, ripping your hull to shreds moments before you sink out of sight. This maze isn't out here as a party game. Instantly, we dropped our speed to limit any damage caused by the coral heads, then hunted, carefully, slowly—first the charts, then the horizon, back to the charts. We looked more closely; what other clues were there? We were approaching the light on the safest side, the north, but not too far to that side? It could be wrong. What if it were the buoy?

As the dawn's light increased and the flashing light neared, Rocco suddenly yelled "Damn! That's the flashing buoy. Have to pass on the south side!" He whipped the wheel for a fast turn to starboard.

We had sweated this out for an hour as we approached the light. When there was little time to read the charts, Rocco wouldn't trust me with that job and his life. What did I know? Rocco had to do it all himself. Had I been allowed to read the charts, would I have read that the buoy was to be flashing every 2 seconds? Looking at it afterwards, it was clear as could be! It's a good thing I was with experts, although I should have reviewed Rocco's resume. Now a lighthouse, visible for eight miles, was supposed to be only a mile from the buoy. Why couldn't we see it? We followed our GPS course slowly, counting down the seconds of longitude, hoping to see the light before the day got brighter.

If we were to run aground, a threat to consider seriously at this point, the boat's owner should be involved; surely he would want to play a role. So I woke Walt: "Hey Walt, you may want to see this. We could use another set of eyes." He responded quickly when Rocco and I both told him we were in jeopardy. Besides the threat of loss of life, his boat was uninsured. Everything was at risk. I watched the navigation screen on the GPS, ensuring the coordinates were moving in the right direction. As we crawled toward where the lighthouse was supposed to be, the sun was still behind clouds. With the sea this quiet, were it not for the clouds, we could have seen any object sticking out of the water within several miles.

Eventually, we came upon a few vertical sticks in the water with two birds perched on them. *Is this what passes for a lighthouse? What happens in rough seas?* The sea was becalmed with only Victorian glass imperfections— a desolate scene. A destroyed "lighthouse" on a lifeless sea, in the quiet rising light of daybreak, with albatross surrogates perched on the partial ruins, nesting material draping down like a windblown comb-over. And no light! Being recently of the Outer Banks of North Carolina, I have seen lighthouses. This was no lighthouse. These ruins were three feet tall, at best. And having a light on a lighthouse would be meaningful.

Passing to the north within 50 feet, we watched the numbers increase on the fathometer (depth gauge) as the sea bottom slowly sank away until we knew we were back in deep water. What a relief! We could breathe again. Almost immediately, a school of porpoise appeared, swimming alongside us, responding as we yelled and Rocco slapped the side of the boat. How surprisingly joyous!

"Does that make a difference?" I asked. "Can they hear that?"

"Hell yeah, of course. They have sonar," Rocco replied, and continued with his drumming, showing a side of him I didn't know existed.

We were not moving fast enough to give them good sport, however, and they soon swam away leaving us to trudge on for another eight hours to Nassau harbor, on New Providence.

Nassau, New Providence:
What a difference a bridge made

By the time we arrived in Nassau, the most economically important island of the Bahamas and containing more than 50% of the population, we had been motoring non-stop for more than 28 hours. The seas could not have been more calm or the weather more temperate. With no wind came no sails, no heeling, little bobbing and dipping, just a few tense moments. As a neophyte ocean sailor, I felt fortunate and grateful. Thus far, it had been a terrific experience, with little sacrifice of comfort.

Sailing into Nassau Harbor with New Providence to starboard, we were greeted by a lighthouse on the port side. The scene was evocative of Edward Hopper's painting "The Long Leg"—a white lighthouse isolated on a point of land, having four round windows rather than two square, with the requisite light keeper's house and, here, a utility building; the foreground a lovely seascape with darker sand than Hopper's, shoals awash with white foam, and half-submerged, rounded boulders. Intermittent clouds hung overhead in a robin's-egg-blue sky, with a gray and white dense cloud bank on the horizon. It wasn't Monhegan, Maine, it was better—Paradise Island.

I'd not seen Nassau since 1970. It was exciting to return to a destination of my youth. It evoked feelings of nostalgia as I mused over all the landmarks I remembered—the lighthouse, a familiar hotel, the bridge my moped worked so hard to climb, the casino, and the marketplace. Walt said we might stay here a couple days. Terrific, we would have relaxed tourist time for looking around, trying different restaurants—what travel is all about. But Rocco and I were soon to learn about Walt's estimates of length of stay.

After passing Customs, we had ribs for dinner at Tony Roma's. Later, I was chatted up by a comely young island girl named Felicia who, supposedly, had lots of nice, attractive "friends." At the time, I did not realize what role these three things—Customs, food, and sex—would play in my life. But before the journey was over, Customs would prove tedious, ribs like Tony serves would be scarce, and Felicia and friends tedious and not scarce. Felicia was greeting people at the boatyard gate. She had a difficult accent and I wanted to be respectful, but soon determined Felicia was a working girl, this was her marketplace, and sailors were her prospects.

I wasn't her prospect, and went back to the boat without Felicia or her friends. This was the first time we'd stopped since the U.S., so we'd probably meet more like Felicia. Sex, food, and drugs: the first two the concerns of sailors and their vendors; the latter the concern of Customs and the trade of pirates—possibly sailors, for all I know. This foray was shaping up to be a stimulating experience, no matter your upbringing; there is always something new to learn.

According to Walt, we'd be moving on to Highborne Cay tomorrow, where we'd finally get into the water for snorkeling. If it had already been two days, then I had stepped through a wormhole or passed out drunk for half the time, because it seemed we arrived only a couple of hours ago. Had time slipped away? Maybe Walt counted as two days the day we arrived and the day we left (like the three day/two night stays offered by hotels), or maybe Felicia frightened him. By Walt's calculations, two days were approximately 14 hours long, saving 34 hours. So if we were in a destination only one day, when would we leave, the same day? Makes sense. A twelve-day week was now possible. Maritime math? Another learning opportunity, especially for those who think math is finite, or a niggling practice?

Sleep came easily in the calm of the Texaco dock, but I awoke early again. Unable to find my running shoes, everything being stowed away in nooks and crannies and lockers, I laced on a pair of tennis shoes and went for a run over the bridge connecting Nassau to Paradise Island. What a difference a bridge made! Paradise Island was green, manicured, and flowing with fountains; Nassau looked like its waste disposal area, including all of the mangy-looking dumpster dogs. Of course, no one was expected to hire Frederick Olmsted to landscape the commercial dock area on any island, but what if I could build such a bridge between Rocco and myself? While on Paradise Island, I bought muffins for the crew and headed back to the boat.

My partners didn't deviate from the schedule, if there actually was a schedule, since it was revised by the captain so frequently. I was harassed for being late and holding up progress, the muffins be damned. Both Walt and Rocco were strong personalities, and I figured mine had better get stronger quickly if I was to survive. They were not soliciting my opinion or preferences. Both had to be proactively stated. This felt like a job. In the future, when I leave the boat, I'll take my wallet and AmEx card with me, not just a couple bucks, because I fear they'd have no qualms leaving me behind.

After a few rushed exercises on the dock to the beat of "C'mon, let's go; hey, we're leaving; release that bow line," as if we were about to miss our plane, we pulled out of Nassau harbor and headed east for islands unknown. Exercising on docks would quickly become a memory for me, and I'd never know in advance how long "two days" would be, but felt one thing for sure—an absence of more than two hours would put me at risk of being marooned.

At the east end of New Providence, we set a course of 134 degrees to travel approximately 30 nautical miles. We discovered favorable winds on our way across the Yellow Banks, put up the jib and mainsail, and sailed for a while under clear blue skies. Clear skies don't last forever, and winds shift. Soon it rained, and we motored. During the sudden rain squall I found out how far a 1/3 cup of orange juice could go. Looked to be 10 to 15 feet! What a mess! Though what was in the cup was not much, it spread throughout the cabin when left briefly unattended before a big wave hit our small boat. More accelerated learning.

Approaching Highborne Cay, we took note of the chop from the southwest and decided to anchor at Allan's Cay in a cove with a northern entrance, north of Highborne. Our first objective was to get in the water; later we would try bathing. Donning snorkel equipment, we swam toward the island known to be populated only by iguanas. As we crawled out of the water and onto the beach, the iguanas similarly came crawling out of the dense brush to greet us. They were the only thing uglier than human beings in diving masks with breathing tubes and big flipper feet; a weird welcoming party in either case. They snapped at each other with razor-sharp teeth, something I hoped they would keep to themselves. There were at least twenty and possibly more than thirty, so we halted our invasion and held our little bit of ground at the water's edge, having no reason or desire to go any further.

Gazing back at the boat, the only one in the cove, I realized this was what advertisements are made of—one lone sailing vessel, anchored in crystal-clear blue-green water among verdant, tropical islands with tan beaches, inducing peaceful relaxation. My next thought was regret that I had not devised a way to get my camera to the beach when snorkeling was my mode of transportation, therefore, no picture, only a memory. Too bad; it would have been worthy of National Geographic.

Unfortunately, the sky was quickly turning dark gray. The impending rain presented another new opportunity. Rain brought fresh water, which we had in limited supply. If we could get back to the boat before the rain started (more critically, before it quit), we could take a shower in the rain, an enticing and romantic idea had I been in different company. Still, a freebie! We wouldn't have to use manufactured and stored water. We could also collect water for laundry from the deck runoff. Men showered communally in most locker rooms, so there was no reason for three guys not to feel comfortable taking a shower on deck. No one was nearby except two Bahamians in the cove across the way, conch fishing out of a skiff that had seen better days many years ago, and they'd likely seen better looking sailors showering on deck.

We swam back and scrambled aboard, stowing our snorkeling gear, dropping our swimsuits, letting the downpour wash salt off the cabin top before collecting the rainwater with buckets hanging under the rear scuppers (deck drain holes), after jamming small sponges in the forward scupper holes on each side. Three nude men were bending over, digging in the lazarettes for flat trays, the handheld shower head, wash cloths, and soap, as Walt instructed us on the steps to take for open-cockpit bathing in the rain. T'was a sight to behold and a feeling of being a kid again playing in the rain without concern—an intense, rare dose of nature, showering on deck with a heavenly rinse, a full moon, and lightning in the western sky.

With a steady, velvet breeze that night, we slept well, but there's no such thing as sleeping through the night without interruption when hanging on the hook (anchored). We either experienced intermittent rain showers, the noisy, disquieting tugging on the anchor chain, or waves coming from a new, unsettling direction (or all three), ensuring we did not get many consecutive hours (sometimes only minutes) of sleep. When dawn broke, we had wind from the west and waves rolling in from the north, broadsiding the boat. The wind positioned the boat with the bow toward the west, so that the northerly waves would make the boat the most uncomfortable and us unable to stand. Hello, paradise.

We had to find a better anchorage before we could attempt a hot breakfast. When Walt asked who wanted pancakes and sausage, there were three "me's." When he asked who would cook them under current conditions, there were three "not me's." Moving the boat to a more protected cove, we saw the conch fishermen sculling their boat to their dive site, causing me to reflect on jobs I would not want. Theirs could be interesting and enjoyable for perhaps a half day since the environment was captivating, but the greenery of the proverbial grass where I sat was already lush, no need to risk it.

After breakfast, we lowered the motor onto *Speedy* and set out into the Atlantic to snorkel over a reef Walt knew from his earlier travels, and dropped an anchor. I was apprehensive about my first time jumping into such a large "pond" this far from land, and I had not yet used my recently purchased equipment, which added to my prep time and made me last out of the dinghy. In addition to the fine tuning of the snorkeling gear, I was donning a wetsuit—because I had one—which is a struggle in the best of conditions, and there was no place to sit without rolling backward, headfirst into the ocean with my legs bound together, mafia-style, for similar results. Rocco and Walt were over the side quickly and never looked back. The buddy system I'd heard so much about in water safety courses obviously applied only to even numbers, and only in the continental U.S. They were headed for land, a fair distance away, surely farther than I could swim without a snorkel, and I'd better follow. Oh my gosh! Apprehension level was off the charts.

Timidly finding a passageway between the coral heads barely beneath the surface of the water, and passing over an intricate reef swarming with fish, all the while I wondered: *where are the sharks?* Though there was no shortage of underwater life to look at, I made my way to the beach to meet up with my "buddies." I was either the only one who owned a wetsuit, or overdressed. Or both. I joined them in searching the remote, pristine beach for items lost overboard or in shipwrecks, feeling like a high-fashion model on a prison chain-gang. Scavenging might become another skill I would learn from my sailing seniors, though it held no real fascination. Five-gallon buckets were a sought-after prize; we found only a round metal float they felt was deserving of passage on the good ship *Godspeed.* I suspected we'd carry it for a while, then discard it so one man's junk can become another man's treasure.

We swam back to our red rubber dinghy, anchored and floating alone, pitifully small against the backdrop of the vast Atlantic Ocean and a flawless blue sky with no end. Before leaving our anchorage, Walt and I decided to try spear fishing for grouper. (I wanted to get maximum value from my struggle to wedge myself into the wetsuit. Probably the last time I'd wear it.) We saw grouper so big we hoped they weren't hunting us. They never let us get close enough to use our spears, which was quite alright by me. Why start a fight you'll lose? A chicken dinner fresh out of a can was likely that night.

Highborne Cay:
Whose aquarium is this?

O nce back on the boat, we cast off for Highborne Cay. We'd been on the northeast corner of Allan's Cay, but with winds from the west and waves from the north, we decided to anchor near the dock on the southwest corner, where there was a telephone we could use to call home. Going into the harbor-like cove, Walt was out of the channel and ran the boat hard aground. This was not sand, but rock. When wiggling and reversing the engine didn't set us free, we tried shifting our weight by hanging on the boom off to one side. Several locals saw our desperate antics and came to our rescue in a speedboat. We tossed them the halyard for the mainsail, which went to the top of the mast, so they could pull our boat over on its side, decreasing our draft, allowing us to float free. Despite our proven deftness at going aground, this was our best yet. Being hard aground can destroy boats and kill sailors, depending on wave action and location. We were lucky this time.

Being anchored well brings a feeling of enormous relief, as it did here, in another picturesque anchorage. We'd picked a site with reasonable depth and room to swing without hitting bottom. The water, in its various shades of green and blue, was pure in color. In the Bahamas, where a sandy bottom approaches or breaks the surface, water appears to be clear or the color of the sand. With an abundance of phytoplankton, slightly deeper water may appear green. Otherwise, the wavelengths of light in the long end of the spectrum—red, orange, yellow, and green—are absorbed by the sediment-free water; the remaining shades of blue scatter and are reflected back, resulting in beautiful Caribbean blue water.

Shortly, Walt fired up the stove and pressure cooker for pot roast and onions, with a few potatoes and carrots thrown in to appease me. Excellent! I enjoyed the garnish, and learned Walt is fond of onions—to him, a major food group by itself.

After dinner, we had uninvited guests—pervasive, vicious mosquitoes that came in swarms at dusk, stayed for a couple hours, then thinned out, leaving a few sentinels to ensure you didn't sleep comfortably. If they had nothing else to do, they stayed until well past bedtime, like wastrels at an indoor shopping mall with a small food court of three humans. The pests found something they liked—me. My skirmishes with the mosquitoes were a source of amusement for Walt and Rocco as I narrated the strafing and biting carnage taking place on my body, any defense fruitless in our open-hatches situation. The little buggers must have known I could never reach them as they chewed on my ankles or the back of my knees in the dining table's curved banquette knee well, nor behind my head in the dark corners of the wood paneling; my only kills were when they rested on the light-colored headliner, which left blood stains I had to clean up.

What did the natives do? Were mosquitoes attracted to skin with less melanin, or were there enough mosquitoes to terrorize everyone? We questioned the reason for the existence of mosquitoes, but no one had any idea, real or imagined, other than the food chain for birds, lizards, and frogs. A recent philosophy was they were devised to keep us humble, in case golf or wind surfing didn't do it, put here for the challenge. Even in Heaven, and looking outside it appeared we were close, it would be boring without challenges to be conquered, chances to use the brain. How would the clever be distinguishable from the lazy? But then, like mosquitoes, would that be necessary? By mosquito standards, these guys were like New York City rats or Lake Wobegon children—above average—and probably grew up in the shadow of "Off!" drinking DEET, and developing immunity to my Jungle Juice.

A thermometer put on the surface of my sleeping area registered 97 degrees Fahrenheit. I thought it might be hotter. You might guess there was humidity, sitting right on the water. When sleeping, the top sheet made an effective line of mosquito defense except for my head (where the buzzing continued to terrorize). Even if the cabin temp was unbearable, the sheet could absorb the sweat. It was all quite miserable. The pests and heat made for a short night of sleep, a long night of trying.

Another challenge at this stop was the issue of telephone service, which was hard to find: will it be working, would our credit cards be accepted, and could we get through, or just reach an answering machine on the other end? The anticipation, then frustration, followed by having to find another working telephone at our next stop, put this challenge in a league with annoying pests. Walt was trying to reach his wife, Felicity, who was, unexpectedly, still in the hospital after her minor surgery, a portent of complications.

Concerned as I was for Felicity's health, and the pall it cast on the team, there was quiet and time for reflection. To survive, I must speak up for myself. My fellow sailors drank coffee early, and beer too soon thereafter. Not having either habit, I started each day in a hydration-deficit. I had to insist on refrigerator space for non-beer drinks, and was given a small allocation— important because we'd only seen ice cubes in Tony Roma's Nassau restaurant. Nothing was routine, so flexibility was required in large amounts. I missed my friends, automatic dishwashers, warm showers, air conditioning, and definitely screens! I'd have passed up sex, not that there was any chance to do so, for screens or, secondly, for an ice-cold drink, unless, of course, Nikki unexpectedly showed up—then we'd shuffle the cards and start a new game.

What would it take to have a voice, as second (and last) mate? Walt and Rocco could talk hours about boats, especially their twin Irwins. There was little I could add; anything I said was treated as an interruption. For the most part, I felt like a twerp, out of my element, except for my navigation skills, developed while on the high school cadet corps map team, now enhanced by GPS. As the boat's computer nerd, I'd likely get an occasional Where-the-Hell-Are-We call, hopefully save our lives, then they'd return me to Ignore mode, and I'd lie in a Wait state, for which I'm ready—all conjecture at this point. Meanwhile, being on a boat, there was always something to repair or improve: a craftsman's dream!

In such a meditative state, my senses were highly attuned. Uh-oh! What was that stench? "Rocco, you smell anything raunchy?"

"Nope, wasn't me."

Walt had moved to the cockpit—it wasn't him—so I followed my nose to discover much of the fresh food we'd purchased in Nassau two days ago had spoiled. All of the carrots, several potatoes, and a package of rolls were in a basket or a knit hanging bag; they'd cooked in the heat alongside us. Heck, at 97 degrees even in the cool of the evening and the shade of the saloon, what wouldn't take on an odious odor? We needed to get better at preserving our food since resupply was difficult. Few things smell worse, not even a dumpster behind a seafood restaurant, than spoiled potatoes ceaselessly swinging in a knit sack, rubbing their putrid juices on the saloon wall. Ho boy! Everything after that will smell like perfume, if I could smell at all. My nose may be permanently damaged. My brother blames me for breaking his, so it may be deserved, but that happened in a youthful pillow fight, which I won fair and square.

After only six days, the experience overall had been incredible. Forgetting for the moment the winged terror, the heat, and the potatoes, my love-for-nature cup runneth over, and Walt had us looking forward to Thunderball Cave near Staniel Cay, an awesome site used in making several movies.

Warderick Wells:
Peace in our time

There wasn't a whisper of wind when we awoke. Becalmed sailors can sit and sweat, sometimes for weeks, if they have no engine. Grateful for engines and fossil fuel, we motored from Highborne Cay to Warderick Wells (part of the Bahamas National Trust) through extremely calm seas, the movement of the boat creating our only cooling breeze. Standing on the bow, the crystal-clear water ahead of the boat's wake smooth and shiny like a polished linoleum floor, I could see all creatures on the bottom as we passed over them. The size and number of stingrays and giant starfish were unimaginable. Though sunny directly overhead, the heavily clouded sky approaching was so perfectly mirrored in the water that a horizon was hardly detectable.

Wherever I looked, constantly changing angles and intensity of light and clouds provided entertainment as moving museums of the best landscape art—unimpeded beauty without end from my foredeck position. Standing on the moon in 1971, an American astronaut, Alan Shepard, chose this area (Musha Cay) as the most stunning part of the world for the colors in the water.

Entering the harbor area, we saw a much larger Irwin stranded on a sandbar, the crew looking calm and collected about the whole thing. We saluted and stayed in the middle of the channel, missing the opportunity to get in trouble ourselves. After anchoring, we jumped in *Speedy* and sped toward the helpless boat to see if we could be of assistance. On the way, one of my superiors ran *Speedy* aground. When we arrived, the folks on the stranded boat, possibly observing our own grounding, declined our help, saying they would let the tide lift them off. They looked comfortable on their large yacht with deck chairs, wind surfers, etc. (where did I go so wrong?) so we left them none the worse for our visit.

At Exuma Cays park headquarters, the ranger station was staffed by Steve and his wife, volunteers-for-a-day. They monitored channel 16 on VHF radio, protected the sea life, dispensed anchorage sites, entertained curious yachters' questions, and fed yellow-breasted bananaquits singing high-pitched trills and willing to perch on your toes.

By now everyone else had run aground, even with the dinghy. Should I be denied? Walt and Rocco were, as usual, engaged in boat talk, so I requested permission to take *Speedy* exploring. The harbor area was similar to a parking lot for a teenager's first driving practice—pretty well closed in, not a lot of things to hit. I jumped in, took my camera to record the beauty, and zoomed out into my new world. Rocco had put a glass bottom into a five-gallon bucket using clear Plexiglas and marine caulking. When placed in the water, I could see all forms of underwater life, amazingly like dry snorkeling or a poor man's portable glass-bottomed boat. I tried taking underwater pictures through the bucket, but the boat was drifting, the bucket was bobbing up and down, the fish were swimming, and I had only two hands to work the zoom lens, focus the camera, and hold the bucket. Too much camera for too few hands, but neither man nor camera fell overboard.

Giving up on those summer camp-like activities, I focused on how to master the dinghy. What power! The small, eight-horsepower motor felt much bigger with two fewer passengers aboard, and it planed easily with just me, even threatening to flip over backwards. When I returned with *Speedy* in one piece and secured it to the mother ship, I was acknowledged by my captain to have earned my captain's license for a tender (a small or midsize craft for servicing larger vessels).

As evening fell, it became obvious we were in for another bout of high heat and mosquitoes, with no wind, no screens, and no sleep. If I could have trusted the sharks not to eat me, I would have tied a rope around my waist and hung in the water all night. As it was, I had no choice but to lie in the bunk and think, swat, and suffer the bites while listening to the buzzing around my head.

The next morning, we were marking one week on the boat. Constant stimulation made it seem much longer, like we'd been halfway around the world. It was hard to remember life before the boat. If this all-consuming trip took another nine weeks, I'd end up a quart low on blood and wouldn't remember my way home. We'd planned a big breakfast as part of the celebration for surviving this long, and it included onions. Walt wasn't just fond of onions, he loved them, with all the concomitant zeal of a recent convert, and he was in charge. Unfortunately, onions don't spoil easily, and they don't sit well with me in bulk. If, for each meal he cooked, ingredients were listed in order of prevalence, onions would be at the top.

After breakfast, we went to Long Island (there is more than one), another beautiful dive site. The area had an extensive, gorgeous reef, as well as interesting rocks and coral along the shore. I was not long in the water, still blowing onion-scented bubbles out of my snorkel tube, when the most majestic creature I'd ever seen in the sea appeared. Cruising through this underwater garden was a spotted eagle ray, potentially as large as 16 feet long, a wingspan of 10 feet, and weighing 500 pounds, and with its trailing suckerfish/pilot fish, themselves one or more feet. Graceful and quick, the ray moved its wings in a smooth undulating fashion, the Elvis of fish. Its commanding demeanor was regal, nearly breathtaking.

Jolted by a voice, I looked to my side; it was Rocco asking, "Have you seen the shark?"

"No. Do I have to? May I pass?" I looked below and didn't have long to wait. Mr. Shark moved in, similar to the ray, but the ray honored the concept of a comfort zone. The ray was awesome; the shark defined breathtaking. Mr. Shark was headed straight for me—afraid of nothing, what brass—staying six to eight feet below me (felt like inches, not feet). His eyes were toward the top of his head, so he could check me out easier by staying below me, especially since I was floating in the water. My thoughts were focused on how far it was to *Speedy*; too far, if the shark took a liking to me. I felt grossly inept, not able to run on water, or fly. I could only watch.

Almost certainly, my heart stopped. Had I not been totally paralyzed, I would've known for sure. The nurse or lemon shark (it wasn't labeled—what kind of an aquarium was this?) continued straight toward me until he was under me, then veered off to my left. Wow! For the moment, I felt I was out of trouble. It must have sensed my pulse returning, as it turned right, right again, then again, completing a full square, and came back at me, eyeing this silly looking, floating thing known to me as a human. Whatever Mr. Shark called it, I hoped I wasn't in the onion spot of his food pyramid. This guy was not near the size of Benchley's monster, nor Melville's *Moby Dick*. However, that didn't bump Mr. Shark off my Top Ten List of Concerns, now uncontested for number one. Was he wondering which of us looked most tender? Or maybe he wanted a good fight. Hopefully, Mr. Shark would use different criteria than the mosquitoes. I stretched out in my most extended position, pointing my flippers and arms in order to appear more than eight feet long. If size meant anything, maybe the six- to seven-foot shark would choose Rocco. If I had to choose, well, not to seem selfish, but Rocco has had twenty-five years I haven't had yet. Or maybe I should wave my hand and volunteer. Did sharks enjoy onions? Marinated, or plain? Should I breathe, or hold it? Nothing I'd read said a shark couldn't have two entrees if it so chose, though we usually only hear of singular attacks, not a slaughter, making my chances 50/50, which was comforting. *If Rocco can keep the shark busy, I'll go get the dinghy.*

Sharks and fish have a lateral line, a fluid-filled tube down the center of their body that detects movement and, hence, prey. So, I froze, repeating "Ho Lee Chit," probably an Asian prayer, albeit a short one, hoping to look more like a log than a wounded or panicked seal. After what seemed a lifetime, the shark headed off in its original direction, perhaps to get a dining companion so as not to feast alone.

Surviving my first shark encounter, I began to breathe again, but was not yet back in the boat—something to consider. What do you do if attacked by a shark? I'd read you pop them on the nose, but those palliatives may be easier said than done. I say stay in the boat.

Intact and unafraid, haha, Rocco and I stayed in the water and kept exploring. He pointed out several lobsters hiding in a coral head. In contrast with the Maine lobster, they were spindly, intricate creatures with lots of legs and appendages, and far preferable to sharks. We saw many fish—giant Nassau grouper, jacks of various types, yellowtail snapper, spotted goatfish, porgy, parrotfish, reef butterfly fish, angelfish (blue, rock beauty, queen), squirrelfish, and triggerfish—and an infinite variety of coral and sea fans. This was an amazing underwater site. Walt had planned to go diving over an ocean reef, but he found this one hard to beat, so we stayed at this site until we were shivering giant raisins, then returned to the boat to sail to Staniel Cay, where he could call Felicity for a health update.

Staniel Cay:
Splish splash, a bloody bath and salvation

Returning from his telephone call, Walt gathered us together in the saloon. "Felicity needs another operation. It's only available in New Orleans. The top doctor is there. They have her scheduled for November 10."

"Oh no, sorry to hear that; sounds serious. Is it?" I said.

"We'll see; we're getting the best doctor, but he has only one appointment open; we need to take it."

"Well, damn . . . what should we do? We can't dependably sail home in time, can we? You're going with her, right? When do you have to leave?"

"I'll take a plane from George Town, the last place with scheduled flights for a while. Got a reservation for Wednesday, should be gone about seventeen days."

"What do you want us to do?"

"That's up to you guys."

Rocco wasn't talking, just sitting, his eyes a little bigger than usual, occasionally looking around, but revealing nothing I could read. He may have had a nauseous sinking feeling or was elated he'd inherit a decent berth.

"Looks like we can sit here, sail back, or sail on. What's your preference, Walt?"

"It's up to you and Rocco, but my preference would be to keep going. I could meet up with you in Turks, or the Dominican Republic if you get that far."

I guessed he would persevere. This was his dream, and it took a lot of preparation. Now he gets shot down a second time. I was needed after Felicity had to drop out, needed now even more, useless as I am, but Rocco would be the brains. If I were left alone, I'd anchor near the grocery store, sit there and travel through reading books. That was all I could do with what I knew. The bell for sailing school had yet to ring.

"What do you wanna do, Rocco?" I asked.

"Don't care . . . either's okay."

Rocco and I hardly ever had anything to say to each other, and now we were forced to decide what to do in Walt's absence. This was bad news. Could Rocco and I bond in just seventeen days, each day having only 1440 long minutes? So far, life with Rocco reminded me of solitary confinement. I'd never encountered anyone like him. I especially didn't want to stay in one place—one of us would start a fight just for something to do. Returning to Florida would likely postpone the trip for another year and wouldn't achieve Walt's dream. On the road of life, you get run over if you stand still and, in another year, something else could detour the dream, put it out of reach. Not good at saying or doing things twice, I wanted to keep going, hoping to complete the trip, stimulate the mind, and focus on something besides Rocco.

"Rocco, if you're willing to take over captain duties, I say let's keep moving on."

"Okay." A man of few words.

I'd committed to making the trip, so I chose to stay on and make it work for Walt. His difficulties enhanced my determination, and there were several things I wanted out of the trip as well, such as learning to sail, and seeing a new world in a way that I might never experience again, though I was getting more than I asked for of things I didn't want. However, this was no time to abandon the effort, just a momentary setback of seventeen days of who knows what, and I had the time. Fortunately, I'd adapted to the modest facilities, and had concentrated on learning GPS; though I didn't know how to sail yet, I could navigate, tell Rocco where we were, and where he could go—there would be some satisfaction in that. Things could be worse, given a little more time, or Walt's leaving could make things worse quickly.

Getting Walt to the airport was our imperative, though he had a few days before leaving. Being our tour guide, he'd show us Thunderball Cave tomorrow, for him a memory of a lifetime, hopefully a better memory than swimming with your first shark. Caves don't usually eat you, but anything is possible; we'd give it a chance. Tonight, the mosquitoes were again terrible: they eat you. Having no wind leads to calmer seas, but in those conditions mosquitoes flourish and launch memorable invasions. Walt was still not getting bitten; Rocco was finally picking up traffic I didn't mind sharing. Sticky, itchy, humid, and hot (95 degrees, no wind) was the market price for what we got—exceptional marine beauty. At night, the price was too high. In the morning, it was affordable. Had it been for sale, I would have paid handsomely for a good night's sleep. The problem had to be solved, somehow, or we'd need transfusions. For the moment, I was really miffed at Noah for not smacking those two mosquitoes off the ark. (They've changed the course of wars, hence of history, and kill two million annually, where sharks only kill 10.)

When I awoke the next morning, I could not deny I'd been asleep, though it couldn't have been for long and not at all a deep sleep. We headed for Thunderball Grotto, a hollowed-out island made famous by the James Bond movies *Thunderball* and *Never Say Never Again*, and also used in filming *Splash*. When we arrived near the island, the current was so swift that Walt had to make four diving attempts to tie *Speedy* to a mooring rod on the sea bottom, then he advised us to swim as hard as possible to avoid being washed out to sea on the changing tide. Uh, yeah! Marketing info said to enter the "fishbowl-like grotto on a slack tide, and become one with the fishes." This was no slack tide, but a near-high tide, a force with which to be reckoned, and near indomitable. *If I miss the island, look for me in Portugal.*

Dutifully following Walt's instructions, I jumped in and got with it. Too soon, wham! What the hell was that? The island. I'd arrived ahead of time, slamming head-on into the island, becoming one with the spiky coral edges. Damn! My head spun in a galaxy of stars. The coral lacerated my forehead and the top of my head was bleeding profusely. Sharks might find me an attractive, bloody chum in this condition. If so, my new concern of "scarred for life" was irrelevant. The extra-large flippers worked better than expected, since I may have been planing when I head-butted the shore. Nothing I could do but hope I would clot before I bled out.

We made our way around the island and swam through an underwater passage between rocks, surfacing into a large, high-domed grotto which had water rapidly running through it. Light streamed through the top where rain had eroded the dome, providing several natural skylights. Stunning! Imagining it as a movie set was not a problem; getting the equipment in might have been. Rocco had preceded me into the cave and was sitting on a coral ledge regaining his composure from the harrowing experience. I needed to do the same. This ill-timed, high-tide entrance into the unknown, with the fast, strong current, seemed life-threatening to me, a novice in underwater exploration.

We swam against the current into calmer pools of water and saw an array of colorful fish, a few rubbing or nibbling on our legs. After the shark yesterday, I feared each nibble might be The Big Nibble. The fish were dazzling but, due to the strength of the current and narrowness of the passages, the overwhelming concern and concentration was on survival. On this all three of us concurred! Would the current take us somewhere we could not swim back from until the tide changed? An ocean's surge around a small island is a powerful force. Another boat of snorkelers was trying to tie up just after we did, but must have decided not to chance the current, which left us to enjoy the danger and beauty alone. Maybe they were staying in the area longer and had options. My option was whether to feel brave or stupid. Sometimes, they are the same.

Leaving the grotto through a narrow passage against the tidal surge, I felt a flipper loosen. If it were lost, I would not have the swimming power and control to overcome the force of the water and bang headfirst into islands, not only here, but for the rest of the trip. Having only one fin would have me going in circles, and I wouldn't hit anything but the boat, repeatedly, assuming I could get back to it. Luckily, the flipper still dangled on my foot. I needed to discern what had come undone and fix it. But not without some mild panic while carried along in the swift current, rolled into a ball, toes curled to keep from losing the flipper, spinning in all directions, banging against the sharp edges of the coral. While reaching for my foot to reconnect the strap on the flipper, I rolled forward which put my head and breathing tube in the water. Every effort to breathe produced water. I was about to drown; I wanted to stand up, rip off the mask, and call a timeout. Not possible. I had about ten seconds, maybe five, before I would involuntarily breathe in water.

Snap! The strap connected; I yanked the snorkel tube out of my mouth, surfaced, took a gasp of air, reinserted the tube, cleared it, breathed in, cleared the mask, spread out face down and took a breath of air that had never been so precious. My heart pounding, I joined the others in swimming back to *Speedy*, now seen as a vigilant rubber island of cocoon-like security. You could lie on the sole and no shark would ever see you. It stood out quite brilliantly, waiting for us to climb aboard to relative safety, looking so good because this was the second time in two days I'd been grateful for its shelter. Whew!

After drying out and decompressing, we went ashore on Staniel Cay in the afternoon to buy groceries. We were also planning to be dazzled and relax with a "famous" Theazielburger at the Royal Entertainers Lounge, but this was not the time and the cook could not be found. (Ever notice how bars are not nearly as captivating when you are sober? Or when the lights are on?) Visiting the two grocery stores, the Blue Store and the Pink Pearl, we bought frozen milk and bread. Freezing was the only way to keep perishables fresh. Otherwise, bread was baked to order, which cost time we would not spend.

I didn't take my camera, but wished I had. Island life is different than Home Owners Association-controlled high density urban living. Generators replaced years ago were abandoned in the field, close to the new one, probably used for parts. Anything that made it to the island stayed. While walking toward the pink and blue stores, colors so vivid there was no confusion, I noticed ongoing rehabilitation of several small, seaside vacation cottages, brightly painted in lime green, yellow, orange, and what I considered Bahama (royal) blue, due to its prevalence in these islands, the small abodes being prepared for the upcoming tourist season. I vowed to never leave the camera behind again, but it was bulky, and the trip ashore would likely get it wet.

More attention-grabbing was a roll of used screening leaning against a palm tree. Looking around for someone I could ask about it, and hopefully purchase it, I found no one. Hoping to find someone when we returned, I counted trees, taking careful note of the location.

For all the intent and effort to find and buy food during our tour of the island, my thoughts were on the screening. You could get food several places, but this was the first screening I'd seen. Like a convict discovering a large sewer pipe through which to make a jail break, I was distracted by the vision of freedom. Surely, it was put there through Divine Intervention—no other reason for it being there, unprotected, placed in my path, at this time. If I didn't find anyone around when we returned, I would know it was, in essence, a constructive apology for the mosquitoes, an apology I planned to embrace.

When we returned to the area, I counted off the trees. The screen was still there but no workmen could be found, even though I looked everywhere. I swear! This was no time to fail for lack of permission—better to later ask for forgiveness, if necessary. That's not a viable approach if you are smuggling drugs into Singapore where the penalty is death, but it may work here. It was used screening, almost certainly removed to make way for new. (With a fair amount of shame, I realized that recently I could justify almost anything: as a re-cyclist, it was only right that I rescue it and myself, giving us both a new lease on life.) No sense littering a beautiful island with trash screening. One last owl-like rotation of the head, a deft extension of the fingers, a flip of the wrist, and the screen and I became as one, headed straight for the boat, serenity swaying tightly by my thigh.

Onboard, so far as I know undetected and unscathed, as with any den of thieves, I was somewhat admired for my alertness, brilliance, and daring (I could go on . . .) and more especially for our new hope of emancipation from winged pestilential terror. Rocco and I would screen the boat as soon as Walt left, if he didn't help us do it before then.

Sizing up the spoils, I started looking for ways to use it. The side portholes were small and had screens in them. Since the boat was almost always set with the bow into the wind, the portholes were sideways to the wind and minimum air flowed through them. The companionway and hatches were unprotected and were the largest openings in the boat.

Not willing to wait another minute, we set to work and quickly found a couple of round sticks similar to broomsticks, a staple gun, and a small saw stowed away. In no time, we stapled and rolled screens the correct width on sticks cut the correct length to jam into the opening of the aft hatch, on a scroll-like arrangement that would unroll and hang over the companionway frame where three hatch boards would otherwise be inserted vertically. By sliding the translucent Lexan companionway cover closed, we had an effective though dangerous mosquito-stopper. Dangerous because we could look aft through the screening and lose sight of the fact the top was still in place. More than once a day when climbing the companionway ladder to leave, especially if wearing a hat, one of us jammed our heads into the heavy unyielding Lexan cover. Ouch *#$&!! Sumbitch! Vertebral compression!

As for the forward hatch, it was a strange six-sided concave polygon with all right angles and defied a solution for now. Closing the hatch worked, and we were usually aft of the larger hatch, so the saloon still received ventilation. We had a moderate breeze, which helped to keep the mosquitoes away. It was still hot, but getting rid of the constant mosquito attacks made it seem paradise was getting closer. Encouraged, we took showers in the evening (Saturday), our first since Thursday morning at Highborne Cay. I was starting to better understand the maritime sayings, such as "Old sailors never die, they just smell that way," or the *Ancient Mariner's* "Water, water, everywhere, nor any drop to drink." Fortunately, we had a reverse osmosis fresh water maker that produced 30 gallons over twenty-four hours, two solar panels, and a wind generator, providing a fair measure of self-sufficiency.

Around 0300, Walt thundered past my bunk. The boat was too small for me to sleep through anything. I always knew when someone moved, when someone used the toilet—indoors or out. Walt was farthest away, in the forward V-berth, but always a light sleeper interested in what was happening to his boat. Something was going on. Rocco was already up.

"What's up?" I asked.

"Not getting any amp output from the wind generator," said Walt.

Rocco's nose was within a foot of the ammeter and other gauges when he was sleeping, so he would have been the first to know he wasn't getting the usual high-powered brain fry. I knew little to nothing about these things, so I jumped up to join in. It helped my comfort zone requirements that we all had on a piece of underwear. Probably that "man thing" that we all want (and need) to solve problems, and we three can solve most mechanical problems—crucial skills for long distance voyagers—so attendance was unanimous, and the challenge sublimated the aggravation of disturbed sleep.

Walt and Rocco had the electrical panel apart in no time, staring at it.

Walt: "I think this wire may belong over here."

Me (the ex-analyst): "Have you moved that wire since it was last working?"

Walt: "No, haven't made any changes."

Me: "Then, why would moving it be the thing to do?"

Walt: "Well, something needs to change; it isn't working."

Me: "When was the last time you had this apart."

Walt: "Been awhile. Can't remember."

Me: "How did we know this wasn't working?"

Rocco: "I got up to take a piss and looked at it before I went back in the hole."

Me: "That's the answer. Corrosion. Probably isolated a wire, maybe the ground wire."

Well, it was that simple, but wasn't that easy or quick; electrical problems can be difficult. We couldn't see any corrosion, so a lot of wires were moved then moved back amidst much humming and hawing. For all the testing, re-wiring, and checking of diodes, we didn't diagnose any electrical problem. It was likely the breaking up of isolating corrosion and a steady wind that eventually had the wind generator cranking out the amperes as dawn was breaking.

We had planned to sail early for George Town, Great Exuma, a trip of fifty miles. Doesn't sound like much, but it would take us all day. The forecast for north of here was for gale force winds. That would be sufficient to charge the batteries and get us moving. But would we be able to stop? If gale winds hit us, we'd arrive in time for a late breakfast, too busy sailing to eat. We programmed the waypoints into the GPS and were ready to go. We can dress while we drive.

George Town, Great Exuma:
Should be Gorgeous Town; MOB

George Town is the administrative center of the Exumas, which is made up of two sizable islands, Great Exuma and Little Exuma, and about 365 smaller cays, including Overyonder Cay, Rat Cay, or Man of War Cay, maybe Lackanook Cay, Ima Monk Cay, all of them collectively stretching across 120 miles. (Don't look for the last two. I made them up.) George Town sits along Elizabeth Harbor, a wonderful sailing ground bordered by Great Exuma to the southwest, and Stocking Island, Elizabeth Island, and Guana Cay to the northeast, providing shelter from the powerful Atlantic Ocean.

After we cast off from Staniel Cay, we had a firm and steady breeze, moving us at 6–7 knots, fast for this boat. The sailing was great: good wind, kind seas, reasonable distance. When we arrived at Great Exuma . . . nothing! Dead calm. The place was sweltering! Up went the mosquito screening on a couple of hatches, and there were only a few in the cabin that flew in before we installed the screens. Ahhh! A small victory and a tremendous measure of comfort.

We were out of vegetables, which mattered only to me as far as I could tell. An ally would have been helpful, but Rocco was going with the flow on groceries. If prepared for him and placed under his nose, he ate it, hunger being a persuasive force. He may have felt nutrition was unimportant if his time on earth had already been more than he expected. Sleeping in the coffin may have promoted this genre of thought. Or maybe he felt like he was in jail and deserved little. I wondered what he would do if the food was really bad. Hopefully, it wouldn't come to that. Or perhaps it happened so gradually none of us noticed, like boiling a frog. The nutrition craze may be a fad or scam upon which Rocco didn't bite. We'd provision at the store tomorrow, the best one around for quite a distance. Actually . . . the only one.

The George Town area and Elizabeth Harbor were divine. Getting the mosquitoes out of the scene helps the appearance of anything, but it was gorgeous, though Rocco may not have thought so at the moment. I dared not ask. Unfortunately, on the way in, he was helping Walt put up a new, larger sail they called a blooper, cousin to a spinnaker, and I was given helmsman responsibilities with minimal instruction. I was unsure if I was told, through hand signals, to point the boat in the wrong direction, move the boat so the wind would hit us in that direction, or a gust caught us. In any case, the wind filled the sail while Rocco was handling the lines. By the time the pain signal arrived where the brain is alleged to be and he realized he could not hold the rope against a wind load of millions of pounds of atmosphere, and not wearing gloves, his right palm was toast, and the left was getting crisp— Wonder Bread-white to scorched toast in half a second. Had he held on, he would have become our first human semaphore, flying straight out at the top of the mast, screaming, "that SOB did it to me again!"

He was probably trying to keep the sail from falling in the water ahead of the boat and getting run over. Were he half the rugged, committed sailor he purports to be, however, we would still be talking him down from the top of the mast, singing "Hang on Rocco, Rocco hang on." Since we were sailing a sloop, that phrase came to mind in a tune, but it may not have been the one in his head which, more likely, was air raid sirens.

He would be out of commission for a while, due to a vicious burn laying open most of his right palm. It was gut-wrenching to look at. Having had two motorcycle dismounts at speed employing a "touch and roll" return to Earth, I can vividly remember how excruciating it felt to leave a lot of skin lying around the planet, several layers deep and, in particular, levitating when the nurses scrubbed the gravel out with hydrogen peroxide and a stiff nylon bristle brush. It still shivers me timbers.

Working with the ropes and lines can be dangerous. Put a body part in the wrong place near a line with pressure and motion, and you may lose the part. Being a mariner is one of the most dangerous jobs in the world. Sharks, lost body parts, concussions, drowning, collisions, bad weather, what's not to like? The 4,000 boats lying on the bottom of the Great Lakes bear witness to the risks.

I'd brought an aloe vera gel for burns, and offered it, but Rocco passed. *What if Walt were to offer it?* There wasn't much else I could do to help on the boat. The love in the cabin was maniacally reverberating in our confined space. He wouldn't talk to me before; would he talk even less now? Maybe I should go for a long walk, let him cuss and scream at me, or anyone, in private, to reduce the pain.

Walt was leaving soon to be with Felicity for her operation. That left me as the only fully functional but non-sailor on the boat. I had two hands to work with, if I knew what to do with them. Finally, I'd learn by doing, and would be waiting on Rocco, doing what required a grip. Perhaps it was proper since I may have been at fault. Would Rocco hold it against me? I'd likely not notice.

So far, this hadn't been a comfortable, sweet-smelling adventure. You would have to love boating more than I to eagerly go without the comforts of home whenever you want or need them, clean clothes and the ability to clean them, and a little personal space. We had received comments from other boaters throughout the trip praising our ability (or intent) to do so much with so little; few sailors endure a similar state of deprivation in making this length of passage. Conversely, most of the people in the world do not have it this good. My upbringing prepared me for less than what we have, I just didn't voluntarily choose it. Were it not for my deprived childhood, I might have been asking for scrumptious cheese to accompany my dry whine. I decided to acknowledge the challenge and try to enjoy the adventure. Not many people have passed this way; doubt I would again.

Walt and Rocco still talked about their boats for hours. Since I knew so little, I might ask "What is a boat?" Then they'd scowl at my question, look at each other as if to say "Do I have to answer that or will you, or can we just ignore him altogether?" which they usually did. So I looked forward to each new port and exploring what was ashore. At this point, the Dominican Republic was enticing, where it was alleged they had fresh fruit. Alas, we could be in George Town a few weeks, waiting for Walt to return. I was willing to push on into the unknown, but how would I do that, not having done much in the way of sailing, only pulling up and dropping the anchor? That's what you do before and after the sailing's done. The only remaining sailor in the group was now handicapped. If ignorance is bliss, I needed to be getting less blissful about sailing.

When we went to bed, it was calm in Kidd Cove. We awoke the next morning (actually in the middle of the night) to rain and building wind and seas. Quickly, I took out the screening and dropped the hatch covers. The wind continued at thirty knots throughout the day, rocking the boat endlessly. The gale from the north had arrived, giving us our first cloudy day. Walt had planned to start training me on the art of sailing, but the wind was too strong. So it was a day for reading in between other small tasks. Too bad; with Rocco handicapped, I could have acquired real-world experience. Learning what I could, I started wearing gloves when handling the lines!

Boat chores for the day included installing the plumbing for a salt-water foot pump at the kitchen sink. Nearing lunch, we jumped in *Speedy*, passed below a picturesque bridge of stone and wooden timbers draped with greenery, into Victoria Lake to a dinghy dock, and went ashore.

After shopping for essential foodstuffs, we had a decent hamburger, fries, and a Coke at the motion-free Peace and Plenty Resort. Comfort food can be reassuring at times, and having it in my stomach improved my outlook. Gazing at the harbor from the restaurant, I was impressed with the photographer's ability to produce a picture of the resort's view for their brochure that made the pool and beach look as if there was nothing else around, when actually they were walled in by other buildings. I held the picture up to the real thing, and imagined what lens must have been used, or the shenanigans performed in the darkroom—marketing wizardry, maybe using nothing more specialized than magic scissors. Still, it may be the best of what's available—in town, close to *de minimis* shopping, and the environment is delightful.

The next morning brought another cloudy day of high wind and rough seas, keeping the boat moving while going nowhere, providing an example of why it takes so long to sail somewhere fairly distant. When you can sail, it is at a speed of 5–6 knots, yielding a maximum range of 50–60 miles on a winter day without sailing overnight. Then there are days like the last three, when you cannot sail at all. Bummer! I wanted to be exploring or moving on. Friends at home asked why it would take so long to make the trip. Couldn't I do it in less time? My attitude was, "why hurry?" and in this particular weather, we would dare move only if the boat was twice its size, and we needed to.

While anchored close to town, we went ashore to do laundry and make telephone calls. I also had my first ice cream in two weeks. We had traveled 350 miles out of an estimated 1,300 for the whole trip. Hoping to find a more protected and calm anchorage, we moved the boat across Elizabeth Harbor to a bay in Stocking Island. The sun broke through for a couple of hours in the afternoon, so we went exploring, enjoying the white sand beaches underfoot, perfect for squeezing silky sand between the toes and walking in the water's edge. Walt was going home the next day, so Rocco and I packaged our outgoing family correspondence and my photographic film to send with Walt in search of a stateside post office, taking a couple of weeks out of the transport time.

The next morning, Walt packed as we compiled a list of things to bring when he returned. Had he been leaving to accept a Nobel Peace Prize, we'd have been in a happier mood. He had to catch a small plane to Nassau, New Providence, then a scheduled airline to Baltimore. Because of the windy weather and high waves, only Rocco crossed the channel to take Walt ashore, allowing the dinghy to ride higher in the water and reduce Walt's chances of getting saltwater-wet.

Later, Rocco and I went beachcombing and dinghy-riding, together but apart. He didn't share any of his observations or comment on mine, and found ways to walk apart from me. If I stopped to examine something more closely, he kept walking and ne'er would we be together before we jumped back in the dinghy. Solitude looked to be something we'd be sharing.

On Stocking Island there were three "hurricane holes" to explore, so the weather did not keep us inside as long as we didn't try to cross the channel. Hurricane holes are bays so named because of their suitability as an anchorage in hurricane conditions. They are large and protected enough for the boats to swing around the anchor(s) with the weather, but the water's inlet is sufficiently restricted to prevent massive tidal surges and waves from destroying the anchoring gear, and the boat soon thereafter.

That morning we had a near-perfect execution of a natural shower, on a small boat that makes its own water and electricity. Rocco lowered a bucket into the sea and pulled out enough salt water to wash the accumulation of dried salt crystals from the deck reasonably well. He then plugged the forward scuppers and suspended buckets from the life lines under the rear scuppers. The rain cloud he saw approaching crossed overhead, dropped its precious content on the deck, leaving 1½ gallons of rainwater in each bucket. When the cloud is of sufficient size, you can take the chance of letting the shower further cleanse salt from the deck before you slide the buckets under the scuppers and catch the sustaining nectar. After the rain stopped, we bottled our catch in half-gallon milk jugs.

After dark, he and I each took a side of the boat, shed our long-worn clothes, and poured a little water in each flat plastic bucket/pan. I then wet my body with a washcloth, soaped up, and wiped it off. Then I drizzled water from a milk jug on my head and shoulders as a rinse, using no more than a half-gallon of water. I moved quickly during this process, because it was confusing whether that tickle was the slight drizzle of water, or a mosquito making a withdrawal. Voila! A free, refreshing outdoor shower. Invigorating, inexpensive would be an overstatement, no burden on the ship's facilities, and environmentally correct since the soap had no phosphates! No exhaust, no noise. This stands in sharp contrast to friends and family I have known who could individually drain a 55-gallon hot water heater.

Weather-bound and not used to this restrained style of life, I turned my reflections to the mechanics of our survival. Electricity is supplied by the wind generator (2–10 amperes), two solar panels (2 amps per panel), and an alternator running off the engine. We had to be sure we were making as much electricity as we were using. How much we produce depends on the hours of sun, wind speed, and whether we sail or motor (if we move at all). Therefore, we constantly watched our consumption, creation, and storage capacity meters to be sure our biosphere remained viable. Unlike life in the suburbs, we could not spend what we did not have, nor save more than our batteries would hold. We had to stay in balance. There was no such thing as an electricity credit card, though if a battery went dead, we'd have to charge it.

Rocco doesn't cook and doesn't want to learn. I fixed a better-than-average meal and . . . no comment! Not a peep! No complaints, though. I shouldn't complain either, then. Walt has empathized that Rocco has probably not received the enculturation that employees of Ma Bell receive on how to get along, communicate, walk on the right, hold the handrail, back into a parking spot—so he seems a little rough at times. Ya think? The strict absence of "thank you" and "excuse me" was glaring.

As for those things I didn't know and needed to learn, there was no change. Walt left without training me. The two experienced guys took care of the sailing activities, Rocco not being one to stand by and patiently watch me do a task in a less seasoned manner than he might, though it's the path to doing it better next time. Walt handled the helm when it was critical, such as during my weighing and lowering of the anchor, after or before which I hoisted or lowered the mainsail and jib, secured and stowed them, the winch handles, and lines for both. What is critical about that is for him not to have to handle the anchor or even leave the cockpit. Rank has its privileges. Otherwise, I could only find room to watch, though you might wonder what was left (not much).

What Rocco did teach me is how to crush a cola can with my bare hands, or rip one in half (so it will sink and stay there) if we are dumping it at sea. Why take it ashore to let it lie there for decades? Return those minerals to the earth, at 10,000 feet deep. Rocco, as my new captain, was truly shorthanded, with burns on his, and lack of experience and training in mine. He would, for two reasons, have to let me do hands-on sailing. Does the training come in time to avoid a calamity? My skill level would more likely cause it. Certainly, there will be a lot of shouting and screaming.

After reading, writing, and watching a few shooting stars from the deck, it was time for bed. We agreed Rocco would take Walt's spot in the forward V-berth and I'd keep my berth in the saloon. We had several rain showers overnight and, by morning, Rocco's water collection system had ample water for two more bathing showers apiece. We worked on a permanent mounting scheme for our screens, achieving great results for two of the three hatchways. The longevity of the screen for the third remained a concern.

The boom box Walt had used to play his music went quiet. His favorites are bluegrass and old-time country/historic country, which sounded a little scratchy compared to the robust sounds of today's popular music, and that is coming from a guy who used to saw pretty wretchedly on a violin himself, which could explain why I didn't find it appealing. Oh, the memories! With Walt away, I would be able to play music I brought along and get familiar songs back in my head and maybe in my heart.

Otherwise, the day was too quiet. Many more days like it and I would be ready to go back to work. Just kidding! One needs time to learn how to be retired. I took a swim and walked on exquisite beaches again; the world is spectacular! Add to this a resplendent sunset, a shower, and a good dinner, and we had an idyllic day in paradise.

Aided by a nice breeze, I thought sleep was certain. Alas, lots of thoughts were going through my head, keeping me awake. A lot had changed, and the next day we were to go where few sailors choose to go, including Rocco.

In the morning, we left our anchorage at Stocking Island and motored across Elizabeth Harbor for fuel and provisions. Rocco procured the fuel while I found a payphone and called the bank, Ray, and my son, Chris. It was bill-paying time again, and Chris was taking care of that, though few bills were not on auto-payment. I also called the dive shop, to see if Nikki would want to join us now that there were fewer on the boat.

"Dixie Dive and Jog, may I help you?"

"Hello, do you have any dives on your near-term schedule for the Bahamas?"

"We have a dive in three days at Andros. We stay at Small Hope Bay, dive the blue holes, barrier reef, Tongue of the Ocean. Have you done that one?"

"I need a diving partner. And I don't know how to dive. Could you be my—"

"Who is this?"

"It's Bryan. You once helped me escape from a too-small Speedo."

"I thought it was you. But when I hear a voice like yours, I get a bit tentative."

"You did fine. Very professional. And you must know not to start guessing who it might be. That's deadly. How's it going?"

"Okay, still running on the energy transfusion you gave me. What was that, anyway?"

"Which one, haha. If you mean the heart synchronization thing, probably a mind/body linkage I felt might work since we seemed to be in the same zone. Everything go down smoothly at the shop after I left?"

"Hmmm . . . actually, I'm not sure."

"Why? What happened?"

In a hushed voice, she said, "Jerry asked me a few questions—who you were, had I known you before? We did spend time together . . . that he knew of . . . talking."

"Uh oh!"

"Uh huh."

"Do you think he suspects anything? Well, of course he does, or he wouldn't have asked. Think he heard us talking?"

"Maybe, but if he suspected what we actually did, I'd accuse him of being insane. People don't do that . . . do they? Not proper people."

"Oh no, that is crazy . . . in a store's dressing room? Yeah, they do. Anywhere they can."

"We were in there awhile—you were quite thorough, thanks be—and the conversations before and after were more than usual, so all he's missing is the video."

"Did you record it?"

"Noooo, no film. Hmmm, wish I did. . . . Have you . . . never mind, it was amazing, exciting for sure . . . delicious, actually. After we closed up, I went back and sat on the bench for a while."

"Ahhh, returned to the scene? You said criminals do that. Do you know any?"

"It's going to become one of my quiet places. I need an image that reminds me of you but no one would know, maybe my necklace. I've been using it when I meditate lately."

"What is your necklace?"

"A cross. You didn't notice it?"

"Not consciously, maybe subliminally, because I did think 'Sweet Jesus' after you got your shirt up."

"You didn't just think it, you said it . . . Thank you."

"Oh! Really? Well there's your connection, I suppose, but, uhhhh, do what you want, but I hardly died to save you from your sins; far, far from it . . . a resurrection, maybe . . . well, whatever works for you, that's a personal decision. And, no, I don't remember it. You covered it with your T-shirt and I was focused on what you uncovered."

"You are so male; look, you did bring me back to life!"

"I should've left the Speedos with you, then," I said. "Wouldn't that do it?"

"Sure, but how would I explain that? He would say 'What are these men's Speedos doing on your dresser?' I'd say, like I told you, 'You probably don't want to know,' and he wouldn't. But you did. . . . It wouldn't be good. And I couldn't sell them and watch them go out the door. Be like selling grandma's wedding ring. . . . No, I really like the other. It's more . . . contemplative. Whatever, something will come to me."

"Until I return, that is gonna be your job."

A pause, then "Yes. Guess I'm busted, aren't I? I think I'm blushing. You've restarted something."

"I hope you can handle it."

"That's my only choice. YOU started it."

"Did not; you did."

"I DID NOT! I was here literally minding my own business. Then you walked in."

"Well, I need to finish what I started, then. Obviously you are able to talk?"

"For a second; Jerry's out back unloading a truck, but I could get company in either door."

"I have another question . . . what was going on when we were kissing at first and you stopped for a moment?"

"You didn't know? Caught me by surprise; I should have told you. A small O."

"Really! Standing up? You were ready, weren't you?"

"Oh my god, worse than that. Back to Jerry, you cannot write to me, okay? He brings in the mail, and a personal letter could start, would be the beginning of the end. Maybe I can write, you call."

"Do you trust him?"

"Not sure which side he would take, if he had to choose. He's a little fanciful, lives in a world of his own. You may have noticed."

"I wasn't watching him, you had my attention, but yeah, he's . . . fanciful is a good word."

"He's creative. A good worker, but he could go either way, in several respects."

"Well described. I'm impressed."

"I won't give him a chance or incentive to be disloyal. That's why I do the inventory, remember?"

"I DO remember you doing inventory. You're good at it. 'Attention shoppers: one aroused customer in dressing room sixty-nine! A blue-light special!'"

"Damn, it's good I'm alone. No one has lit me up like this. If I said 'keep it up' you wouldn't take it the wrong way, would you?"

"Oh heck no, can't imagine a wrong way, but it's been a problem."

"I like that picture. But look, we need to be serious for a moment. This thing could take a while. You need to live your life—you've earned it is my guess. . . . Do you realize I don't know anything about you?"

"Nothing? Didn't we . . . you know a lot about—"

"Anyway, have fun, don't worry about me, but don't forget me. And don't get married or committed without asking me . . . I mean, checking on my status, if it's okay, okay? Hope you know what I mean. That way, I'll think there's hope. That sustains me right now."

"Actually, I am a bit worried about you. It may not be my business, but if your fiancé is a serious drinker, and you said he was mean when drinking, my experience has been you need to get away. Nothing but tragedy comes out of alcohol abuse."

"I agree. It's serious."

"If you go ahead with the wedding, we can hook up after the inevitable divorce. But if you don't and need a place to run to, I operate a halfway house; you can go there."

"Do you really?"

"Well, not officially; I've put a few people up. Certainly have room for you."

"Don't worry; I've a good education. My dad saw to that. Said 'It only will do you good and can't be taken away,' about a hundred times. So, I can always find work to support myself. I might need . . . emotional support. By the way, where are you?"

"George Town, Great Exumas. You probably know, it's beautiful. Wanna join us? We've had a man go overboard and now there's more room."

"Yeah, I'd love to but can't. Overboard? What's going on? Everything okay?"

"Not really; not at all. Trip is falling apart. Captain's wife is sick, needed him at home, so he's gone. Now I'm stuck on a small boat with a guy I don't know and can't figure out."

"Wow. What's he like?"

"Odious. Maybe not that bad, but nothing I've ever seen before. Not this close for this long."

"Now I'm concerned about you. Come on back. I'll meet you at the airport."

"It has to be near the water. I'd arrive by boat."

"We're on the water. Close to it. Think we can run away together?"

"Keep a bag packed. You never know. Right now it looks like we will try to press on. I guess there are options, but it took me four months of preparation and I'm 1,500 miles from home, on a chance of a lifetime if it pans out. Walt needs me, and I feel committed. If I leave, I don't see how the trip continues—it can't! But, if Walt can fly out of here, so could—"

"Hold on . . . DamnIgottago! Thanks for calling Nixie Dive!"

Click!

At the beginning of this trip, I wondered about my motivation—in search of adventure, altruism toward Walt, escapism, all three? Now, the antithesis of escapism was in play, though any future with Nikki was so distant, I had to be realistic, responsible, and control my emotions.

I headed for the best grocery store in the area, which was modest based on those in the States. There was no Beltway traffic though, so overall this was better. I picked up a lot of canned food: fruit, green things, canned butter, fruit juice (two cases), and locally baked bread and banana nut muffins, all the while wondering if they were foods Nikki would enjoy.

At the dock, Rocco told me to pay for the fuel. I added the cost of the groceries to it, divided it in half, and told Rocco the amount of his share.

"I'm not paying it," he said gruffly.

"Someone has to. It's not free. Who is?"

"The captain. Walt."

"Well, the captain isn't here! You're the captain, I'm certainly not. Did he give you money?"

"Nope."

I was paying a third, then figured I'd be paying half after Walt left, until I found out I was paying for it all. Flicker, flicker, blink; the light went on. The basis for Rocco's behavior was becoming clearer, and his willingness to eat whatever Walt cooked was unmistakable: Rocco was an employee, and was being paid to be here, at least all-expenses-paid since he won't pay to feed himself. That made me an adventure capitalist until Walt returned. It gave me pause, but the only option was to keep moving forward. He had his deal; I had a different one; but neither deal specified who paid for Rocco when the captain was absent, or who paid the captain's share. Someone forgot to clue me in. After a moment or two I was over it. No doubt Walt was good for it, and my discovery explained a lot.

How Walt had so quickly assigned Rocco to sleep in the coffin became obvious. As a compensated crew member, Rocco could be "instructed" better than a volunteer, so I received the better bunk, probably not only because I'm a foot taller. I'd pay extra, if I had to (in effect, I was), not to be in the coffin. Rocco might have seen this coming from the beginning, explaining his disinterest when we first met. If I had to pay all expenses until the captain returned, the coffin was his rightful resting place, though, in fact, he was elevated up to the V-berth, a double bed in the bow of the boat. Good thing I brought more than bus fare. What would Rocco do if I were not here? Fly home? Not likely he could come back, and this dream of Walt's would be over. Stay here? Two or more weeks of cold beans? He's gonna love his new sugar daddy so much, I may have to sleep with one eye open.

After paying and loading up, we went out the southeast end of Elizabeth Harbor on a twenty-mile motor/sail to Cape Santa Maria on the north end of Long Island. We arrived at our anchorage south of the cape in protected water north of Calabash Bay at 1600, only one other boat in the anchorage.

We started cooking dinner at 1715 and the mosquitoes arrived before 1720. Screens went into place, and we had twenty or more mosquitoes at the door in no time, ready for dinner. We sprayed the screens with an appetizing cocktail of OFF! and were relatively bug-free for the rest of the evening—if we stayed inside. I worked on Spanish, thinking it would be useful for the upcoming countries, and read other books. I slept between 2100 and midnight, but it was too hot to sleep long. I read until 0300, then tried again. Perhaps I wasn't getting enough exercise to sleep well, or my mind was too active.

There was a lot of time to think under these conditions—quiet partner, short distance days, calm seas. Felt lucky, sometimes lonely. Felt stuck while feeling fortunate. Guess it "depends on where you stand as to where you stand," a Walt-ism, before he left. I enjoyed his ability to philosophize, to look at the broader picture. Not everybody could do that effectively for the betterment of their life. It was certainly a skill he could use at the moment. Taking his "ism" a step further, I also liked "If you change the way you look at things, the things you look at will change." I wished I had someone to attribute it to; my children would give it more regard than if I'd said it.

We awoke at sunrise if I wasn't already awake. Though the blinds were drawn over the eyes, the mind was too often still open for business. The mental angst of on-board personal relationships was as exhausting and interminable as going through a divorce. Continuous monitoring of the environment was always tugging at my nightcap—the rocking of the boat, the heat, the whuff, whuff, whuff of the wind generator, receiving rain or mosquitoes through the hatches, or the banging of the anchoring gear on the hull—conspiring to float me under a thin veil of sleep at best. The prospect of a one-eyed pirate with a knife in his teeth, pistol at his side, coming down the companionway steps was also something to consider when the best we had for defense was a roll of paper towels. Our door was wide open and we had no clue who was outside. A couple hours of deep sleep were a distant memory, possibly last captured in the stillness and safety of the Texaco dock in Nassau.

We had an early breakfast, hoisted sail, and headed for the cape, planning to sail on a bearing of 106 degrees toward Port Nelson on Rum Cay. We would be there in four hours, traveling 21.6 nautical miles at a ground speed of around 5.6 knots (motor/sail). I tried to start a conversation: "Hey Rocco, guess what?"

"Gimme a couple turns on that winch, sail's luffing."

"Okay. Hey, we're in the cradle of history here."

"Now! Dammit. . . . A little more . . . that's enough. We'll need more once we round the cape."

"Right. Did you know Columbus's first discovery was San Salvador, only 30-40 miles from here?"

"Hurry up, tighten some more."

"Ya know what he discovered second?"

"That'll do it. Put the damn winch handle in the pocket before we lose it."

"Rum Cay."

"Where?"

Rum Cay and the Bermuda Triangle:
Columbus comes in second

In August, 1492, Christopher Columbus set sail for the Spanish Crown, not to discover new lands but to open up a trade route to the "Indies" or Asia, which would allow Spanish merchantmen to bypass the Muslim pirate fleets controlling the Mediterranean Sea. The overland trade route known as the Silk Road had been cut off by the fall of the Mongol Empire and the conquest of Constantinople by the Ottomans. Together, they were depriving Europeans of silk, spices, gems, and other luxuries from the Far East.

Columbus felt a potentially lucrative alternative was to sail west to reach India and China, and tried to interest the Portuguese in his scheme. They were not persuaded, feeling the world was much larger than Columbus reckoned. (They put their money on Vasco da Gama, and a route around Africa.) Chris would have been spurned by Spain, too, had that nation's centuries-long war with the Moors (Muslims) been going badly. Fortunately for Columbus, the Spaniards were winning handily, and victory was in sight. Spain was feeling expansive, having enhanced its economic interests via the consolidation of several kingdoms of Spain, under Isabella of Aragon and Ferdinand Hapsburg of Castille, in the last half of the fifteenth century. With the increased political and financial strength of the combined monarchy, Spain could bear the costs of supporting exploration.

When the last Moorish stronghold fell at Granada, the Italian sailor from Genoa was ready and waiting. On Oct. 12, 1492, Columbus made landfall in the Bahamas, significantly changing the course of history. He never found an alternate route to the Far East, but called the Antilles islands the West Indies, having found dark-skinned natives he assumed to be of India. Over his four voyages to the islands between 1492 and 1502, Columbus set the stage for the European exploration and colonization of the Americas—two continents and a collection of islands later named after another navigator, Amerigo Vespucci.

The Bahamas also has a history of skullduggery. The passages between the islands charted by Columbus were used by the Spanish conquistadors to ship back to Europe their riches obtained by pillaging Central and South America. However, they were frequently attacked and plundered by pirates— hard to know which crooks to root for—hiding among the islands, fostered by the secluded cays and islets, shallow waters, sandbars, and reefs. For centuries, pirates used lanterns in tandem with the reefs to lure sailors to their demise, then looted the wrecks.

During Prohibition, the islanders trafficked in alcohol. It was likely during this time a boat laden with rum crashed upon the island and the residents dropped Columbus' original name of Santa Maria de la Concepcion (taken from the name of his flagship) in favor of Rum Cay, a win-win for cartographers and any spelling-challenged residents. Chicanery has continued through the recent cocaine era. Pirates, in practice crooks-on-water, are still a reality.

We arrived at Rum Cay around 1300 after a pleasant sail. Channeling Chris Columbus, every island arrival felt like we were discovering a new country. Other than Nassau, our stops were at small, unheralded islands with sparse populations. Rum Cay was covered with palm trees and other bush and tree foliage around sporadic modest dwellings, all sitting behind tan sandy beaches. It was a pretty picture, and an interesting one for the lack of commercial development in such a desirable environment.

We anchored at a sizable concrete government dock in the Port Nelson area, which allowed us to go ashore in a respectable fashion with dry feet. Nearby were a canal and floodgates, ruins of the salt industry of prior years when water was let into the canals which flooded the salt pans/evaporation ponds in the interior. Salt rakers gathered the salt after the floodgates closed and water had evaporated. Hurricanes destroyed the pans beyond justifiable repair, and the island turned to pineapples and cattle, until these fell on hard times as well. There were multiple settlements on Rum Cay in the 1800s, though most of the remaining 70-100 islanders now lived in Port Nelson. It's believed more natives were living here when it was "discovered" by Columbus.

Rum Cay is used as a stopping point for sailors like us, heading south or southeast to points like Clarencetown, Mayaguana, and Turks and Caicos, or to points north and west such as Conception Island, Long Island, and Great Exumas. That day there were no other boaters in the anchorage. Few sailors come this far—not wanting to take the beating—just the serious passagemakers. However, Rum Cay claims to have the best diving in the Bahamas, with a necklace of prolific coral reefs and the Underwater Museum of the Bahamas featuring the HMS Conqueror, a 1,400-person, 100-gun troop ship that hit a coral reef in 1861 and now lies in 30 feet of water. The shallow water and coral reefs that make diving rewarding also make navigation errors deadly for sailors.

It was sweltering, as usual, so we went snorkeling around several coral heads to cool off and admire nature's incredible underwater beauty and variety. I assumed Rocco admired it; he would never share his emotions, if he had any, but was willing to jump in, swim around to explore and did point out rare finds like sharks and lobsters. When back at the boat, the screens were besieged: there may have been more mosquitoes here than we'd seen anywhere.

A memorable sunset filled the sky and painted the sea with color. The frequently present elongated clouds to the west were back-lit across the sun, radiating multiple shades of blue, gray, and pink, and left a gap on the horizon filled with orange and red as the sun slowly disappeared behind the curvature of the earth. It was an exquisite moment, except for the soft high-pitched tune of mosquito wings singing around our ears.

By current standards, not at all ambitious, I had a good night's sleep despite the heat. In a bunk this narrow, one has to wake up to turn over, a feat achieved by levitating and spinning in place, rotisserie-like, while trying to keep the sheet near as a mosquito shield. Sound sleep is unheard of.

The wind started whipping up around daybreak. On such mornings, the boat listed, then rotated around the anchor, changing the direction and view you might expect when you peer out of the companionway. Each morning, a differing land- and seascape awaited, affected by changing weather and sea conditions, angle and intensity of light, and occasionally new neighbors.

The roar of the wind generator signaled the wind speed was rapidly increasing, promising rain. We rushed topside, checked out the eastern horizon, noted the approaching clouds, pulled yesterday's drying clothes off the lines, then battened down the hatches with little time to spare. Working in the rain, we collected several gallons of rainwater for later use. Since most of life aboard is spent in a swimsuit and sandals, the warm, invigorating rain had me feeling like I had returned to my youth, playing in the flooded gutters, racing rudimentary "boats" against my playmates.

We took the dinghy into Port Nelson to explore the island interior, being sure to use mosquito repellent. It was Sunday, and an attractive, one-room solid masonry white Catholic church was empty, as witnessed through the Gothic equilateral arched red doors now wide open, while the patrons of the Baptist church were belting out gospel music. On such a small island, I had faith the Catholic singers were invited to cross over and join in, making a joyful noise together. We saw a hand-painted sign nailed to a tree for Two Sisters Take Away, a local bakery, and decided to order a loaf of bread over the VHF radio on channel 16 to be picked up tomorrow.

Continuing along the packed-sand roads bordered by mostly volunteer vegetation and coconut palms, I wondered how my view differed from Christopher Columbus' view, 501 years and one month ago. Did a path, over time, become the road I'm on? Did the path determine where the pier was built, or vice versa, and did Columbus come ashore where the pier is now? Being where the most unobstructed depth exists on the sheltered side of the island, there was a chance.

Circling through the overgrown interior and back to the waterfront, we stopped to talk to Ralph, sitting on his porch with a leg propped upon a spindly rail, not daring to put both legs up while his chair was rocked back. He flew in from his home on Long Island, NY, to spend the weekend in a house that looked like it would be a fold-up in a hurricane, possibly the reason all buildings here are one level, and why he hadn't made a major investment beyond basic housing. U.S. regulators wouldn't know where to start in their condemnation, but they would approve of the view: waterfront, with a picturesque aging boat hull and a few wooden remains between him and the beach, and only a few feet above sea level. His radio handle was "Seclusion," and he suggested we radio "Sun Seeker" (John), over on Long Island (Bahamas), for a weather report that evening.

We had an otherwise lazy afternoon, waiting for the easterly winds to stop blowing in our faces so we could move east from here, hopefully tomorrow or Tuesday. A low-pressure area from Florida was expected to hit the northern Bahamas that night, causing the winds to shift to the southwest, great weather for our next leg to Mayaguana, an overnight sail of 130 miles. Ralph cautioned we'd be sailing through the heart of the Bermuda Triangle, where many boats and airplanes had perished—a little something to contemplate.

I was focused on learning Spanish when a 100+ foot yacht came into the area and sent out a call on channel 16. Tony was the captain of *Fantastique* out of the Mediterranean port of Antibes, France. Piloting a deep draft boat, and faced with coral heads all around, he wanted to know how to safely get closer to the shelter of the island to anchor. I checked the local charts, radioed back the information, and he anchored successfully. Tony then asked what he could do for me. What could I possibly need? We had learned to get by on minimal electricity and ambient temperature water. We'd have bread tomorrow. I asked if a tour of his ship would be possible. He suggested a tour when he and the crew returned from dinner on Rum Cay. They came by on their way home asking us to excuse their sudden withdrawal of hospitality because the crew became dinner for the mosquitoes and were in no mood to socialize after having been bitten so rapaciously. I could see, by flashlight, one crew member in particular had skin eruptions akin to a severe case of measles. What misery! Being a recent and frequent victim of such ravenous attacks, it pained me to see it, making my bites itch all the more.

In the morning, we took a brief tour of Tony's yacht and felt A/C for the first time on this trip. Tony was from England, as was Jenny, the alternate captain, and Elaine, the cook. The rest of the crew was from Australia.

The ship's owner was from Germany and planned to board the ship in the Virgin Islands. His large chain of grocery stores paid to float the boat. The ship was transported on a super-carrier from its home base in Antibes to Port Everglades in Florida, for $70,000. The cost of ship-shipping was stag-staggering, though not so much if you considered the fuel consumption of crossing the Atlantic on a ship that size, plus time and all the other expenses. A one-way trip would buy two used boats the size of ours. Either the owner loved the Caribbean, or chartering *Fantastique* in paradise was lucrative, possibly both.

Tony handed me a glossy, full color tri-fold brochure of pictures and specs of the boat. I could readily see why the boat came over on a ship-shipping ship; the range was 2000 nautical miles. Even if they came through the Azores, they would have to depend on a friendly drift for the last thousand miles. And that's after spending $13,000 on fuel on one leg. *Fantastique* carried three metric tons of fresh water, and one ton of it was hot (we had none). It was a fantastic boat, with or without ours for contrast.

I finished my ice-cold Sprite, then climbed back into *Speedy*, opening up a gash on my leg courtesy of a sharp piece of hardware on our transom. *Fantastique* would set sail soon after us, around 1000. I wondered too late whether they would be willing to tow our boat, with us reclining on their afterdeck. Big oversight.

The expected wind shift to the southwest did not happen. The winds were still coming from the northeast and would prevent a decent sail. Disregarding the adverse conditions, Rocco planned to leave anyway. I didn't agree—the wind would be in our face, pushing up waves we'd have to fight—but my opinion also didn't matter—like the rear bumper on a car, I just absorbed the hits and followed the shining lights, feeling as qualified to take on the Triangle as I would be to climb Mt. Everest in a T-shirt, tennis shoes, and a compressed air cartridge of Fix-a-Flat.

Once back on *Godspeed*, we made ready and weighed anchor. Within two hours of casting off, like the wind compass, conditions swung from Heaven to Hell and we were ensconced in a long and punishing fight for life, hanging onto a boat on its side most of the time. Long before Rocco's late-night command to go forward to drop and stow the jib when I was nearly washed overboard, I was in a long, drawn out panic and all but certain I'd not see the dawn. Or Nikki. She talked about emotional support; I was sooner in need of prayers, hoping to see another day.

For ocean sailing, we should have had a jackline, from bow to stern, one on each side of the boat. To this, sailors tether their harnesses before ever leaving the cockpit, and even tether in the cockpit when it is this rough. Statistics reveal more people are lost overboard from the cockpit than the foredeck, because of the lack of grab points. Using a jackline and a harness, if you are ever tossed from the deck, you would still be attached to the boat, and a rescue would more likely be possible. Sometimes, sailors get thrown out of the boat, and on the next wave get thrown back in, perhaps not leaving them in the best of condition or mood, but much better than the alternative. Without a harness, once you have left the boat in this kind of weather, life for you is over. These waves were so tall you could not see beyond the next wave. You are just a tear in a rainstorm.

The sail from Rum Cay to Mayaguana follows the break of the Continental Shelf, where the slope into the depths of the Atlantic begins. The Bahamas (part of the Lucayan Archipelago) sit on the Continental Shelf in shallower water, though quite deep enough (up to several thousand feet) to swallow anything in trouble. It would seem the squeezing of water up that slope would produce large waves in the same way water rushing toward a similarly sloped shoreline created great surfing waves. Other theories that explore causes of the Triangle's dangerous waters, its penchant for producing freak and rogue waves, include spontaneous releases of methane gas from underwater storehouses, destroying anything above in its path, and potential large waves emanating from tectonic shifts in the five-mile-deep Puerto Rican Trench-corner of the Triangle. On that night, the steady, wind-formed, and occasional cumulative rogue waves gave us hell.

It was a night of terror, with many hours of feeling all control had been lost, and maybe all hope, wondering if the cockpit would drain as fast as breaking waves were pouring in, and were we making any progress at all toward our objective? Wishing we could just call it quits by turning off the TV, turning on the lights, and leaving the room, we were relieved to spot

Mayaguana and its light on the NW point around 0700, and reached the Betsy Bay area, a recommended anchorage, around 0930. I was ready to throw down an anchor and collapse. Rocco commanded that we continue on and anchor in Abraham Bay, Winston Churchill-style: "If you're going through hell, keep going." Making a slight turn to the southeast into the lee of Mayaguana, putting the wind on our nose, I considered his stand to be more like General Custer's last—the waves steep, orderly, and repetitious, coming at us like Indians with Winchesters: bang, bang, bang, bang, bang, bang, bang . . .

Abraham Bay didn't appear to be far, based on the sketch in the *Yachtsman's Guide*, but getting there was similar to going up the down escalator—we didn't reach anchor until 1400, another 4.5 hours! (I had time to do the math.) Of course, it was not a straight course; we had water mountains to cross; straight up, straight down. Rocco had tried to go to the bow when I refused, but quickly returned, angry and defeated.

This was a 28-hour cruise unlike anything in the brochures, with no food, water, or bathroom breaks. Exhausted, hungry, thirsty, we were almost too tortured and shaken to change those conditions. The boat seemed bigger because we both had shrunk.

Mayaguana:
Hello? Hello? Oh hell!

Once inside the bay, we looked for a strategic location, far enough from land that rats wouldn't walk up the anchor line, miscreants couldn't easily swim out to the boat, and out of the way of other boats. Of course, there were no other boats. Who would go through what we just did? Finding the right spot, Rocco yelled, "We'll anchor here!" By then I was on the bow, the sail was down, and the water surface was settled in a bay so big I felt we were standing still.

Anxious as hell to anchor, and because I'd been given the command, I had to move smartly or pay the price of another harsh performance review. I lowered the anchor and chain overboard, hand feeding the first fifteen to twenty-five feet. Suddenly, the anchor rode (the line connecting the anchor to the boat) was yanked from my grasp as it sprung out of the anchor locker, as fast and dangerous as a striking cobra launching from an Indian basket, streaking over the starboard side and aft to the stern. The probability I had made my move too soon became a certainty.

Nothing to do but safely stay out of the way; I knew the bitter end was attached to the . . . ooh hell! . . . Nothing! The anchor chain should have been secured to a U-bolt inside the anchor locker! Whose bright idea was that? Murphy's Law was in play.

"NOT HERE!" came Rocco's next and belated bellow as he watched the anchor rode pass alongside. I imagined he was, at least initially, surprised to see it back by the helm; it was supposed to hang gently off the bow. Or it may have been confirming for him, looking wide-eyed behind the boat, thinking, *Oh Jesus! What is that dumb son of a bitch doing to us now?*

Too late! The anchor rode fed out so fast, any effort to stop it guaranteed serious injury; Rocco's raw palm came to mind. Not for me, I wanted to keep mine intact. The anchor was down, gone, apparently set in the bottom, and the boat was still moving. Maybe now we would always be moving except when we ran aground, which seemed frequent enough. With no anchor, what choice did we have?

Rocco coarsely "informed" me I should not have lowered it. We were going downwind and he had no control of the boat's speed. I was unaware there was such a thing as "downwind." Everything has been upwind. He had screamed at me several times for not dropping anchor the precise moment we lost all forward progress, and I was eager to avoid a tongue lashing in my fragile, emaciated condition.

As a postmortem: in passing over the anchor's watery grave, Rocco had said, "We'll anchor here," like he'd found a big shade tree with a picnic table and barbecue grill. To me, barbecue grill=cheeseburger and I wanted to reserve the site before we lost it. Plus, I knew he meant now. I don't need, nor get, a day's notice, usually just seconds. I'd never been given advance notice. To my way of thinking he had, in effect, said, "Jump," and my only option was to gauge how high, head or feet first, and to get on with it. Without further ado, by looking down into the water, I knew, to retrieve the anchor, it would be a head-first dive of thirteen feet—three feet of freeboard, ten feet of water. Sumbitch!

At least it wasn't thirty feet, and irretrievable.

Tired, hungry, and thirsty, I had to dive to the anchor before doing anything else. Luckily, the chain was lying within my diving max, or so I thought. The anchor and dark chain were all that I could see on the sandy bottom, and would be heavy and difficult to swim back to the surface. A manila-colored rope was connected to the anchor after twenty-five feet of chain, but I didn't think playing with the rope underwater to find the end 100 feet along was yet in my skill set. What would dragging a 100-foot rope over sand with ten feet of water on top of it be like? If I pulled on it, would I move before it did? I hadn't done this before, but I felt I would make something happen. I had to. We had to have an anchor. For all I knew, it could be easy. Rocco was a better diver than I, but he was not going to leave the boat, unanchored, in my hands while he dove for the anchor, and I wouldn't advise it.

I could look for someone to share the blame on this, but there'd be few takers. If I just picked you-know-who, his refusal to accept any blame would leave me with a life-destroying toxic resentment that would be an anchor around my neck for a long time, and I would still have to dive for the real one. Better to accept responsibility, dive for the anchor, and be without burden as soon as I could tie it to the boat.

I dumped it. I should fetch it.

After considerable anxiety and struggle (more of the former than the latter), I created slack in the damn line and secured the damn anchor to the damn boat by having Rocco take the rode from my hands with a boat hook, secure it to the bow, then turn off the engine before I climbed aboard at the stern. Then I went about making up for the deficits of food and water suffered during the crossing.

With all that out of the way, appreciation ran high for being safely anchored in a quiet place.

When I had time for retrospection on what went wrong, other than miscommunication, it was not always discernible we were moving, in water that was moving, in a large bay where there were no stationary objects for comparison. Looking over the pulpit to the bow at the waterline might have worked. What I usually did was hang the anchor partially in the water and see how it and the water moved. But being so eager not to be yelled at, and so ready for this crossing to be so over, I hastily lowered it. Then when the anchor caught on the bottom, the rode started flying uncontrollably out of the anchor locker at the speed of the boat, or about six feet per second.

What if the anchor rode had been attached to the U-bolt? Would the boat have slowed and spun around, would we have a big hole in the anchor locker, the cable caught in the prop, or something worse? It may be lucky we didn't find out. There could have been carnage with snapped lines and wires all over the deck, a falling mast breaking stuff, with me in the middle, cut in half. Or the anchor may have dragged until it pulled the boat around in a graceful four-wheel-drift style of parking. THAT might have impressed Rocco: *Damn, Byrd, where did you learn that? In that Spanish book? Now we don't have to back it down to set it.* With my luck, we'd likely have a hole in the boat that, on nights like the last, would easily fill with water and sink us. Were the rode cleated at the rail, it might work. Maybe I would try it—closer to home.

Effective communications between two people, over the length of a boat, are difficult. Only a few couples will have the hand signals already worked out. Those who don't are courting divorce. The boat is usually pointed into the wind, the luffing sail is whacking loudly, engine's running, wind in your ears is blowing bow to stern, and conversation is impossible without raising your voice—usually the point of escalation, when things start backsliding in any urgent discussion.

Strangely, I felt a smidgeon of sympathy for Rocco, having also incurred a bait-and-switch dilemma. He was stuck on a boat he had to be paid to sail on, now with captain responsibilities by default, with a guy who didn't know spit about sailing. He could have helped his situation by training me a little, explaining things before they became crises (sometimes with my stewardship), but he was a do-it-himself sailor. Except for anchoring.

At this point, had I ever thought about owning a boat of any size, there was absolutely, unequivocally, no desire to do so now, or even for continuing this cruise. Sailing without sufficient water, food, or sleeping space, and confined to a small boat with a stranger possessing oddly different behavioral traits, was poor sport. I hoped Walt could rejoin us to keep this cruise moving forward, and Rocco and me apart. If Walt couldn't return, and I had to backtrack to Florida with the boat, it would be my greatest "mind over matter" challenge, exceeding even nausea control.

If we decided to turn around, I wanted a new captain. Rocco was making this worse than it had to be. After more than two weeks, I was accustomed to the challenging living conditions, but we didn't need to sail last night in those wind conditions pushing up big waves on the bow to power into, with no stability provided by being under sail. That was stupid! You lose a day by waiting, but save two lives.

More than usual, I could appreciate how good it felt to be safely anchored in a quiet place. That I needed rest was also apparent. To bed, perchance to sleep. And dream. Of pleasant people, if that wasn't too much to ask.

What a difference a day makes! After a good night's rest—in bed at 2130—I awoke for the day around 0700, then may have overindulged on pineapple pancakes for breakfast. Rocco said his stomach did not feel right, either. That was a frequent meal, so the problem wasn't the cook. Perhaps our digestive systems were not used to the intrusion of food.

My thoughts and prayers were with Walt's wife for her scheduled surgery, partly attributable to my survival needs moving lower on the priority list and religion bubbling up. Lest you tend to be agnostic about this, we had learned to pray during our last voyage, honed to a fine edge. You might even think Rocco was born again, listening to all his "Blessed Jesus" statements. Rocco must have suffered mightily. Was he a believer? Perhaps. He invoked religious names frequently, usually in conjunction with an expletive. Perhaps it was a short, emphatic prayer. It's been said that old sailors may have odd ways of showing their religious feelings, but there are no infidels at sea.

God's world and touch were in evidence all around us (it would be a great day to sail). I hoped it parlayed into good fortune for Felicity. One thing I'd been feeling more certain about every day, though, was that He was not going to save my ass if I screwed up, unless it was after I passed on. While St. Peter was guffawing at the very idea of my induction, He could intervene. Meanwhile, I'd better make my own plans for staying alive. Or maybe He did play a role, when that wave hit while I had my arms wrapped around a life-saving sail. That we were in Abraham's Bay tied all those thoughts together nicely with an, umm, Biblical cord.

We spent the day cleaning up what spilled during the passage, mainly a 40-ounce bottle of Dawn dishwashing liquid. Concentrated, of course, so we produced lots of pretty suds. Folks prefer their beer with a head on it. We had a boat with a head on it. Picture a small boat anchored, all alone, in a vast bay, with a plume of bubbles from the cockpit to the heavens, reflecting rainbows of light. I'm not making this up. It may look like it to anyone on shore but, believe me, this ain't no party boat. Secretly? It was kind of festive! I hadn't made this many bubbles since I was seven years old in a bathtub after drinking several Coca-Colas. How do you meet a challenge of this nature? One way was to open the seacocks, let in 10,000 gallons of seawater, 3" above the floorboards, and hope the batteries that power the pumps did not short out. Risky, but it was the quickest approach. Of course, then you would have to clean the whole boat, since it was salt water.

The other way was to take the boat apart and rinse, rinse, rinse, *ad nauseam* (which came pretty quickly. My stomach was akin to an eight-year-old car battery—not much reserve). When we finished, everything was spotless and Dawn-fresh! My forearms ached from all the wringing, especially the scatter rugs. The bay had a pernicious but pretty coating of bubbles floating on top. I wondered how the locals felt about it. An ecological disaster? I felt we were cleaning up the environment.

That evening, after a yogurt and fruit salad (Rocco would have none of what he called curdled milk, so he made a sandwich), I used the shipboard laundry facilities to wash a load of clothes. Darn! Had I thought to use my dirty clothes to wipe up the soap, I wouldn't have had to do it again. The onboard laundry operation is thus: As usual, start by filling the laundry tub with water. That is the red bucket with the rope on the handle. Throw it overboard and, if you remember to hold on to the rope, you won't have to jump in to retrieve it and bump into me while I'm down there looking for the anchor. Bring it up filled with crystal-clear (salt) water. In this, wash each piece to your heart's content. Next, if someone did their laundry earlier, you may choose to use their rinse water. In that case, you also get a second bucket of fresh rinse water, as the better mechanical washers afford. The fresh water is taken from captured rainwater through the scupper plug and bucket system, or if it has not rained recently, but you had good wind to power the wind generator that powers the water maker, you may take fresh water from the holding tanks. Put the rinse water in the gray bucket.

After the wash and hopefully a double rinse, you get that luxury of line drying, another throwback to my past, where I first learned to use clothes pins. How often we miss that fresh air scent in clothes when we opt for a mechanical dryer, though not here, where we share and enjoy many of the finer foregone luxuries of necessity.

The whole hand-washing process was integral to my youth, when we always washed clothes on a Saturday. When else would I have gotten a crack at it? Sunday was devoted to church; twice, to ensure retention. Our wringer washer was stored under the steps, behind a curtain, under the mayonnaise jars, their lids screwed to the underside of the steps, holding nails, screws, buttons, and Halloween candy, if any survived the first week of November. The alternating dark green and black twelve-inch squares of asphalt tile on the floor made rolling the washer eight feet to the kitchen sink the easiest part of the operation. The drain hose was hooked over one sink, the water hose attached to the faucet. We filled the washer with clothes and water, added soap, and the cycle began, shifting the lever for the agitator to spin. When the washer had ground on the clothes long enough, we had to feed each piece through the wringer without jamming it on buttons or zippers, into a second sink filled with clear water. Sometimes the wringer would jam, and spin on the clothes not moving through. Back up, try again. Swish the clothes in the rinse water, reverse the ringer, and feed them back through to wring out the rinse water.

Then we hung the clothes on the lines, overlapping garments to save pins. On the really cold days, the clothes would freeze before they dried. I could usually get them hung quickly enough to keep my hands from freezing to the clothes, but not always, and that's when we learned not to touch aluminum hatch covers with wet hands.

On wash day we usually had a lot of water all over the kitchen, as we do here. It always seemed a shame to me it wasn't wash day the early morning our dad was frying his prior day's catch of Potomac River catfish on a gas stove and, while he was upstairs shaving, he set the house on fire. There would have been an abundance of water to quench the blaze if it could have even gotten started. At worst, we would have had more time to exit the premises in a less spirited state of undress. Dad should have done with the fish what I often wanted to tell Rocco to do with his profane eruptions—put a lid on it.

That's the long way of saying washing clothes in two buckets and drying them on the lifelines of a boat that is not freezing or on fire can be a good thing.

Besides recharging my personal "batteries," I also felt better because this remote outpost might be our last before visiting the other countries and civilizations I had come to see. We didn't stop at any of the publicized Bahamian resorts, and I'd had enough of the unknown islands. There are reasons they are not better known. A concession should be made, however, to the islands that we breezed past: they had shops, dive leaders and sites, and many things to investigate and enjoy if we had not been on a mission from hell. Rocco was like a furniture mover taking on a boat job. Give me a more curious partner and more time and I would be experiencing a different cruise. Our objective was not to enjoy ourselves; it was to move the boat—in my mind a waste of a potentially great journey. But this trip would probably take all the time we had to give it. Somebody must have had a schedule in mind, or Rocco was getting paid by the day and Walt wanted him off the clock.

Whenever we could safely leave, probably sooner, we would sail for Caicos, then Turks, where they have food, as rumor had it! We were overdone on packaged noodles and rice, although Rocco wasn't complaining. We understood Caicos had Mexican, Chinese, French, and American food that somebody else cooked for you! And, of course, the adventure capitalist would be buying. Whatever it cost, it would be worth it. Things could be looking up, but our main information source, the *Yachtsman's Guide*, had been wrong before, though the bigger challenge was comprehending all it had to offer.

The looming question was the weather. The winds were generally southeasterly. Where was Caicos from here? Due southeast! We'd have to figure out how to get the winds to blow from another direction, maybe east-southeast, which didn't work earlier. It briefly crossed my mind that Walt chose to stay home until we were going in a direction other than southeast. Couldn't blame him, and might bet money on it.

For the second night in a row, I took a shower on deck while watching the sunset, a sentient, physical experience. With a little more sailing knowledge, I'd feel respectable. To do this all the time would be a dream; no one around for miles, nothing but horizon toward the setting sun, and shooting Rocco a full moon.

In the morning we went into the settlement of Abraham Bay to make calls, but we had no clue whether we would find a phone, especially one that worked. Usually a payphone was close to the telephone company's microwave tower. We found the tower easily, on a rise with a large, decayed building behind a small white hut with a red roof. The standard telephone booth was six yards from the hut. Nearby was a U.S. military satellite tracking station, one of several located on Caribbean islands, down range from Cape Canaveral. This site was built in the 1950s to track ICBMs; over many years it also tracked manned and unmanned space vehicles orbiting the earth in the early days of the U.S. space program. It was currently closed, the buildings and rusting DC-3 airplanes abandoned. The military-built runway was 10,000 feet long but was overgrown to where only 5,300 feet was usable as the island's airport. Notably, the nose cone from a Thor missile, one of the early rockets sent into space in 1959, was recovered on a beach in Mayaguana containing the camera used to capture the first color photographs of Earth from outer space.

Here on Earth and feeling abandoned, we placed several calls that were not answered. A conversation with someone civil would surely have helped my sanity. It seemed as if Walt had sworn Rocco to silence, and there were few others around.

The settlement was rather large by recent standards, though the area looked impoverished. The Bahamian islanders' decision to leave British possession in 1973 in favor of home rule must have hurt their economy. Mayaguana, where many buildings and much equipment had fallen into a sad state of disrepair, is the least developed and most isolated of the Bahamian islands, with a population of one person per square kilometer. Wyoming has 2.3; of all the States, only Alaska has less— 0.5. It was quiet here.

We passed a small green bungalow with yellow trim where an adult was working on a small boat, and a young person was tearing the not-yet-brown tassels off a few ears of corn growing in a helter-skelter garden. I wondered how well they ate here. Those tassels or silks are important. If they are not present during the pollen shed or pollen drop period, the ovules will not be fertilized and the kernels will not develop. There was one silk per kernel before the kid started his work, but not anymore; they will have to share. I was an uninvited visitor, so I kept the already uneasy peace. There were too many unfriendly faces here to be showing off farming knowledge, and they may have been doing this style of "farming" for a long time. I wasn't feeling as chipper as Mr. Rogers, and I saw no Sesame Street signs, so I could easily forgo the desire to fix the neighborhood today. Fresh corn on the cob would have been great, but just looking enviously at it might have gotten me arrested for stalking.

If attitudes were projected through the looks they threw our way, this was either a penal colony or they equated boaters with polluters (or many other options). Islands and prisons do share the element of captivity (as do boats), albeit to widely varying degrees. Unless they had something here to sell to boaters, then we could only be polluters. As for products to sell, the place exuded a sense of their "Cocaine Islands" reputation. An unexpected number of speedboats skimmed around, with no obvious industry to support the habit. But any community that could afford to tear the tassels off corn must have had a better way to put food on the table. I couldn't see it from where I stood, and it may have been best that way. My view was this was a waystation on the path to elsewhere. The sailing guide said the inhabitants see few visitors (certainly believable) and that they were especially friendly and helpful, "eager to make your stay a pleasant one." Of that I hadn't been a witness. If I was prematurely severe in my speculation and we did get invited to dinner, I wasn't going to be so insensitive as to ask for fresh corn.

Back at the boat, we checked the charts to determine which channel to take when departing. If we left at Guano Point, it would improve our angle with the wind. We took *Speedy* out to the breakers to ascertain where it was deep enough for us to leave the bay toward the southeast, avoiding backtracking to go out the way we came in, from the southwest. The wind had been coming from the east most of the day, but by evening it had swung around to the northeast. Not much of a weather opening if it vacillated, but still decent, since our path would be about 135 degrees.

Around sundown, Rocco and I decided to go for it. We had to move fast to get past the breakers before dark. After weighing anchor, I stayed on the bow to try to spot any coral heads in our path. It felt useless, since they all looked to be near the surface in water this clear, and you couldn't stop anyway if you didn't see the obstacle sufficiently early. I correct myself; you would stop, just not on your terms. You might prefer to steer around them, but we had yet to discuss whether my pointing to the left is pointing at the coral head to avoid, or suggesting he steer to the port side. You had better have it right before you set the plan and the boat in motion (we didn't). Otherwise, the pulpit serves as a convenient perch for me to be thrown from the boat when it crunches to a stop. Rocco enjoyed that as a no-lose backup plan.

We cleared the bay, then set our sails under cover of darkness. Keeping the lights off so as to avoid unwanted attention, we settled on a modest speed which kept the boat more upright, not wanting to reach Caicos before dawn. We took our time, enjoying the fact that the environment did not seem to threaten our lives at the moment, and observing the brilliant stars, undimmed by artificial light. I wondered if there might be another boat traveling without lights as we were, that would cross our path. There was scant pleasure boat traffic this far down the island chain, so it was as likely as winning the lottery, but people still play the lottery, and win. I kept an eye open.

The wind held firm in the northeast, hitting us on the beam, and the autohelm did its job nicely in the benign weather, unlike the last overnight sail. As the sun rose, the wind died, so I dropped our sails and motored, heading directly toward the sun. Long hours of sailing to our compass point of 135 degrees became tedious, and I amused myself by watching flying fish do their amazing feat of evading predators: Gossamer wings propelled them on a woodpecker-like sine wave flight—or it was I who was bobbing up and down—several feet above the water, then they disappeared into the sun or dove back into the water. The world appeared pretty simple—the fish, me, and the orange blaze on the eastern horizon painting the sea golden.

That was all there was, a tiny boat carrying two men, one of them asleep. Not so much as a cloud, boat, or stick in view for 360 degrees, just endless sky and water. Where else but on the water could this be the case? What would you do without charts and a compass? Sometimes I sang to break the monotony, but only a monotonic chant would have fit this flat, monochromatic scene. It was beautiful and, though not an artist, I could have drawn this easily with a sheet of white paper and an orange crayon.

Not fighting to stay afloat left time for contemplation. One moment, my thoughts were many miles away, musing over how this scene compared with the traffic crush on Interstate 270 between Gaithersburg, Maryland, and the Washington, D.C. beltway during rush hour. Only the sunrise shared those polar opposite scenes. The next moment, why hadn't we waited another day at Rum Cay? Bad judgment like that kills sailors. Other thoughts were of past friends, friends who would have moved on in their lives. Thoughts of Nikki were ever present and varied wildly due to our pleasurable but fleeting introduction. She could be elsewhere in her life by the time I returned, though with her complicating factors, it may not be immediate. Our connection was special in so many attributes and interests. Still, she was geographically challenging. There may be plenty of fish in the sea, but you need to be where they are to engage them. We were going in the opposite direction, 4–5 knots at best.

As we grew closer to our destination, I double-checked our navigation. Beneath the smooth, reflective surface, extraordinary in its simplicity, lies an underwater world seemingly inert and beautiful, but dangerous. If I wasn't mindful of the ubiquitous low-lying coral heads that have doomed many a sailor, we could run aground and still be there when future 30-foot waves crushed the boat and us into small pieces, turning us into another "lost at sea" story.

I was eager to remove that risk, to see land and settle my stomach. These were low-lying islands, and we were teased by occasional elongated clouds appearing as islands on the horizon. Being sea-weary and anxious to tie it down accentuated the feeling that little progress was being made. This sail was one of the better ones, but life is always uncertain until you are securely anchored.

CHAPTER
Five

Turks and Caicos Islands:
Providenciales:
Alice's Restaurant, R₂D₂, and John Lennon

W e sailed through Sand Bore Channel into Sapodilla Bay on the
south side of Providenciales, referred to as Provo by locals.
Provo is the largest and most commercially developed island
in the Caicos group. It covers 38 square miles and, in 1993, had around
6,000 folks from many countries. Caicos comes from a Lucayan term "caya
hico," meaning "string of islands," geologically part of the Bahamas string.
Columbus was said to have discovered the islands around 1492; Ponce de
Leon was alleged to have arrived at Caicos first, around 1512. Better yet, we
arrived around 1130, having left Abraham Bay at 1730, an 18-hour crossing.

We immediately sought to clear Customs which, at Provo, was done on
the boat. After hailing Customs on VHF channel 16, two hefty agents in two-
tone brown uniforms showed up on the dock. Once aboard, they admired
and appreciated treats from the larder, in fact made it seem we would not
gain entry if we didn't have special bribes, specifically fresh oranges and
root beer. *Hey, that's my food! Have some sausage and beer, I'll throw in three
onions! Okay, two onions. One? Please?* Those guys got more comfortable in
five minutes than I had in several weeks. Chatting was the marine version of
"How were the roads, traffic, and weather west of here?" Perhaps that was the

Customs version of an interview, observing behavioral tics betraying dope smugglers versus sailors. *You boys carrying dope? Gimme some!*

Rocco was more than anxious to have them leave—what was he carrying in his baggage? I was happy to have someone to talk to; they could stay the day for all I cared. After they were orange/root beer-bribed and ferried back to the dock, we had a quiet lunch of fried rice at the Mandarin Chinese Restaurant near our anchorage. On a nearby hill, Mt. Sorrow, there were stone markers and shipwreck remains representing less fortunate sailors. The volume of detritus suggested there were many who perished, having made a navigation mistake or sailed when the wind and seas were unfavorable.

We bought fresh bread from a baker at the Mariner Hotel and tried to find a telephone. But the closest telephone was in town, 4.5 miles away, on a sizzling, near-desert island. Incredible—a hotel without a payphone! Only a baker in the hotel; no cars in the lot where asphalt dissolved into a large area of rock, sand, and gravel. Apparently, we were at the back door of the island, no one around, just a pier and what may be a wharf. Town was closer to the north, the Atlantic and unprotected side of the island. It would take a full day to sail around the island, and then we would be on the wrong side of the island when we departed for South Caicos, across the Caicos Banks. Tomorrow, we'd try hitchhiking into town, to find a phone and see what's there.

Returning to the boat with the treat of a good restaurant meal in my belly, I found a U.S.-style radio station, a welcome companion for the evening, which helped boost my spirits. Then it was time to catch up on my sleep.

The next day, we went ashore and headed toward town. Our dock was past the end of the paved road; we had to walk to the hardtop. A driver coming out of a warehouse parking lot stopped to look both ways. I waved and showed the hitchhiker's thumb of my youth. He nodded, and we ran to the car. Vincent Ewing drove us into town and dropped us at a Texaco station with payphones, which I used to talk with Chris for a while. Afterward, we walked through town toward the Atlantic side of the island.

Shortly, we were called out by two thin, dark-complected island men sitting in a small pickup truck. The back window to the cab was slid open, and the driver, resembling Eddie Murphy, said "Hey, where y'all from?"

Moving around to the side so I could see more of them, I responded, "United States."

"Where ya goin, mon?"

"Other side of the island, to see the Atlantic."

"Ya won' see it wit what ya got wit ya."

"What do you mean?"

"Issa long ass way from here. You cain't walk it. Issa loooonng ass way."

"How far is it?"

"Miles, mon, not just over a hump or two. Miles. But we take ya dere, if das where ya really wanna go."

"You will? And how'd we get back?"

"We bring ya back, mon; ain' gonna dump ya; you buy da drinks, we buy da gas. Deal?"

Hmmm . . . somewhat unconventional, but fair enough. Mutually Assured Destruction kept both powers in check during the Cold War with the Russians, so it may work here. "Okay with you, Rocco?"

"Hmmmph" with a small acknowledging head dip.

"Okay. . . . We ride in the back?"

"Yeeeaah. Les get drinks first. It's hot! C'mon."

Cash up front! Our guides, Evan and Appie, popped open their doors, jumped out of the cab with gusto, and led the way into the convenience store. Evan got something a designated driver would drink. Appie got a beer, because he was driving Evan's truck. Maybe Evan drove only if Appie fell face down, shitfaced, in the middle of the road, and they needed a reliever. The possibility that Evan had a DUI conviction and AA imperative putting him in the shotgun position was the only way this made sense.

We climbed in and took off, on a strange narrow winding road on a strange windy island with two strange island guys, sitting in the back of a small Toyota pickup like trash headed to the dump, while the guys up front were probably high-fiving, saying, "Hey, look whats we got! This counts as community service on that last drunk driving charge."

Driving from a convenience/liquor store past nothing more than scrub, sand, and an occasional cactus, to a bar overlooking the Atlantic for more drinks—what could go wrong? The future was bright. We went in and found a table for four. Once settled, I felt I was back in charm school: *Okay, students, here you are with two strangers—three, really—with whom you have absolutely nothing in common. Now make pleasing, intriguing, and meaningful conversation.* I didn't speak Rastafarian, had never sat at a table with someone with dreadlocks to his waist, Rocco was bald of hair and word, Evan was short and thin, like Appie, otherwise unremarkable. But the local patois was so thick Rocco's grunts were the most intelligible. Looking around the table, by appearances, we comprised an unconventional collaboration, possibly a drug deal or murder for hire negotiation; Appie, a narco, or undercover cop who would bust us; Evan the unexpected hired assassin; and Rocco, the gangland boss. An Alice's Restaurant menu of potential.

Unless we were part of the Star Wars bar scene.

Giving another glance around, it clicked: We were. This was a movie set, and R2-D2 was in the back of the room talking to C-3PO. A big fan, I asked to be excused to go make introductions and invite them to join us. They were all that was missing. As I was getting up, I asked the waiter for a cherry Coke, and to please impale the cherries on a miniature light saber. As I moved toward the back and my eyes adjusted to the dim light, R2 and Threepio turned out to be a Wurlitzer Model 1015 Bubbler jukebox. Chagrined, I looked for Sheb Wooley's *Flying Purple People Eater* for solace and to further enhance the mosaic, dropped in a coin, punched the C, 3, buttons and headed back to the table as the FPPE was "...knockin' em dead, playing rock and roll music through the horn on his head."

It fit.

Back at the table, though not the leader on the boat, I still had to carry the anchor. "So, what do you guys do when you're not driving around drinking?"

"Drugs!"

"Oh yeah? Wow, that's great. Do you get good quality on the island, easy access?"

"Yeah, mon."

"That's rich. I guess you get it before it gets to the States, when we finally get whatever is left. Supply comes through the Bahamas, according to our news, is that right?"

"S'right."

That's about how it went. I know to ask questions like "how did your relationship with your mother and father affect your attitude and behavior with women?" Or "how do the limitations of a small tropical island and its year-round sameness of warm weather affect your career aspirations and world view?" Much as I would like them answered, these questions didn't cross my strangled mind as I struggled to understand the few words in their local patois they did allow me. I may have subconsciously wanted simple answers, unable to understand anything more complex than "yea, mon," or "no, mon."

"How big is the island?"

"It's big, mon. We show you if you keep us wet, mon. We don' drive dry, mon."

That wasn't likely, given the intemperate beginning.

"Rocco, wanna have a look around?" I mean, where's the risk in that? It's not like we're going sailing in the Bermuda Triangle on a bad weather night, wind on our nose. No one would risk that. Anyone surviving must be immortal anyway. It's more likely we will hit somebody and be thrown from the truck to face life in a wheelchair or death. But only if the other driver's drinking. The chances there are two drunks on this small island at the same place and time? Not so much.

"Hummhh."

I knew "Hummhh" meant "yes," and his unrelenting cussing reflected a tendency toward disapproval. So, it looked like we had a "go" for the tour.

It had been a longer drive to the Atlantic shore than I had guessed, so we accepted the guided-tour-for-drinks offer. Being the largest island we'd seen since Nassau, there had to be something to see. We left the bar, sadly before Princess Leia arrived, and mercifully before Darth Vader. Anyone with a hood over their head and a weapon in their hand elevates my anxiety. We were active captives on the tour, examining beach exotica and taking photos of red, green, and yellow racing boats. Appie insisted on being featured in every picture, striking a gallant pose like a yard art silhouette. If I whipped around to get a clean shot of another boat, he was there. Only a picture of the mast top was likely to be unobstructed.

We visited Turtle Cove Marina, where we saw Aquanauta, a new type of boat alleged to be in a movie (these two guys knew details only up to a point—they peaked early), then went to Smokey's for lunch, fixated on a much-ballyhooed grouper salad. When the salad was delivered, the grouper was still at-large. Appie yelled at the owner to show us the grouper. Neither of us could find much of it, but the price had suggested there would be plenty. Obviously, the operating margins were at high tide on the most expensive lettuce this side of Tokyo. Our guide was likely on the Cash Kick Back for Tourists program.

The ambience was tropical—an open air, ceiling-fanned, thatched-roof restaurant directly on the beach, not much else nearby. Absolutely delightful. This wouldn't last. On this beautiful site, development was inevitable. Let the grouper live; it was worth a couple bucks to sit here, absorb the scenery, and dream up questions, trying to make conversation with three unknowns.

Our next stop was the Ramada Inn, a full-scale resort in Grace Bay, where we could buy a root beer float. I had to have one. Where else would I see a root beer float unless I threw a can of root beer overboard encased in bubble wrap to hide it from Customs? Not a risk worth taking. Without root beer, second only to a passport for clearing Customs, where would we be? We then roamed the hotel indoors, enjoying the shade and the magic flush toilets I didn't have to pump by hand. Outdoors, we found the shark-free pool attractive, more a reflecting than a swimming pool, its poolside human *objets de'art* having no intention of getting wet other than by spray lotions and misters being used like basters.

Further down the road, we pulled up to the gate of Club Med, where Appie asked the guard if we could come in and tour. The way Appie was dressed and groomed, the guard probably felt if he hadn't thrown Appie out yesterday, it was the day before. Had we arrived on my private jet, no doubt the latest Gulfstream, sporting Louis Vuitton luggage, in Appie's company and this truck, we'd still be denied. "Registered guests only!"

We took that as a strong "NO!" and drove to the end of the road where we observed people boarding a cutesy, not-very-serious-looking ferry, so much like a children's book feature I checked the front for moving eyes, eyelashes, and a smile, maybe a name like Capt. Li'l Toot. It went to Pine Cay, an exclusive island off the northeast end of Provo. Doubt these folks would invite Appie aboard either. I was content to leave them to their vacation of one or two weeks, preferring adventure a bit more raw, active, and of longer duration. However, I wouldn't have minded being comfortable as a woman's boy toy or chaperone (I could cook) until the wind swung around to the north or northwest, especially the tall brunette with the fabulous slacks boarding Li'l Toot without me. But Rocco was my date and the cross I bore.

We drove on to Leeward (should have been "wayward") Settlement, a nearby partially developed residential area that raised serious questions of just how thorough the tour would be. This wasn't a feature on "Show and Tell" or a stop on the Boulevard of Stars, and Appie wasn't a real estate agent. We were looking for a "drug store." No commercial establishments in sight, it quickly became apparent we had located a "cottage industry" of sorts. Appie aroused the "druggist," dressed in long white cargo pants with spacious pockets, from his post on a white, cinder block wall near an intersection of two quiet roads and, after a hushed conversation, money and product surreptitiously began to change hands. My guess is there was a standing or easily communicated prescription that was being refilled; "one nickel bag or two?" I further educated myself on the need for such a transaction when I looked through the sliding window between the cab and the truck bed where we were risking it all and imagined I saw a light on the dashboard, flashing "Low on Drugs."

Looking up from the information readout, I felt antsy, exposed, akin to the ducks in the shooting galleries of amusement parks at closing time, the ducks having come to rest. An easy target! No chance here for us, not even to duck, with what the salt air had done to the sheet metal of the truck. It wouldn't provide any more protection than a cardboard box.

For a moment, I thought of getting all puffed up in a Puritanical rejection of drugs and their negative effects on society, and objecting to the trade relationships being conducted here in the islands. Or, at least, taking shelter behind a bush, were there one. But I was a guest, and while in "Rome," if sitting still as Nero had done was all I was asked to do, it shall be done. Moreover, I had no idea where the hell I was. Or how I would get to someplace else! There were few roads and virtually no traffic. To set out on foot might have taken overnight to get somewhere, if I knew which way to go. I doubted Rocco would have wanted to walk home on principle, which may have a moral compass but little arch support.

After an uneasy, extremely long time to get an order filled, we made it safely back to town. Perhaps that dealer owned the island franchise, and there weren't any gang or turf wars like those at home. Needing other groceries, perhaps a little something for the children in the family (confectioner's sugar as a training aid), Appie stopped in a supermarket parking lot. I was happy to be there. Appie's sobriety was on the wane, but we were still 4–5 miles from the boat, so we couldn't make a practical run for it. Next door, we purchased a cone of soft ice cream apiece which helped lower my anxiety level. If police will buy cones for lost little boys, then cones should work for bigger boys who'd lost all options. Ice cream in hand, Rocco and I jumped in the back of the truck and, with Appie at the wheel, headed back to South Dock, our anchorage in Sapodilla Bay.

Finishing off their liquid refreshment, possibly their last free drinks for a while, our true-to-their-motto we-don't-drive-dry chauffeurs were noticeably fluid by this time, making our bed-of-the-pickup perch precarious. The last leg of our ride was longer than a map would indicate, what with the weaving, but not by an unforgivable amount. Our driver's condition provided something on the order of an amusement park ride among few cars, many cactuses and sand. If he veered off the narrow road and hit a saguaro cactus, we'd be stuck. Getting that pickup stopped for the last time was sweet relief. Risk elevates the sense of adventure, and we'd had enough of both to hold us until Monday.

But they weren't done. Our new buddies proposed we get together for a crawfish dinner on Monday. Charming as we may have been, my guess was our official function would be paying the bill. We must have been a big hit, though, because they also wanted to supply us with women, blind dates, to host on the boat as guests for the weekend. Which, and again I'm just guessing, we would also be buying (or leasing). But, to extend that much hospitality? How thoughtful. (And I could only imagine the possible negative outcomes—charges of rape, kidnapping?) Posing falsely as paragons of virtue (speaking for myself), we respectfully declined the female companionship on the hallowed grounds surrounding the sanctuary (in this case) of the institution of marriage, happy to feign attachment, forgoing any curiosity to see their "Gentlemen's Club" portfolio.

"We're both committed men. Maybe just dinner on Monday?"

"Whezya weddin' ring, mon?" Appie asked

I winked at him, pulling at my ring finger, "I didn't want to risk losing it."

Exhausted from carrying Rocco socially for the last three hours, I could not imagine spending any more time with another person who speaks unintelligible English, and paying for the torture.

Saturday was a day of recovery; Sunday was a true holy day of rest, observing the Christian Sabbath by denying ourselves the hot island women. Hopefully, that sacrifice was recognized and recorded, offsetting other failings. I baked muffins for breakfast, and brownies, before fixing a lunch of pork and beans with Vienna sausages and grilled cheese sandwiches. Dinner was fruit mixed in raspberry yogurt, with crackers; then brownies covered with rich Haagen-Dazs vanilla ice cream and Mrs. Richardson's hot fudge with a trickle of raspberry coulis, all smothered with whipped cream, topped with two tongue-knottable long-stem cherries. Would you believe dessert was a buck-naked brownie? Was I hallucinating from second-hand inhalation of dopie's Ape?

Between meals and dreaming of food we didn't have, we took *Speedy* for a ride to explore the coastline and the interesting homes sitting back from the water-carved rock forming this coast of periodic small beaches. The sun was setting, making the coastal scene glisten in gold, appearing even more dramatic and desirable. Today was how the trip was sold in the "brochures"— pretty scenery, time to relax, an uncommon opportunity to do something different, explore a new country. It had been slow coming.

My work on Spanish in the evening was inspired by a recent encounter with a gentleman who spoke only Spanish. It was fun to work at communicating with him, more fun than not understanding people speaking your native language, like Appie. Rocco seemed surprised that I was able to get useful information from the man just as Rocco was walking away, frustrated. I kept hoping for improvements in my relationship with him, that his air of contempt would abate. No sign of it yet.

On Monday, the weather was dissuasive to sailing across the banks to South Caicos, our next stop. Rumor had it that tomorrow would be different, so we motored up the coast to the Caicos Marine & Shipyard (CM&S) to refuel and visit Customs. One of our boat neighbors, John, sailing *First Light*, was going there also. At CM&S, I picked up a couple of books from the lending library, pervasive at most marinas, and we met John and his wife, Wendy. She worked for IBM, he worked for Bell Northern Research (Northern Telecom). They were on a two-year leave of absence and had been working to improve the boat while sailing it. They would return to their jobs next July. Both were young, probably in their early to mid-thirties. When not closeted in an office building working a standard 40-hour week, you discover people like John and Wendy in interesting jobs with unusual arrangements.

Checking the weather forecast, it was obvious the wind would not be cooperating tomorrow, so we canceled our meeting with the Customs officials at the boatyard and sailed back to our anchorage with the wind at our backs, a delightful experience referred to as a sleigh ride. John told us later that our route was too close to the island, and we were lucky to have avoided dangerous coral heads. Our shallow draft may have kept us from becoming detritus on Mt. Sorrow. There was a full moon in the evening, providing light to sail by if we soon had favorable winds. The sun went down around 1700 this far east in the Eastern time zone, which made for a short evening unless you chose to stargaze. We would be entering the Atlantic time zone before too long, which would give us more daylight in the evening relative to the clock, not that the clock mattered at all. It was our Circadian rhythms that drove us.

In the evening, our local well-wheeled and -connected hosts did not come a-calling to take us out to dinner, but stood us up, evoking Rocco's description of this being "about the best thing that happened all day," his first, best line of the trip. In his uplifted state, Rocco started discussing how to know when to do what when sailing, and he talked until 2230, one of our latest nights and our first real conversation. Of course it was beneficial to me with so much to learn. He had an enviable set of skills, though not such that everyone needs. He had built a railway to tractor his boat out of the Maine winter waters and store it in a shed, where he could lay up fiberglass if he wanted to redo the hull or make repairs. With his sewing machine, he could sew all the sails, awnings, and make other canvas covers as necessary. He'd built a sawmill and facility to cut and cure lumber, and could work with stainless steel—stuff most of us city boys don't do. Then, when it got quiet, without saying another word, he stood up and went to bed.

It didn't occur to me to ask if he had served in WWII, but he was the silent type, writ large, and most of our veterans don't discuss their war experiences, even if asked. His age made it almost inevitable that he served; probably born around 1922, putting him at about 19 when the U.S. joined the war. Might have been a ground-pounder if he was in the Army, and kept doing it for the post office when he got out. But the way he loves water and solitude, the Navy may have given him his start, plus he easily cleared the hurdle of one who "swears like a sailor!" He most reminded me of a Trident submarine, something that runs silent, runs deep for a long time and then, without any announcement to the world, suddenly all hell breaks loose.

Rocco is possibly not the bad guy he would have me believe. That was pitiably late-breaking, and potentially good news, though I may not experience it in practice. Pure theory, so far.

When we awoke, the wind was still blowing strongly from the wrong direction, keeping us weather bound and requiring us to go into town to get an extension from Customs for more than the standard 7-day stay. Once ashore, we reserved a loaf of fresh bread and three pastries from the baker at the Mariner Hotel, all he had, then stuck out our thumbs when we came to the hardtop road, which was also baking. Considered semi-desert here, it looked and felt parched, flat, with Cactaceae (cacti) flora, and a cloudless sky. Eventually, an Asian fellow in a pickup truck gave us a ride. Not much was said; I suspect he did not speak English. His truck had A/C, so I liked him. Since hitching was the standard here, if the driver is not going all the way into town, they will usually take you pretty close or to an intersection where you have a good chance at another ride. It is a sign they have done you a princely deed when they turn around and go back the way they have come, which was the case. Our prince dropped us in town and we walked to Immigration.

After we filled out the extension requests, we were told interviews were held at 1400. It was then 1030. Were they kidding? This was either a big deal, or Rocco has his photo in a post office somewhere. If we were required to swear to something, Rocco had it covered. Spending a day getting an extension for another day seemed wasteful.

Needing a cool drink, we went to the Tasty Temptation. I ordered a Ginger Ale, Rocco requested iced tea. When it was served, there was no ice in either. Asking about the missing ice, we had consensus when told there was none. Whatever made me think that iced tea might have ice? That was dumb. But at least it was cold.

The town reminded me of Arizona border towns, a cross between Bisbee and Sierra Vista. Orange-to-yellow desert landscape and heat prevailed. After our drinks we ran a few errands around town and grabbed lunch. Walking out of the restaurant, we crossed paths with Appie. He'd had a "severe" Sunday, as he described it. Didn't recall that as a biblical term, though the culture here was different. Was he doing construction and taping drywall for fourteen hours, or working with the white powder we bought the other day? He took Monday off to recover, preventing him from making good on hosting us for a crawfish dinner Monday night. Damn! We feigned disappointment. So did Appie. In any case, it felt better that I was inquiring of his absence than he of mine.

Arriving at Immigration at 1400, it took our interviewer nine more minutes to recover from lunch. The interview was extensive; he told us to fill out the section marked "Official Use Only." Apparently we had been deputized or elected without knowing it, having survived the statutory waiting period. We waited 3.5 hours for this? The only resemblance of an interview was when he said to fill out the official space, and I asked him: "Are you sure? This 'Official Use Only' section? Right here?"

"Yes."

It took two hitches to get to the boat. Our last helper was John Lennon, whom I thought had died. If we kept hitching, we may meet Elvis who "had left the building" but possibly not the island. Who else may be hiding here? They had cars that appeared to be reincarnated. John mentioned there was no income tax on the island. That's only initially attractive; the absence of benefits was obvious. I asked John about the antique-looking schooner anchored in front of our boat. David Douglas spent four years building it, and now used it to import fresh fruits and vegetables from the Dominican Republic to Caicos. It was an interesting boat, new but of historic design, with giant leeboards on each side. Leeboards are used in place of a deep keel, retractable to allow passage in a shallow draft area, and still prevent sideways drift when sailing. That provides more unobstructed internal room for freight and a watertight hull as opposed to a centerboard design. John also told me where David set up his stand in town to sell his produce. He would have a visitor! The stores were supplied by a fruit plane, which arrived on Wednesdays, and the stores were empty of fresh produce by Saturday. David had found his niche, and I had found a godsend in John—two if I could find David.

Tick tock, rock around the dock. Much of each day was spent sitting around reading, rocking with the waves, waiting for favorable winds. The weather forecast was for more of the same in wind direction and strength lasting several more days. We talked to Walt today, for the first time since the operation. He dearly wants to be here, but Felicity needs him. Her operation went as planned, but it was too soon to know how successful it will be. Walt encouraged us to get to Luperon, Dominican Republic. He had heard and read good things about the country, and I on the availability of fresh fruit. My banana-a-day habit would have been happy with one per week.

While wandering on shore, more appreciation for my life in the U.S. surfaced when looking at two adjacent boats unloading at the Customs dock. One was a Haitian boat, having unloaded what is known in the Caribbean as ground provisions (roots and tubers, such as viandas, cassava, malanga, taro, and sweet potatoes), sugar cane, plantains, oranges, mangoes, and old bottles, all spilling out of gunnysacks onto the ground. Alternatively, it may have been the result of a Customs inspection. Definitely unappealing. The other boat was a large, modern freighter, with gunwales (pronounced "gunnels") higher than the top of the Haitian mast, hailing from Fort Lauderdale, Florida, unloading speedboats and jet skis, all mounted in shipping crates or on pallets shrink-wrapped in sparkling clear plastic film. A stunning contrast; the two countries are as disparate as any two in the world.

Another Haitian boat sat dockside on the ocean bottom, partially submerged in several feet of crystalline water, the crooked mast top lashed to another three feet of a slightly crooked tree branch with the forestay attached.

Most of the rigging was collapsed. A red-topped blue box on the deck looked like a companionway to slight storage below. In this water, depth was hard to measure, but it looked like the last days for this boat as it sat in its shallow, watery grave. It may have been intentional, perhaps scuttled by "immigrants," now somewhere on the island, who may have had no intention of accepting Custom's invitation to an orange/root beer chat.

Had you been born in Haiti, the story of that sunken boat might be familiar, as would dictatorships, wrecked economies, and digging in the dirt for a living. No chance of riding on those jet skis offshore with the dolphins, then zooming up the Intracoastal Waterway wake-surfing behind big yachts, enjoying worldwide travel, or achieving financial independence. Even if you have the discipline to do the right thing, being born where you have the opportunity to do the right thing can make a big difference. Good government, rule of law, and property rights provide the opportunity, for which I, standing there in amazement, was very grateful.

Wednesday morning, I woke up mildly excited, knowing the fruit and vegetable plane would arrive. Weird, what passed for excitement. Because Rocco was not in charge of food or associated in any way but for the eating, I alone headed into town early to ensure a good selection. Not many cars passed, so I walked quite a distance. I saw American-looking couples in rented cars, but they didn't mess with hitchhikers. Too risky? No longer a part of their culture? They were guests, not hosts, and didn't have the luxury of time. They had to get to Immigration. Or maybe they were French. Or British. They all looked alike. In any case, I walked my ass off. I took letters written last night to the Post Office. Mail would go out Thursday to Turks, and out of there on Friday. It doesn't sound fast, but it was what you got.

Yeah, mon, we have no bananas! Town Center grocery store was still out; plane had not arrived, had no schedule, but it usually showed up—sometime. That's good. John Lennon said David would have fruit at the Marketplace, which was another long walk. *How much would he have? Perhaps I should hustle. By the time I get back by the store, the plane will have been here. Cripes!* Island time would be considered a degenerate's disease by any Type A personality.

When I arrived at Marketplace, David wasn't there, but was expected soon. A shopkeeper, Kathleen Grant, showed me around the small cluster of shops, and sold me a postcard of her sitting in her shop. I had her sign it, in case she and John Lennon became famous for something. At least John had name recognition. Kathleen had a beautiful, stuffed, wind-up talking parrot that I had a use for, but didn't think it and Rocco would get along.

David soon arrived with a trailer-load of foodstuff. I bought a dozen oranges and a dozen bananas, eating one immediately in the style of, "life is uncertain; eat dessert first." Four grapefruit, three tomatoes, a dozen potatoes, a cucumber—almost more than I could carry, and I was on my way. Fresh food! Could you be robbed of food? Perhaps, and I might have done so as recently as yesterday. Skipping down the road was tempting, but my sacks of produce were too heavy and awkward. I felt conspicuous stopping at Town Center grocery for the things they had in stock, carrying fresh produce into the store and past the empty shelves and envious shoppers. I had no receipt, and didn't dare set the fruit down. I checked out without incident and headed for the edge of town to hitch a ride home, pleased with my success.

When I was back aboard, a thought struck me. I looked around and saw David's boat. Looking to land, there was our dock and, to the right, the bigger dock with the freighter and Haitian boats. Where would David have unloaded his boat?

This trip continued to bring back childhood remembrances. Not too strange, really, since both were light on frills, heavy on fundamentals: hitchhiking and walking to get everywhere, including to and from the store with bags to carry, and washing clothes by hand then air drying them on a line. There were many other similarities to life in the government-subsidized project on Knox Hill in Washington, D.C. Even the discussion with Rocco reached back, as when he mentioned how he did a lot of sewing by machine, making a lot of covers for his boat. Instantly, my recollection was of using mom's Singer sewing machine to make and repair things, usually ripped clothes from jumping fences or catching the pants leg in the chain/sprocket of my bicycle. Many times it felt as though I had gone back in time 30 years. Life here was pretty basic; most of the modern conveniences and abundance didn't exist. We'd traveled from a land of plenty to mostly second/third world countries, and the facilities of the boat bore a lot in common with our host islands. Waste was greatly reduced. Would I revert to free-flowing showers (with water-savers, of course) when I returned home? Definitely.

Unable to take food for granted, I noticed that our dinner was international. A fresh salad had tomatoes from Dominican Republic, carrots and lettuce bought in Great Exuma from California, ham from Caicos. Not at all exotic when written down, but interesting in discovery.

We were still waiting on the weather, and it didn't look good for a departure tomorrow. I washed the dishes and, after sundown, took a shower on deck in the middle of a long sequence of lightning. Beautiful exposure to nature, but all those volts dancing around made me a little skittish. I wondered if the lady on the boat next door caught any of the action. I didn't hear any hissing or jeering, so maybe not—would have made a sexy scene in an R-rated movie if the sexes were reversed. No one cares about a naked man, do they? Going to bed clean felt luxurious, almost sensual.

Another day and, boy-oh-boy, was I ready to move on. But it was another quiet, boring, windy day in port. Weather came up, providing rain in the afternoon, which was interesting to watch as it moved around the bay in scattered dark columns from the clouds to the water's surface. So, early to bed, all the while waiting for relief in the easterly wind speed. If it didn't change direction but dropped to less than 20 knots, we may try to power across the banks. With these wind speeds, we didn't have to run the engine to recharge the batteries. The constantly howling wind generator replaced all the electrical power we had used in the past week. The airplane-like prop spinning at high speed at head level (sounded like we were at the airport) combined with the motion of the boat and the rhythmic pump/suck ummmphh ahhh of the water maker made up several predominant ambient sensations that would become lasting memories.

With unrelenting easterly winds, we watched the sun go down through the companionway. As eager as we were to move on, a regrettable decision was possible, which would guarantee more abuse from the sea. Having cleared Customs, Rocco would think we had to move on, death be damned. Better that than another visit from Customs. On the other hand, sissies never leave sight of the dock, never turn the GPS on for anything other than a system check. Arrrrghh!

At daybreak of a heavily clouded day, we pulled up the hook and were off on another (ill-advised) adventure. Wind was still nukin' (windsurfer term for nuclear winds) from the east. We could have left a week ago under the same conditions and died earlier, leaving a week's worth of fruit and vegetables for someone else. At least Rocco avoided the Customs man. He wasn't going to come out in this weather for anything, not even a root beer.

We hung out a reefed mainsail and the jib for our sail to the southeast, and later, the mainsail only. Our navigation from Provo was to a point in the middle of the Caicos Bank defined as 72 degrees west longitude, 21 degrees 30 minutes north latitude, staying northeast of many coral heads on the starboard side, but avoiding shoals northeast of the specified waypoint, a critical channel of sail. Using GPS, we could track that vector within feet, as long as we computed it correctly. If not, all bets were off, and so may be the hull.

When we turned from our southeast vector toward the east at the shoals, we had to drop the mainsail and resort to diesel power. Waves hit us dead on the bow, making the trip an athletic event. The water was shallow and, with the wind coming from the east-southeast, the deeper water of the Atlantic piled up on the shallower water of the banks, making the waves steeper and closer together than they would be if we were running in deeper water. Our little boat was doing some serious tail-dancing, and we didn't dare lift a foot, unsure of where the boat would be when we put it down again.

If conditions didn't deteriorate, this could be our second-worst crossing. I hoped nothing exceeded our trip from Rum Cay to Mayaguana. Being daylight, we could see what was coming, and not be blindsided like a vicious mugging in a dark alley. We discontinued using the autohelm in order to steer by hand, because of the numerous coral heads that had to be avoided— if we could see them in time in the low light and high seas. Rocco thought the autohelm would not allow sufficiently fast course correction to avoid a potential accident, and everything was at risk. Nor could anyone stay on the bow as a lookout. At least steering kept us vigilant. If we stayed on course, and the charts were accurate, we could stay afloat and live for another day.

Sitting was out of the question; the seating surface behind the wheel was arched to provide additional height to see over the cabin top. Pushing the wheel to port pushed you to starboard and out of reach of the wheel, and vice versa, keeping you sliding and rolling on the seat from corner to corner like a prizefighter with an invisible opponent. It was necessary to stand to steer, single-handedly, the other hand holding onto the backstay to stay balanced and in the boat. Whoever was not at the helm was standing in the companionway with the slide pulled across the top, holding on with both hands, looking aft and trying to breathe fresh air without getting nauseated or swamped from the pouring rain and sea spray. Today Rocco was more than willing to share helmsman duty—one of the few times he wanted to act as a team; I kept hearing, "your turn!" "your turn!" "your turn!" *Thank you, Rocco, I was hoping you'd share. But you're quitting early; you have 58 more seconds to go, or 15 more breaking waves.*

Light displacement, shoal draft boats are more affected by rough weather than heavier and deeper boats, and we paid dearly for being a lightweight. After a long day of being bounced, smacked, slammed, dunked, and generally disrespected by weather coming at us from all sides, it began to look as if we might make it across. Approaching our destination, we had to sail south of 21 degrees 25 minutes north latitude to clear numerous coral heads extending southwest from South Point on Long Cay, then sail north along the Atlantic (east) side of Long Cay to round its northern tip, south of South Caicos, before settling in the lee of the cay on the northwest corner. We picked out a desirable anchorage and set the hook barely in time to escape the rapidly deteriorating weather closing in, with the wind and rain picking up in withering velocity.

Finally, we could sit down. I sat propped up in a corner of the bunk for maximum support.

The anchorage was well protected from the swells coming from the southeast, giving us a settled, peaceful evening, except for the unceasing, howling wind keeping the rigging strumming like guitar strings. The wind generator was roaring like a propeller airplane approaching take off, with wind speed so high the generator's automatic brake kept engaging to prevent an unscheduled disassembly. NOT the marketed image of paradise, though once I was confident the boat was not breaking apart and the anchor was holding, being securely cocooned inside a small, snug boat felt both precarious and comforting.

The coziness of the boat reminded me of the childhood forts and tree houses my friends and I used to build—sometimes in standing trees, but usually from old Christmas trees or larger fallen trees—like a cave with only one way out, which was easy to protect and provided great solace. The boat, with its bow pointed into the eye of the wind, had just one companionway, opposite the threat of driving wind and rain, and could be boarded up for a secure and dry hunkering down to outwait the weather.

I was increasingly aware we were but a mote on the surface of planet Earth. We didn't die that day, but 150,000 did, ten of them drowned, on average, without a ripple in the news; lightning strikes Earth eight million times a day, and you likely didn't see any of it. In our big world, we were so small, only two people knew where we were.

The wind continued, without pause, past the arrival of sleep, slipping away before the break of dawn.

South Caicos:
Nothing to see here, keep moving

I awoke feeling it had been several lifetimes since we left a month ago. Looking around outside the cabin was like surfacing out of a hole in the ground after being transplanted in the dark of night: not a single thing outside the boat, not even the warm sun, looked familiar. Nothing offered a path to the past.

Hoping to improve our quality of life, I made banana pancakes, a first and an overdue treat. I still couldn't read Rocco on whether he enjoyed anything I placed in front of him; invariably, he was mute when it came to expressing his opinion. Apparently, if it was paid for and cooked for him, his meal would be acceptable. Life with just him around was solitary confinement with a teaser—knowing what having a travel companion could be like but wasn't, although he had uttered a few intelligible words the week we were in Provo.

Rocco inspired a recall of several "monks working in silence" jokes, especially where the new monk got to say only two words every ten years. He started with "Cold food," then, at twenty years, "Hard beds." By thirty years, it was, "I quit!" The head monk retorted: "I am not surprised; you've been bitching ever since you arrived." That was about how it would go down here, I supposed. After saying little more than six words, Rocco would tender his resignation and be off the boat before the ink was dry if he had someone to receive it. He'd have to be quick about it; mine's already written.

While in town to find the Immigration officer, we discovered the yacht *Fantastique*, from Rum Cay, tied up at the dock. After ten days or so, they hadn't made any more progress than us. Few passagemakers came this far, and protected anchorages were limited; we may see them again. We walked the town as I took pictures of the salt flats/pans, and a few concrete block dwellings along the waterfront, where a now-closed one-level market and warehousing structure with a wide overhang and decaying roof supported by a dozen pilings on the front stood behind a bare flagpole. I wondered what it had been like here at its peak. The only business that appeared to be operating nearby was a small marine biology college.

Noel, a native islander, talked with us while we took cover under the overhang during a brief but strong shower. He was a talkative guy with a 30-year-old Chevy truck, twenty-seven of its years spent in the South Caicos salt air. It couldn't legally operate on our streets back home, but much of the truck was still intact, minus the doors and most fenders, like a decomposed WWII army truck. Replacing yesteryear's donkey-pulled carts, the truck skeleton was used to haul water in giant open barrels to the boats that docked in South Caicos. Noel had worked for the U.S. Coast Guard while they had a station in South Caicos and patrolled these waters. Now, though the islanders were getting along the best they could, it didn't seem they were succeeding famously, just about everything having closed down. Sailing guides stated emphatically that South Caicos was not worth a visit. So, here we were, finding out why. The practical why is continuing across the Turks Channel to Turks would have been insane, not that we didn't qualify.

During our afternoon snorkeling trip, I saw my first barracuda in his world, where he looked even more badass than he does on ice. On the dinghy ride back, we met Les, skipper of *Gaia*, headed next to the Dominican Republic. Les would stay at Samana, D.R., for a week before going on to the Virgin Islands. Based on his long beard, relaxed dress, and physical condition,

I guessed he was a permanent sailor, having the long, sloping front of a sports car but not possibly the performance. The deck of the boat looked well lived on, something only the boat's owner would abide. It seemed to be working for him. What else mattered? Pretensions weren't high at this remote outpost.

As we pulled away, I pondered why *Gaia* was so named: a replica Viking ship? A lust for a Greek Goddess? Or the man living in his own ecosystem? He had no engine, few amenities, and a female bust for a figurehead under the bowsprit, so it could be any of them. He may have been living on two or three dollars a day, outside of repairs to the ship, for food and thread. I may admire someone who can sail without an engine, though I wouldn't want to do it. An engine can compensate for finicky weather and sailing errors, though also enabling the latter. If we'd had only sails, we'd be traveling today instead of yesterday. As it was, to stay on schedule, we were making a habit of leaving port a day before good weather arrived. Hmmm . . . how can I sabotage our engine? Kill an engine, save a life.

Back from our snorkeling and island tour, Rocco took *Speedy* back to South Caicos to try again to line up the Customs event in case the weather would soon allow us to make our passage east to Grand Turk on our quest for paradise.

We had anchored in Cockburn Harbor in the lee of Long Cay, quite a distance from town and all alone but for *Gaia*. Yesterday's rainstorm and thrashing winds had moved on. In the welcome, therapeutic heat of the afternoon sun, while Rocco was ashore, I sat reading a book on the bow, my back to the pulpit, reclining against the jib stowed in its sail bag, feet propped up on the cabin where it rose out of the deck. In stark contrast with yesterday, the weather was Caribbean-beautiful and relaxing; the water a gorgeous blue, seas were calm, the sky mostly clear, temperature in the mid-80s. Being alone, I broke out a Speedo-style bathing suit to soften the tan lines from the longer-legged style that had been my daily uniform. Unlike yesterday's weather pounding, the warmth of the sun felt restorative, the gentle motion of the boat was seductive, and the reclined position was comfortably supportive. That I had fought hard to earn it made it all the more divine.

I took note of small motorboats off the port side a quarter mile away, with swimmers in the water wearing snorkeling gear, diving, and returning to the boats. Judging from the high-pitched voices in this otherwise noise-free haven, there seemed to be a prevalence of women among the divers, probably from the university of marine studies we passed while walking the island.

Later, one of the motorboats slowly crossed the bow behind me and came by on the starboard side. There were three women in the boat and, whether in fact or due to my having been at sea with Rocco for so long, they looked fabulous. I waved and, since they all were looking at me, they waved back then slowly motored around to the stern of the boat, appearing to talk among themselves. At a pace consistent with proper decorum and hospitality, though not necessarily dressed for the part, I rose and walked to the stern of the boat, then waved them closer.

As they neared, we exchanged hellos, and they said: "We're just checking you out. Where you headed?"

"Would you want to throw me a line so you can turn off the motor and we can hear better?" They hesitated, looking at each other. I quickly realized why, found a line in a locker, and said "I appreciate your security concerns. Hold onto this line," and I belayed my end to a cleat on the stern. I told them where we were headed, that we had been sailing for nearly six weeks since leaving Florida. We exchanged our home ports; one lady happened to be from Potomac, Maryland, a nice neighborhood not far from my own. Finding a connection always helps the conversation.

"My name is Bryan; may I ask yours?"

"I'm Elle."

"My name's Kay, I'm an advisor."

"I'm Dee."

"Do you always work in teams where the names sound like initials?"

Elle said, "There is a team of Sara, Barbara, and Cleopatra."

I was being put on, I thought. "Cleopatra? Hasn't that number been retired?"

Kay said, "We have a Janice, Phyllis, and Eunice team."

Fast thinkers, these students! "If Kay were named Esse, you might be druggies or, rearranged, proselytizers," I said.

"Oh, we believe, and get high," said Kay, "on our studies. We love what we do. Who's sailing with you?"

"I'm Bryan, and I'm sailing with Ryan and Lyon." Smoke that!

"You're lyin'!" said Elle.

"No, I'm Bryan, and I'm kidding. Only one other guy's aboard; Rocco." They were marine biology students from the School for Field Studies conducting research used by the Fisheries Department. "Sounds interesting, something I know nothing about. Seems more likely a site for a photo shoot for the Sports Illustrated swimsuit issue."

"Well, you're in pretty good shape," said Elle. "You must work out?"

"Pretty regularly, but not lately. Having to eat my own cooking keeps the weight down. And I get to raise and lower the anchor. Every time." *Maybe my idea of 'make the best of what ya got by staying in shape' actually works with women.*

"What you're doing is really cool," said Kay. "How do you get that much time off?"

"Well, that's a bit of a story, as has been the trip up until now. How much time do you have? Would you like to come aboard for a drink and have a look around? . . . Of course you can see most of the boat from where you are," I had to admit.

"We can't right now," Kay said, "we have to get ready for dinner. If you miss it here, there's no way to make it up. Can't send out for pizza."

"I'd noticed that. Well, it's been a long trip, having only one guy to talk to who really doesn't like to talk. After six weeks, we've said about all we have to say. Any chance you could come back after dinner for an hour or two? My partner goes to sleep before 7:00; could we chat for a while after that?"

Resigned, Dee slowly shook her head suggesting there was no way, while Elle was talking to Kay as if there was. They continued to talk until Kay nodded to me and told Elle, "Ask him."

"What's your last name?"

"Byrd."

"Really! Do you play tennis?"

"Yeah, lots."

"Where?"

"Anywhere I'm invited."

"Ever know a Janice?"

"One ... maybe two, both at work. One worked with me. Is she here? You said you had one."

The buzzing between them became animated as I sat clueless, feeling they had discovered my third foot, or an eye in the center of my forehead.

Kay looked like she was mediating, thought on it for a minute, then it was resolved: "We'll come back at seven for a while, if you promise to be a gentleman."

"I'd love the company, and to know more about you and the island."

"Okay!" They started their motor, threw back the line and, as they left, suggested I turn on the anchor light after dark.

Well, that was stimulating to the mind, perhaps as likely as finding a true mermaid. But what the hell? They can't say yes if you don't ask. They do occasionally push their way in the door, but not often. Not often enough. Perhaps having survived a near-death experience at the gates of Hell had me unconcerned over the embarrassment of rejection, a slight ten-second emotion. Disconnected, unaccountable, and I could die tomorrow. So what about tonight?

I was unsure what to expect, if anything. The most probable result would be a "no show," the least probable would be they'd bring a flippin' pizza, but one can dream. They had more than two hours to lose their nerve, change their minds, or find another distraction, and I was almost sure they'd not be returning in the middle of the evening, after dark, to chat with a stranger who was as transient as a boat can impart—able to sail away to anywhere. In any case, it was fun to talk to someone besides Rocco, however briefly. If they did return, would it be all three, or just the advisor? She was probably not more than low to mid-thirties, but closer to my age—an ancient mariner of forty-eight, though Elle seemed the most insistent. I was intrigued by their private conversation, which seemed to sway the decision in my favor—unless they kill unwitting sailors for fun and they were just diving over the decaying remains of their last mark. No one said I couldn't be at risk, but what was that chatter about?

Many fantasies had occupied my mind on this cruise in the abundant time available for such mental meanderings, but this was the first one with real faces and in-the-flesh, scantily clad, golden-goddess bodies. For better or worse, men have great appreciation for, and a lifelong servile bondage to the beauty of the female form, of which there were three in one boat. If we were on a 200-foot yacht with elevators, a helicopter, a ballroom with a dance floor and strobe lights, I'd have had more confidence they would return. They could tour this boat from the outside looking in, but something caught their attention. If an unexpected vessel showed up in my backyard, I'd want to know 'Who are you? Where did you come from? Where are you going?'

Spoiling my dreams, Rocco arrived next, cursing about the Customs process. Having been to many countries and being comfortable in the security of the Rule of Law and all rights and privileges accorded U.S. citizens, backed up by a Big Brother who buys bullets by the freight car, and has bombs about that size, I merely thought of Customs as a necessary nuisance if you want in. Perhaps Rocco had less-favorable experiences. Customs collected five to seven dollars for the boat and captain, and it takes a lot of time. But time is what they have here, by my reckoning, and it's for sale. They have to protect the borders from yachties, or any immigrants who want to steal a country. Having a trail of who was where when sailors go missing would be helpful to any search effort. Some seamen may be scurrilous characters and need watching; not all are dapper do-nothings.

I made sure we had soda and beer in the refrigerator and fixed a quick meal. Rocco didn't take long to eat nor did he comment on the food. After dinner and a few loud, unexcused belches, he retired to the V-berth in the forward cabin. This was another day I didn't try to engage him in conversation. He quickly fell asleep, announced first by snoring, which eventually diminished after he turned onto one side. If he moved, I'd hear the berth squeak with the weight shift, so I always knew his state of activity. When he got up to go to the head, the berth squeaked three times. Had the captain been here, this dream fantasy wouldn't have had a chance, plus Rocco would have been sleeping aft, in his coffin. I'd have had to entertain in the dinghy. That's less attractive than the old overstuffed, threadbare couch in your mom's basement.

I turned on the anchor light, went out to the cockpit, and looked toward shore, feeling pretty much the chump for even thinking they'd return. How implausible! Already modest, disappointments such as this were sure to keep me that way, though life is long and good things do happen. It was only 6:45. Alternately hopeful, then realistic, only the arrival of 8:00 would make me give up and free me from this anxiety. I made up the bed for the night as a distraction, pulled down a pillow from the shelf and laid back.

Around 7:00, still lying in the dimly lit cabin, I thought I heard a motor. Couldn't be. Not likely. *Don't get too excited, probably Customs returning with Rocco's passport, or to jail him for past transgressions.* I casually stepped into the cockpit. My eyes adjusted easily to the night with a three-quarter moon; I could make out it was the three mermaids, probably coming to say they couldn't stay—school rules, but they'd brought a pizza as a consolation prize.

They circled to approach from the stern, then Elle handed me a line, which I fastened to a cleat. Elle and Dee began to climb aboard after I showed them the folding step on the transom and where to grab the bars and place their feet. I'd only been this excited two other times since setting sail, both when I thought I was near death. I may yet have a heart attack, but busied myself in the requirements of safe boarding.

"Aren't you coming aboard?" I asked Kay.

"No. I have things to do, but I'll be back around 9:00. Can you get along for two hours?"

"Sure."

"Yes."

"Uh-huh."

I released the line and threw it to Kay. After she pulled away, I turned and smiled at my guests. Now what? Everything went smoothly in my imagining; now I had to make something happen. I supposed two was better than three. Just conversation with two 21- to 22-year-old ladies was more than I could have hoped for just hours, or even ten minutes ago. We had a deck of cards if we needed it and could play Old Maid or Spin the Wind Vane. They could sit downwind.

I sat on the port side of the cockpit, and Elle sat next to me. Dee sat across from us on the starboard side, several feet away.

"How about something to drink?" I asked.

"I'd love a beer, if you have it. I haven't had one in a long time, but could use one now," replied Elle. Most of the boat's food storage space was occupied by beer, the foundation of our food pyramid.

"I'll just have a soda, Coke or Pepsi, if you have it," said Dee.

"Sure," I replied, "we don't have ice, but it's cold. Want a glass, or in the can?"

"Can is fine."

Great. That made it easy, quick, and quiet.

I went below and opened the fridge, a couple feet from the V-berth, being careful not to awaken Rocco, thankfully a sound sleeper and hard of hearing. I returned topside and, while enjoying the drinks and company, we talked about the coincidence of us being almost neighbors at home, the things we liked to do, the familiar places we went, and their studies.

In the next lull of the conversation, I asked, "When you were deciding if you would come back, you had a lively discussion. What was that about?"

"OH! Oh yeah. Okay, so, you know a Janice, and you play tennis, right? Ever play tennis with her?"

"The one who comes to mind was a co-worker; she reported to me, so we didn't socialize. But, yeah, we did play tennis once, at a charity round robin event; her partner dropped out at the last minute, she asked me to sub and we played that evening. You know her!"

"I was there; do you remember me?"

"Hmmmpf . . . I guess, vaguely. I had several partners. Don't tell me one was you!"

"Yep! Janice and I were college roommates and on the tennis team. We talked about you afterward—after the tennis."

"I wish Janice had said something. So you put it together, decided you knew me, or about me, and I was safe to spend two hours with?"

"Worth a try. I told Kay I'd swim back if she didn't bring me."

It had been a long and lonely wilderness, mentally more than physically, though it seems my last human contact was years ago. No hugs, no touch, nothing! When things got quiet again, I put my arm around the shoulder of my long-lost tennis partner. "Well, it's great to see you; glad you didn't forget me. By the way, did we win while playing together?"

"Of course." Then she leaned into me; "It's chillier than it was a few hours ago. We don't often come out on the water after dark. Forgot it dropped this much."

"Anything I can do to help? How about a blanket?"

"Could we just share some body heat?"

"Sure. Let's try this," and I sat with my back to the bulkhead, spreading my legs, putting one up on the cushions and one toward the cockpit sole, then placing her, sitting, between them.

"That's better . . . would this be okay?" she asked, as she turned and placed her back against my chest, snuggling up between my legs.

"Much better!" I encased her slender body within my arms, being careful to keep my hands in bounds. After a minute or two of soft purring on her part and a few comments on how warm it felt, she placed my hands directly on her bare midriff. A flat, firm stomach, not in my dreams but right here in my arms and hands. It had been a long time, in many ways. Knowing that hands do not stimulate unless they are moving, I soon started to lightly touch her abdomen, running my little finger just under the elastic waistband of her shorts, then coming out again, moving in a circular motion toward her breasts, not quite going there, then moving back to just below the waist band. In time, receiving murmurs of encouragement, I tried teasing with two fingers from each hand under the shorts before pulling back. We kissed.

"So Elle is your real name; at first I thought you might have made it up?" I whispered in her ear.

"Tonight it is. Sometimes it's Eddie," she whispered back.

"Oh? Sounds too masculine for you."

"Well, there's nothing else masculine at school."

"What does that mean?"

"You've probably heard of BMOC, Big Man on Campus? We have what we call LTOC . . . Low Testosterone on Campus."

"That'd be cute if you weren't living it. I can appreciate your position." Which I truly did, the reason she was now in this position. Moving one hand under her panties, I turned my lips to her ear and whispered, "May I?"

"Oh yeah . . . please," she whispered into my ear, then gently sucked on my earlobe before nibbling on my neck. She pivoted her hips upward and spread her legs, putting herself within reach. My skin suddenly electrified, be it the chill of the night or the heat of the moment. I felt tasked with her pleasure, happily so, her three words fusing our souls, at least for the moment.

I kissed her again, her breathing getting heavier, her hips moving rhythmically. I stayed with her, probing her mouth with my tongue, feeling the soft cushion of her lips. She countered my probing with her own, the angles perfect for deep coupling, passion we enjoyed for many long, hot kisses, until I felt a deep shiver roll through her body.

"If you're cold, we can go below. It should be warmer."

"Uhhhhh . . . gimme a minute . . . yeah . . . okay, but . . . is your partner on the boat? Don't you have someone with you?"

"He's in the forward berth, sound asleep, and hard of hearing . . . we'll be okay."

"If you're sssure, okay. For sssome reason, I'm really sh-shaking!"

"I think I can help." We started to uncurl from each other to go below. While doing so, I looked over at Dee and noticed she was up against the bulkhead with her hands in her shorts. She was cold, also.

"What about Dee?" I whispered.

"We discussed this; she'll be okay . . . Dee, I'm going dow . . . inside, for a few minutes."

"Okay. You wouldn't have a spare blanket, would you?"

"Sure, I do. Coming up!"

With that done, I backed down the companionway, then Elle did the same as I held her at the waist. The sight of her backing down the steps firmed my desire. I guided her to beside the divan which, at night, served as my bed. We shared a full-body hug while kissing hungrily, our hands slipping under the other's clothes. I helped her remove her abbreviated top, slowly pulling it off over her head like an exotic dancer, the low-level night-lights perfect for viewing her lithe body. I knelt and kissed her breasts as she stood in front of me. She seemed suddenly demure, now more alluring than her earlier assertive self. Her soft cotton shorts came off easily, and she stood naked but for a small pair of panties. A rapturous scene. I kissed her abdomen and murmured my approval: "Hmmm, perfume down here, too."

"It says on the bottle to put it wherever you want him to go."

"Good advice, it's working. . . . May I take these off?" I asked, looking up as I hooked a finger in each side.

"Uhhh . . . let's leave 'em on for a while."

"Sure." I rose and, as I took off my shirt, she followed by putting her hands on my stomach, sliding them up my chest, then wrapping her arms around my neck. Holding her gaze with mine for a moment, I put my hands on her shoulders and held her in place, leaned back and took in the full length of her, bent my knees until our thighs touched, and restrained her embrace, only letting her highly aroused nipples touch my chest. Then we came together like two magnets and, with eyes closed, I focused on the touch of her silky smooth skin, the fingertips truly sensual organs.

"I, I've gotta sit down," she pleaded.

I helped her sit, swing her legs up on the divan, and put her head on the pillow. I took my time recording the scene before me, knowing this would be a memory to keep, and wanted an indelible exposure in my mind: her pert breasts, flat stomach, well-toned legs, and the seductive look on her lovely face.

I slid in beside her and my fingers continued to reveal the silky sensuality of her skin. Erotic sensations rolled through me. After enjoying my attention for a while, she tried to return the gift of touch. Turning on her side to face me, the touching and kissing continued. Our legs became intertwined and she began a thrusting motion on my thigh, held firmly between her legs as she pursued her pleasure. Her soft cries, the shaking of her body and her tightened grip on my back and arm told me what I hoped to know. After a moment of heavy breathing, she began again, on the same pursuit of satisfaction, isolated in a world of her own.

When she reached out for me, I encouraged her to lie on her back again and the touching resumed. As she thrust her hips, she separated my fingers to isolate one to penetrate her, turned her head away from me, spellbound, focused on her passion, amazing to watch in her pursuit of ecstasy. Soon, she lay exhausted, eyes closed, breathing heavily, arms and legs limp.

As her breathing slowed, she turned her head, opened her eyes, and looked at me with a glowing smile and wet eyes: "What about you?"

"Me? I'll never forget this. It's a compliment when you respond so passionately. Is that why you're tearing up?"

"I should've explained . . . I went too far. Too fast. It wasn't right."

"It seems right, it's wonderful. Or is there something to . . . explain?"

"Yeah. Okay . . . this semester, I decided to take a BC holiday, and didn't refill my prescription 'cause I didn't expect to have sex. Then you came along at exactly the wrong time of the month. I want to make love, but know I don't dare . . . unless you have a condom . . . I don't. Looked all over my room, even asked classmates, got nothing but snark.

"Well, I'm like you, didn't expect to need it . . . the urgent feeling I had earlier is not feeling as urgent. Don't worry about me. I'm fine. Let's lie here for a minute, hold each other and relax in each other's arms. Enjoy what's happened."

Soon, the furrows relaxed from her brow and, while tracing little trails with our fingertips across each other's bodies, calm returned. "Let me satisfy you," she said.

"Nice of you to care; confirms how precious you are." I wrapped her up and held her closer, then backed off: "Wait a minute. Your concern is about getting pregnant."

"Yes, very. Unless you have a—"

"No, but would this erase your fears?" Whispering.

Her eyes opened wide. "Oh jeez, I never thought about that. Really?"

"Family planning is not just the responsibility of women. Now do you want—?"

"Oh, fuck yes; desperately!" She immediately reached inside my shorts, gently embraced me and, with her persuasion, it was back. She helped me out of my shorts, and then removed her panties.

"I'm pretty stirred and excited," I warned her. "I'll try to be careful. Bring your legs back, I want all of you."

"Take it."

She showed me the way. Released of any constraints, she began to make up for so many lonely nights, unfulfilled dreams, maybe distant memories. Indefatigable. When she could go no more, I met her last desire.

We'd found heaven so far up, it took a long time to float down. On the way, a few tears ran down her cheek onto mine, her chest rose as she sighed in relief. We enjoyed the moment as we continued to lie together—I resting in her cradle of love, of thighs and arms, cheek to cheek—feeling our hearts beat together, relishing the honor and comfort of having shared something personal, intimate, and much needed.

I had cupped her head in my hands, my arms under her shoulders, scanning her face, enjoying her gaze. The afterglow was delightful.

"You okay?"

"Soooo okay; I'm floating," she cooed, in a sense of delight, "what flight am I on, when do we touch down?"

"We're in a holding pattern for angels." I kissed her lightly on the eyelashes, cheeks, lips, and forehead. She returned the favor. "We touch down when ready."

"I like this," she said.

"Like what?"

"The way you are holding me. I feel safe."

"I'm holding your very essence. This is what makes you the beautiful person you are. It makes me feel close to you."

"Me too."

Eventually, we rearranged our bodies, me on my side with legs bent under her knees as she lay on her back. We relaxed and sighed deeply. Our hands never stopped, most times aimlessly brushing, relishing the touch of another.

"I like this," she said, "I wish you were staying around." After a few minutes, "I'd give you an appreciation for the name of the harbor. Isn't that a hell of a name? Cock burn? I lie awake nights just thinking about it. Of course, the Brits don't pronounce all the letters."

"Yeah, and I like knowing how you think. That's how we get to know each other. I know you have a hot streak and a sense of humor. I'll lie awake thinking about tonight, something to remember. Unfortunately, my schedule is not my own."

"But, you're doing what you want to be doing, aren't you?"

"I was when I stepped aboard. Then I entered another man's kingdom, subject to his rules, whims, and schedule. Boat captains can be tyrants; sometimes it is necessary. This owner's okay, but I'm still a guest. You're right, though, I don't have to stay, unlike in Cockburn's day."

During our whispering, I had pushed back the blanket and was kissing and caressing her, creating memories to carry me through the remainder of my time at sea and, probably, years beyond.

"I bet you have a girlfriend, don't you?"

"That's a strange way to ask . . . well, maybe not, may be the best way. . . . Nah, I don't think so. Not now. If I do, I don't know who it would be. If I make it home, everything starts anew."

"Oh! So, in May, you're available? Think we could become 'a thing'?" she teased.

"You know, after our deep, lengthy, and exhaustive engagement, with a years-long cooling off period, I'd feared you wouldn't propose. We were running out of time."

"Didn't it sound like one? What should I have said?" The look on her face showed she was enjoying the relaxed intimacy and playfulness.

I chuckled. "I'd consider it; just give me a little more time. Not sure it would be fair to you, though. May I have until Kay arrives to decide?"

"What's taking you so long? You're just in it for the sex, aren't you? . . . How long before she gets here? Should we get dressed? What time is it?"

"We have a few more minutes . . . it's 8:30."

"A year ago, had you heard of South Caicos?"

"Not even two weeks, but it's now on my map; I'll never forget it. In fact, it's my favorite anchorage. What do you think of it?"

"Truthfully? It's the fucking foreign legion! On the Isle of South Deprivation. The swimsuits, relaxed dress code, water, physical exercise, the sun, is all pretty stimulating. And we're stuck with LTOC. Other than that, I enjoy the school. . . . Tonight was the best."

"Good. I arrived with a trounced spirit, hopeful somewhere I'd find a touch of humanity. Just talking boat to boat earlier was uplifting. Now you've given me . . . you, and a whole new attitude."

"I'll miss you. It's already started. Tenderness is hard to find, hard to give up. Can we do this again tomorrow?" she asked spiritedly.

I heard the noise of Rocco waking up, and put my finger to Elle's lips. "Shhhh, he may be getting up." I reached across for a blanket, struggling to get it free. "Quick, turn your back to me." She did, and I spooned behind her, pushing her toward the hull side of the divan, hoping to shield her from view. Not much time to spread the blanket in such a small space with one hand, I heard footsteps, covered Elle and hoped Rocco would be polite enough not to stare. He hardly sees me in daylight.

He opened the door to the head, about three feet from my elbow, and closed it behind him. We stayed still and quiet, hoping he wasn't so dazed that he might still go outside. He quickly came out and climbed back into the berth. Wow! One of us could flush it in the morning. I wasn't complaining; it's complicated, especially in the dark. We held each other until we heard him roll onto his side, and his puffing and growling noises of sleep resumed. We calmed down, slowed our breathing, enjoying the touch, the cozy position, and the shared intimacy and risk.

"Why don't we get ready for Kay? He's usually a sound sleeper. We should be okay now."

"Alright, if you're not going to make love to me all night, I need help getting up."

"You can stay; okay by me."

"Grrr!"

I rolled backward off the divan, stood, and helped her sit up, then knelt and pulled her forward, to lay kisses on her lips and breasts one more time before dressing her. I put on my clothes, and helped her stand.

I said, "You gonna be okay?"

"Yeah, I think so. Gimme a minute."

"You're gonna need to be steady to pivot over the rail and climb into the boat."

"I'll be ready, but I'd rather go back to bed."

"I know."

I gave her a boost up the companionway stairs as we went to the cockpit to check on Dee, who was alert and composed, wrapped in the blanket. We heard a motorboat approaching, so I turned and gave Elle a hug.

She handed me a card: "Here's my home number, good after May 15. Please don't lose it."

"I won't. When we both get home, there are lots of things we can do."

"You've got all I need right here," she quipped, pressing her hand on my heart, then her index finger on my chest, running it down to my waist. "Thanks for making dreams come true . . . and driving me crazy for the next six months!"

"It's been a pleasure! You're a brazen angel of mercy. And give my warm regards to Janice, just not all the details. I have an out-of-date, probably undeserved, reputation to maintain."

"IF she believes me. She'll probably ask ten times if it's true."

"Hmmm . . . I know—ask her when she started using salad dressing. She'll believe."

A long, deep kiss and hug followed, and we were the picture of propriety as Kay motored alongside. "Did everyone behave and have a nice evening?" Kay asked, as she grabbed the transom and turned off the motor.

Did you expect us to not behave? You may already know. Might make people envious. "It was a great evening, thanks," I answered, feeling I could speak for two of us. "And thanks for your support."

"No problem. We have to take care of each other at this remote outpost."

"I'm glad you have each other. Must be a special relationship."

Once the painter was fastened to a cleat, Dee, then Elle climbed over the rail, pivoted, backed down the transom, and into the boat. Their waving and "good nights" were too soon cut short, swallowed by the cool darkness of the night, their speck of a running light lost among the few on the South Caicos coast.

Wow!

Unsure whether to swoon in the cockpit or cocoon in my bunk, I chose to sit in the cockpit, listening to music, and relive the night in the capacious theater of my mind while staring into the featureless, vast darkness, nothing but water for a hundred miles or more. My emotion was amplified by the music, initially of Dobie Grey, stirring me to my soul: "Gimme the beat, boys, and free my soul, I wanna get lost in your rock and roll, and drift away." All consciousness was in my core, all boundaries were down. The boat did not confine, the mind was drifting away like deep meditation, when you cannot sense where the body and spirit begin and end.

I remembered feeling the warmth and luxury of touch when I took Elle and Dee's hands as they came aboard. That was part of what had been missing. The trip had been so physical, anchor handling and trying to stay upright and aboard, I had not given much thought to the absence of human touch. Now I was fully aware the deprivation of touch had been a hardship of the journey. Other than a rude bump in the passageway, maybe when huddled around the ammeter, Rocco and I hadn't so much as shaken hands.

Contemplating my unusual situation, I wondered why me? I'd never felt particularly lucky in love—it may look so in the distortion of retrospection: time frame is compressed, memorable events seem larger and closer together—but lucky enough. Sure, right place, right time, with the right goods and words, but subordinate to their wanting to check out our boat, and the crew, apparently, for their reasons. They were the only boat to leave the dive site and come looking. I had no mobility; they came to me.

By bedtime, the lyrics of Sinatra's "Strangers in the Night" had captured my imagination, making me think all things were possible. But I had to consider I may mean nothing to Elle, just another worthy, weary sailor at the Isle of Desperation and it was all about location and timing. Reality intervened and had me creating a personal note to self: *You may have enjoyed the friendship of Nikki and Elle, but do not assume they will be there* or *you have a choice to make when you get home. They will be pursuing their own career paths, needs, and desires. In this age, they can take a bite of the apple and move on. You're a unicorn—not easy to find a partner in a compatible situation, more likely to find frustration, heartbreak, and fatigue. Not all is what it seems.*

Regardless, the pair-bonding drug must have been kicking in, making a future seem possible, though the future was also distant. The downside of creating friendships while traveling is the length of absence before the next meeting, during which things quickly fall apart. A lovingly planted garden can wither if not maintained.

When I went to bed, I realized Elle had left the gift of her scent on my pillow and sheet, a delightful remembrance. I pulled the pillow to my face and drifted off into a full night of sleep.

The weather report was favorable for a departure to Grand Turk tomorrow, and Rocco had checked us out of Customs. He would almost certainly set sail for Turks, even if the weather were to deteriorate. His job was to move the boat. I would have liked to stay another day, but sometimes it's best to play the hand you are dealt and keep moving—as if I had a choice.

A loud belch from Rocco woke me with a start from a semi-dreamy state resisting wakefulness. Dawn had come and he had to choose—set sail or go to jail. Looking around as I was folding the blankets, making the boat ready to head out, I realized it looked just as it did last night: no evidence of anything interesting going on. What would it be, other than the smile on my face? We had no furniture, no crystal or china, no burned down candles with spilled wax—unless Rocco was counting the beer inventory, and that product moved through this boat rapidly. The can was gone; Elle or Dee may dive on it as sunken treasure. Could bring a smile. Rocco would never suspect a thing, and who cared anyway? I was still buying, so it was my beer, to use as I wish. Memories are made of this.

Anchors aweigh and away!

Grand Turk:
It's freakin' nukin'; where's my board?

The weather on the sail to Grand Turk was sunny and pleasant. Initially, I did look over my shoulder for angels waving or speedboats pursuing us. The first turn at the helm was mine, when we seemed to hit our most disorderly waves, drenching the helmsman and spraying the passenger. Rocco occasionally gave me hell as being the cause. Since a light sailboat swerves back and forth all the time because of the wave influence, steering is constant course correction. (I tried several times not putting up with such silly vacillations, holding the wheel in one position. The water didn't care. It would turn you around.) Someone could look at your compass setting at almost any time and think you are off course. They might be correct at that moment, but the course that gets you where you want to be must be the average of those alternating swerves.

Having read the sailing guide for the area, I learned it was the current in the Turks Passage, ripping to the north, combined with wave action driven by the strong wind from the southeast that was creating the cascades pouring over the starboard side. We were on a bearing of 95 degrees, close to the wind, and veered closer as the boat turned back and forth. Rocco didn't enjoy the wet ride. Normally hostile, my tutor was becoming enraged, but it did not improve when he was at the helm. He cussed as much then as when it was I who was screwing up. Was the point lost on him?

I took shelter on the port side beneath the dodger, detached from his anger. I didn't give a damn whether Rocco was loud or quiet about it. This water was to be expected on this point of sail, and I was encased in a virtual suit of armor, willing to go back if Rocco insisted. We obviously weren't going down; I'd seen much worse, and nothing else mattered. Being in a rare, impervious mood, I smiled when he cussed at me, possibly further pissing him off because I would not join in his misery.

We arrived at Grand Turk Island near 1330, anchoring in the North Creek area. It was the farthest anchorage from town but with seas coming from the southeast, it was the best choice to sit it out and wait for Walt. The anchorage was totally protected and the water was calm, despite the increasing wind speed.

After we changed into dry clothes and made things ship-shape, we went ashore and headed to town, a few miles away. A local offered us a lift to the far side of the commercial area where there was a telephone. I thanked the driver—for both of us. It had become my job to handle all civilities; Rocco quit months ago, if not years.

Rocco called Walt, who was relieved to hear from us and wanted to join us as soon as he knew our location. Felicity was better; the stitches would come out Monday, but I heard no joy in her voice. Hopefully, she wouldn't lose any functionality in her arm; we'd have to wait and see. Walt would try to join us on Tuesday. But American Airlines was on strike, which would affect his ability to fly standby using his Delta employee/family passes.

We hurried to get back to the boat before dark. Our end of the island was teeming with dogs roaming free, clearly not sensitive to the value of the minimal tourist trade. During our hopscotch back to the boat we had plenty of incentive to put spring in our step, though zigzagging back and forth across the street lengthened our journey. When one dog dropped off, another picked us up—something of a cellular or turf thing, I supposed—as if a dog could only scare or bite someone in their area. At one point, five to seven dogs came charging at us. We stopped and stood our ground, nowhere to run, ready to swing my camera at them if necessary, but they stopped at their property lines. Whew! Nerve wracking. I'd rather drown than be eaten alive.

We escaped the onslaught, but amidst the concern over the dogs, we got lost, perhaps because we didn't think it possible. Town was south, boat was north, the island was narrow. Simple navigation. We flagged down a car to ask directions, and they offered us a ride. The island was so small (7 by 1.5 miles) it would not take them too far out of their way if they took us to our destination. They may have enjoyed talking to people from off-island, and we indisputably were. I craved a little conversation myself.

The next day, while admiring the picturesque government buildings in Cockburn Town, we met a policewoman, Linda Rigby, who, in response to my question, enumerated the crime problems of the island. There were 42 people in jail, many of whom received 18 months for stealing cigarettes, beer, or something rather small by U.S. standards. Sounded more like a temporary housing program, a free homeless shelter on the American plan (includes meals). They were tried and incarcerated within a week, if the officer had done the job correctly. Knowing crime against the tourist is non-existent here was comforting. Linda wore no gun, consistent with Turks being a UK island, and was smartly dressed in a colorful uniform. She was from Antigua, had been here eight years, and her only other travel was to visit family in Brooklyn, New York. I'd found limited travel true of all the native islanders I had asked that question. To my next question, she recommended The Salt Raker as her favorite restaurant.

Grand Turk and Salt Cay make up the Turks Islands, known primarily for outstanding snorkeling and diving on many shipwrecks, magnificent reefs, the Grand Turk Wall, and their fishing and picturesque beaches. If you wanted nightlife, you had to bring it, much as I had done . . . Rocco was spoken for (but available; make me an offer).

We went into town early the next day to check in at Customs. I took a few pictures of a Haitian boat tied up near town, crooked mast but still floating, then walked down Main Street. The city streets were relatively unoccupied, making it easy to photograph bougainvillea-covered historic buildings made of boat timbers and stone ballast, truly lovely and picturesque. We ordered lunch at the Salt Raker's Inn—a cheeseburger with fries, and were soon joined by a delightful couple from Miami whose flight home was delayed when their plane ran off the runway. They ordered a dessert while the damage to the wheel was assessed. Conversation with them was as refreshing as finding cool, potable water on a desert island. She was alert and playful; he an open and sincere person. It only took meeting compatible people for me to realize, once again, I had more-or-less been sailing alone. Unfortunately, the couple was informed the plane was ready to go before the food they had been eagerly anticipating could be served. I asked if they knew how to sail, thinking Rocco could go in their place, but they did not. It was a brief dream.

After lunch, while I was taking pictures and calling my son, Rocco scowled at me and abruptly left, concerned over the Customs man now scheduled to show up at the boat at 1530. I was laid back about it all, thinking we had plenty of time, and chose to continue making calls, taking pictures, and buying fruit at a church bazaar before walking leisurely to the boat.

Back at the dock before 1530, I waited patiently, having no place to go. Rocco would not come pick me up, afraid the customs man would radio him, if not visit. Might as well sit on the pier as on the boat. Company's about the same. The Customs man didn't call or show up that afternoon! How dare he treat Rocco that way! No surprise to me, mon; we be on island time.

Otherwise, the people on Grand Turk were fabulous. Though there were not many cars, I was given rides in both directions as soon as I decided to stick out a thumb. Friendly and helpful, these drivers drove past their destinations to take me to mine, because we were literally at the end of the road. Small-island hospitality. I walked through their exceedingly modest neighborhoods with no fear (other than the overexcited dogs). Most of the people seemed poor and, with the cost of food being so high, I imagined that would persist. Whatever jobs they could get didn't spin off value beyond basic needs, limiting the potential to prosper. Education was an answer for younger folks who would deploy it elsewhere—either Provo, or abroad.

Back on the boat, I worked on my Spanish, and read a murder mystery in case I caught the urge. The few times I had the urge were fleeting so, for now, Rocco lives. Sensitive flower that I am, skirmishes with Rocco, like the one in town, reverberate in my brain long after they are over. In the silence and stillness of having nothing to do or discuss, Rocco and I sat against each of the bulkheads under the cockpit awning (bimini) staring into the distance beyond the stern.

"Hey, Rocco, got a minute?" (Of course he did, we had little of everything but time.)

"What?"

"May I ask you a question?"

"What?"

"First, the Customs man, sorry about that. He's an SOB."

"They're all sonsabitches. Bureaucrats."

"Clearly. So . . . what about this trip? Is this what you had in mind? Working out for ya?"

"Hell no. I don't want to be responsible for this damn boat. I could be on my own boat."

"Have you been this far down the Bahamas chain?"

"No. . . . Great Exumas."

"You were probably pissed you had to sail with a novice like me and all my mistakes. But am I a problem at this point?"

"Nope."

"And Walt will be here before we have to move the boat again, so will that help?"

"Yep."

"And I'm not a problem?"

"Nope."

"Good. . . . By the way, how's the food?"

"Boring. . . . As good as can be expected, I guess."

"Maybe Walt will bring something different."

"I hope."

"I miss his sweet potatoes and ham with his brown sugar, pineapple, orange juice, raisin, and carrots glaze. It's good, probably his best dish."

"Why don't you make it?"

"Good question. I dunno how. I'd have trouble with the proportions, and the corn starch. Meager food that we have, I don't want to put it at risk. Do you put the cornstarch in when the liquid is cold, or warm, to keep it from balling up?"

"How the hell would I know?"

"Yeah, me neither. . . . Do you really not know how to cook?"

"Nope. Never learned. Don't want to."

". . . If I made that dish and it was inedible, you'd be okay without food for a day?"

"Hell no."

I left it at that; a conversation that could help me sleep nights for a while seemed adequate. It always helps to understand what bothers your companion, as opposed to suffering all of the ruminations your mind can devise, though he wasn't much different, if at all, before Walt left. Having an insufferable bunk might have played a role, to which he would soon return.

Another day, shot. Never had it taken so long to do so little. At home, even as a new retiree who had earned my peace, I'd have been feeling the guilt and stress of non-productivity. It felt like it would take forever to get to the Virgin Islands. At our speed, it would. The knotmeter didn't work but, for the last couple of days, it has been deadly accurate—zero knots! If it measured wind speed, we'd have been getting much higher readings. Had I not been impressed into service, would Rocco handle (or prefer) this much solitude? We're both, essentially, alone—him by choice.

Rocco and I were getting along well, no tension on the boat, which made for a quiet evening. He knew Walt would lift the burden of being captain before he had to move the boat again, which had been the heat in his Hell. That was valid for him, but it wouldn't shake me. Cripes, he had an identical boat, so he knew how to sail it.

Only later would I appreciate that navigation in the Bahamas chain is uncertain compared to the well-charted and -marked waters Rocco was used to sailing. Here you had to sail, without serious error, by "eyeball" as well as using charts and GPS, being aware of the tide and water depth, while watching the water surface ahead for "shoals awash" and any impediments in water so clear it looked like you would surely hit them. All I had to do was cook, raise and lower the sails and the anchor, program the GPS, monitor it, and fund the expedition.

I awoke knowing this would be another dead day, there being no chance Walt would arrive before tomorrow. The airline strike meant fewer planes flying, making travel exceedingly difficult for those traveling stand-by. We were counting on Walt to bring *The Thornless Path* to guide us through the rest of the trip, since we had exhausted our *Yachtsman's Guide to the Bahamas* and our good chart set. We could also use a short-wave radio, as well as personal and alimentary reinforcements.

We had not located a supermarket or a Laundromat here on Grand Turk, so I decided to use the shipboard facilities to do laundry. Our generally eclectic "dryer" was working in tip-top condition: dry and hot, close to thirty knots, better than any machine. You could dry out a drunk in this wind. Hopefully, the clothes would not blow away. Since all of our horizontal lines pointed into the wind causing the clothes to bunch up against each other, our vertical clotheslines worked better. I hung my sheet on a shroud (vertical mast stabilizer) and stood by while it dried, watching the water evaporate. This wind gave laundry the appearance that the law of gravity had been repealed; twin-bed sheets flew like oversize semaphore flags. If I'd had windsurfing equipment, my whole attitude about the high wind over this enclosed calm body of water would have been entirely different. Bet I could set personal speed records—perfect conditions to fly.

To get maximum bang for a bucket of wash water, I cleaned the cockpit floor while doing the laundry. This ship was shaping up to be spotless, since we were adding no dirt or salt, and spending days getting rid of it. I could reflect on whether this was a good way to spend this part of my life, but I was here, choices were few, and the wind was still blowing 25 knots or more from 135 degrees, dead-on from the Southeast.

After completing my Spanish word list, I showed it to Rocco up on deck, don't ask me why, as if he cared, then glanced at the shoreline. A tall white man in white slacks was carrying a duffel bag and a white canvas tote. Like us, he stood out on this island. He even resembled Walt, but there was not supposed to be plane service today. I waved tentatively; he waved back. Launch the boats! I dispatched Rocco. Nothing would erase his dogged look faster than to fetch his savior.

Thanksgiving came a day early. I was thankful Walt made it back and thankful for the bounty of food in his duffel bag: noodles, canned chicken, tuna, cookies, and cashews. Also granola bars, a welcome first for this sailor. Like a castaway on a deserted island, I hungered for one of everything. Walt shared his travel experiences, then stories from home—the activities of the dog, Felicity, kids, the weather—and we still made it an early evening, since Rocco gave the boat report. You might guess it was brief. Walt had left Annapolis on Monday, spent the night in Atlanta, flew to Nassau on Tuesday and stayed there a night since there was no plane to Grand Turk until Wednesday, and he was tired. Free tickets aren't free if they require two overnight hotel stays, meals, tips, and ground transportation, but they may still be a bargain.

"Buenos Noches."

After breakfast, our revitalized captain, fresh from too-long a stint in dry dock, announced his readiness to move on. The weather forecast was for winds from the south overnight, becoming southwest Friday and Saturday. We could sail south to the Dominican Republic that evening or the following day if we had that southwest breeze.

We motored out of North Creek, around the north end of Grand Turk, along the west coast to a dock at Main Street where we could tie up while going through Customs. We hoped to catch a Thanksgiving buffet in town, and then sail to Salt Cay, a protective outcropping south of Turks. As always, Customs acted slowly. You had to find the fellows, then encourage them. After that slog, it was too late to eat here and be able to anchor at Salt Cay, 8–9 nautical miles away. A tradition of another culture, Thanksgiving was not a holiday they celebrated with enthusiasm here, though I was hopeful when I spotted a restaurant advertising it earlier, thinking it would be better than canned beans. Alas, it was not to be; Customs, in effect, pulled the plate away.

We sailed to Salt Cay and, not bothering to anchor, kept sailing south toward the Dominican Republic. The seas were calm, the breezes had lightened, we'd had no lunch and it was getting dark; the possibility of sailing all night without eating was an opportunity to get sick not to be missed.

We hadn't prepared any food while in the lee of Salt Cay because we had to determine whether to continue or turn back, depending on how rough it was. Of course, winds were light in the lee of the island, but sufficiently rough after we passed the island to make preparing food below deck a nauseating experience. When have we ever been wise enough to turn back? Walt couldn't eat for a while anyway, not yet having his sea legs, so he wasn't cooking. Rocco and I could walk on anything that moved, but stumbled, staggered, and swayed when on land. We had only sea legs. That didn't mean I could cook for any length of time while sailing, and you know Rocco's cooking resume—on a level with our Thanksgiving feast: peanut butter and jelly served between two slices of bread, assembled in the cockpit. No messy, four-hour, twenty-pound golden roasted stuffed turkey with vegetables and pies all around for us! We were sailors—Arr-ugghh!—together again as a dysfunctional crew.

The crossing to the Dominican Republic was better than we'd hoped for with a southerly wind forecast. A port-side full moon followed a lovely starboard sunset, highlighting the puffy, thin clouds, with frequent lightning in the distant western sky. Nature enveloped us, with nothing to obstruct the stunning sight of the first edge of the moon or the last edge of the sun. A lightning bolt reminded me of our vulnerability—one strike down the mast and we could disappear. We motor-sailed into the night, piercing the blind-like darkness, confident of our charts and the curvature of the earth.

Later, it was nauseous smells from the engine that enveloped us, nature in second place. Luckily, the odors were in the cockpit, not the cabin; it smelled like exhaust and felt woozily like carbon monoxide. The only option was to get as far upwind from the smell as possible.

I slept snugly in my bunk from midnight until 0500, when it became obvious we had changed from motor to sail after I had fallen asleep, and were sailing with the wind east of due south. When the forecasted wind shift to the southwest occurred, the mainsail backwinded with a loud whacking noise as the sail went slack then forcefully filled, followed quickly by a jolt and sudden roll of the boat as if we'd been hit by another vessel. I was sleeping without lee cloths (functionally sleep seatbelts), and the change to a starboard tack instantly dumped me onto the cabin sole (floor). I shook it off, crawled to my feet, and stumbled toward the cockpit, hoping for fresh air and someone to check me for lacerations while wondering if we had lost anyone.

CHAPTER
Six

Dominican Republic:
Bring in the whales, you clown

I
t wasn't long before the sun came up. This was particularly enjoyable after seeing stars when I was dumped out of my bunk. Several hours later, we spotted the mountains of the Dominican Republic—so different from the low, flat islands of the Bahamas chain, it felt otherworldly. Approaching the coast, we had an escort of twenty or more porpoises splashing, dancing, and arcing along the starboard side and in front of the boat, their sleek silver-gray bodies gleaming with the golden rays of the rising sun.

"These guys are a joy, such grace and personality. I love their smiles," I said, not having seen a smile for a lonnng time. "I wonder if we'll see any whales."

"Holy crap; you oughta know they're only here in February," growled Rocco.

"Thanks, Rocco; I didn't know that. Dunderhead that I am, I don't even know why I oughta know it."

Less than thirty minutes later, on November 26, as though he were in the crow's nest atop Columbus' ship *Santa Maria* pointing forward, trumpeting *Land ho!*, Rocco stood in the cockpit, feet spread widely, left hand on the dodger, right hand pointing toward shore, boldly proclaiming, in essence,

Whales ho! Launch the boats! "There's at least four whales off the starboard bow!"

Wow! That call took guts. Or senility. Were I him, I'd have waited to see the whites of their eyes and not contradicted myself quite so soon, this far out, having just dressed down the second mate.

"Where are they?" I asked, excited I might be exonerated from my innocent question.

"What's wrong with you? Are you fucking blind or fucking stupid?" Rocco doubled down in disgust, offering such good choices that I, loving the luxury of options and being simultaneously greedy, was waiting for "All of the above." Otherwise, it was hard to choose. I could have gone with either one.

The ocean was exploding as was his genius, to be respected and recorded. He could see water columns erupting into the air and imagined a whale under each one. Why couldn't I? If those were whales, they were hyperventilating. I only saw waves splashing on the shore, possibly forcing water up through holes in the lava or other shore rocks, emulating blow spouts in a surf rhythm, as I had perceived much earlier, causing me to eventually ask about whales in general. The DR is volcanic and I (cheated) had seen this phenomenon where the geology contained lava, as it did here. In contrast, the Bahamas sits on a limestone plateau which contributes to its alluring white sandy beaches. "Well, excuse me, Rocco, this is the year February follows November, isn't it? I should have known. I just hate to miss Christmas and the blizzards of January."

He took his eyes off the wave-induced water columns momentarily to look at me like I was the crazy one. Some days I felt it; but not that day, when Rocco was depriving a village of its idiot.

So much for my alleged stupidity (it wouldn't have been the first time); however, a few more of those targeted comments and I would forever be cured for which my children would be pleased and surprised. They had considered me foolish ever since they became brilliant, as Mark Twain so aptly put it: "When I was a boy of 14, my father was so ignorant I could hardly stand to have the old man around. But when I got to be 21, I was astonished at how much the old man had learned in seven years."

As we approached Luperon in the Dominican Republic, the island's lush vegetation was striking. We had not yet seen such hills or greenery. The excitement of a new country was more than that of moving from one low-lying Bahamian island to another, and was mitigated only briefly by Rocco's black-cloud efforts to show how relaxed, observant, and on top of things he was now that Walt was back in charge.

The island's topography ranged from Lake Enriquillo, the lowest point in the Caribbean (475 feet below sea level) to Pico Duarte, the highest mountain in the Caribbean (10,500 feet above sea level). Lake Enriquillo has the distinction of being the only saltwater lake in the world inhabited by crocodiles. Adventurous as we were, we wouldn't be going there. And we would miss most or all of the three major mountain ranges, unless something disastrous occurred, like what happened to Christopher Columbus' ill-fated encounter nearby on his first voyage. In December 1492, the *Santa Maria* hit a coral reef offshore, broke up, and Columbus went back to Spain in the *Nina*, leaving forty crew members behind, without a ship or a choice, to start the first European settlement in the Americas, La Navidad, which could have been aptly named La Deyalldied, given that the crew perished before Columbus returned in late 1493.

With better luck, we'd be looking at part of the 1,600 kilometers of coastline and a few of the nine million inhabitants. The island was diverse enough to warrant major exploration, particularly the resorts and hotels and their twenty-three golf courses, though I was getting ahead of myself.

The Dominican Republic (DR) occupies the eastern two thirds of the island of Hispaniola (second largest in the Greater Antilles after Cuba), Haiti has the western third. I was curious about Haiti. Having seen the ramshackle condition of two Haitian boats, I had no compelling desire to go there as a tourist—possibly as a relief worker. The DR had been moving toward representative government since the assassination of Rafael Leonidas Trujillo in 1961 at about the speed of sailing—not so fast—though well ahead of Haiti.

Luperon:
Going back in time

We arrived at Luperon around 1000, having traveled a distance of roughly 100 miles. I piloted the boat into port, which I could only do with Walt on board. Rocco did not instruct. Although I wasn't learning anything from Rocco, I was appreciative of him at the helm when I was almost washed overboard at night in the Devil's Triangle. It worked out for the best. If he had been on the bow when that same wave hit in the middle of the night and washed him down the deck, it would have been something I did and, had he survived, a fist fight might have ensued. To have been alone in the boat in those seas, looking for a man overboard—I could imagine my panic. I would not have left him—wouldn't have known how—and would have perished with him. It's still disquieting; forever will be.

As soon as I had the anchor down and secured, Walt and Rocco investigated the exhaust smell we experienced last night. With a little pulling and tugging on the suspect exhaust, it came apart in their hands. Fortunately, this was accomplished before we met with Customs agents. Felix, an informal concierge on foot who shows up at the end of the pier and knows people, would help us hire a car to take us 50 miles to Puerto Plata tomorrow for repair parts. We could forage for food while there and, since my buddies didn't speak up loudly for fruits and vegetables (they suppressed such speech), that would be my focus.

The small, remote community of Luperon was portrayed in our guide book as a beautiful village with a bay that looked more like a Swiss lake. It looked low-income but charming, in a picturesque setting of thatched-roof, one-room homes, many with concrete walls, others wooden, all close together, a few coconut palms sprinkled among other vegetation where possible. There were concrete sidewalks and curbs under construction; the dirt streets were mottled with raw sewage, awaiting installation of the nearby large sewer pipes to carry the sewage away for treatment. The lake seemed to have little flow through, and the yachts and the villagers must have been straight-piping their sewage into it. I'd seen Swiss lakes, and suspected the perfectionist Swiss would disavow this one—for now. Swimming in it would be inadvisable. Still, it was an exotic locale, worthy of our time, so it was strangely beneficial we were broken down.

Dinner was corned beef hash with onions, or rather onions with corned beef hash. The portions were too big but, however big the meal, it all got distributed onto someone's plate—we were unable to deal in leftovers; no taste or space for it. Perhaps I'd like onions before the trip was over. Tomorrow, we would meet the taxi driver at 0800. Felix was arranging it, all for $45 U.S. At that price, it wouldn't be a Bentley or a Benz, maybe a manure spreader, a cart behind a burro, or a large four-man moped. Not intending to be derogatory, but three hours and 100 miles for $15 per person before commissions to the agent was more than a bargain, even on the moped.

Our driver was Dari, a short, thin, affable man who only spoke Spanish. I tried a word or two in Spanish, which he no comprende, but he gave me a big smile for trying (I was his village idiot). The 50-mile ride into Puerto Plata would take 1½ hours. The long and bumpy road up to the main highway, combined with the well-worn, un-sprung seats in our ultra high-mileage, low-comfort Toyota painfully compacted the spine on the bigger bumps, since we were basically sitting on the chassis. Needing to save my back for anchor-raising, I tried levitating when the front wheels warned a hard bottoming was coming to the back wheels, which was all of the time. That became hard on my wrists, and Rocco was probably wondering why my hands were occasionally slipping under part of his butt. It was a small back seat, hardly two butts wide.

Unfortunately, the main highway was no better. It was similar to posting English saddle on a horse with no saddle or stirrups for 90 minutes, but worse. The kinesthetics were all wrong, trying to levitate from a deep well, a true bucket of a seat. Shock absorbers must not have been in Dari's budget. Standing would have been better, legs bent to absorb the impact, but no can do. I understood now the price. What could we get for $30 each? I'd pay more. Some bargains are insufferable.

I loved how the locals went anywhere and everywhere with whatever it took to keep moving. There was more traffic here than we'd seen since Florida: Men and boys riding mules, many men on motor scooters, possibly for hire, with female passengers wearing dresses riding sidesaddle, and seldom a car. One scooter had clear plastic bags of freshly baked loaves of bread piled high and overhanging the saddle, nearly scraping the ground. The saddles on the mules and burros were wide-ranging in design and construction, from practically nothing but burlap rags held on by a large belt or rope, to artistically ornate with silver surrounding colored gemstones, leather belting securing the saddle.

We were passing wonderful scenery and local sights that included burros carrying truly massive loads. I wanted to take pictures, but had no way to let Dari know because, for the life of me, I couldn't remember the Spanish word for "stop." Dari was getting paid for "Go," not by the hour, and with our language differences, he was tired of smiling big, not really wanting to mingle and fake comprehension, so he was laser-focused straight ahead. We couldn't give him the five-year-old's time out signal, nor the slash-your-throat motion to quit, without getting out on the hood, a posture Walt was slow to render. The view from outside in must have mimicked the Three Stooges—hand signals, heads turning, shouting—absent the hair, not a full head between us. We hastily threw out many words, in retrospect most of them French, hoping for a reaction: "Gauche! Pousser! Halt! Arrete!" Of all the inquisitive words I studied, in case I encountered a lovely senorita, the now-critical word I had left for later was "stop." We never saw so much as one road sign of the red, octagonal design; everyone just merged and peeled off when they could. We continued to use the trial and error method, and eventually thought we'd found an utterance, not our first choice by far, that caused the car to come to rest. We used it sparingly, lest it had another usage unknown to us.

Actually, we never did figure it out because no word worked every time but, like with any training, if the driver could correctly associate an action with a sound, he probably thought it was him learning a foreign language, not us. I thought it was "arrete" or "halt" (sounds close to pare and alto) that applied the brakes, but that's French. Maybe it was "stop." Maybe Dari spoke French. No matter, it could have been "bow-wow," as long as it worked each time. Being the only one caring about pictures, I took fewer than I wanted, the best ones were lost because of this language conundrum. Not in a million years could I tell Dari to turn around and go back to where the palm trees and giant cacti scene looked like posters of Outer Mongolia, a poster he had never seen, a country he will likely never see, a scene that looked precisely like his own neighborhood. This landscape and culture, though, was quite different from what we had seen until now, and I was amazed that in less distance than from Washington, DC, to Richmond, VA, there could be such a distinction. I felt it was my mission to take back, if not sea chests of gold doubloons, photos of our discoveries on a real hard-core adventure. Other than tourist spots that had been built new to look old, there was little "original vintage charm" like this remaining in the U.S., which is the allure of travel.

In the Puerta Plata hardware store, Rocco and Walt found the two different-size pipes needed for the engine repair ($6–7). Being unimportant to their mission, I searched for a restroom and a place to stretch out and rehabilitate my back. At the curb, such as it was, there was a line of unique plumber's vehicles made from the rear end/axle assembly and wheels taken from a discarded vehicle, with a flat wooden tabletop over it, attached to the pulling quadruped with a thill on each side. Being wide open gave the plumbers plenty of swinging room for their PVC pipes, as long as they didn't poke the horse at a sensitive spot in a sharp turn. There were several around, enough to convince me it worked, though a serious step back in time, doubtful we had them in the U.S., if ever—using auto parts in a horse-drawn culture.

Understanding sign language pertaining to a template of what was next required, Dari drove us to a back-alley machine shop that cut a hole into the side of the larger pipe, inserted the smaller pipe, and welded it in place, all for $4.25. No way would you get a custom exhaust system for that price in the U.S.! On second thought, add the taxi driver charge, the orthopedic specialist fees, and the value of three person-days-—it may not have been as cheap as it first appeared. But we were getting a memorable experience and a tour of the country.

Feeling thrilled about our essential success, we went to the open-air marketplace, parked, and walked in. Shoppers were driving through the marketplace on a narrow dirt road in anything from a small pickup truck to the plumber's rig, or on a small burro with a rope around her middle holding a large straw basket on each side and a pink ribbon on her head. Food was piled on the bare ground or stored in small contiguous huts with corrugated tin roofs and chain link doors. Bananas and plantains were piled as high as my waist, whereas an overnight sail ago, Provo had no bananas five days of the week. Distribution is important. Slabs of meat were lying uncovered on a butcher block, a portable circulating fan blowing to keep the flies at bay, waiting for customer orders. Surprisingly, food prices were not much better than the U.S., possibly because Walt had all the pesos but no yen for negotiating. He didn't want any fruit, because he hates to peel it. I asked him, "If I peeled and cored the pineapple, for the love of God and for Pete's sake, would you eat it?"

"Yeah!"

Well, hot damn! Maybe Pete was a good friend. I negotiated a bargain price on two golden ripe pineapples that smelled sweet as candy, bought oranges, mangoes, potatoes, carrots, and cucumbers, and came away heartened. Perhaps one must travel outside the U.S. to know initial prices elsewhere are suggestions and negotiable. It'd been a challenge raising two children older than myself.

We completed our provisioning, buying cereal and packaged goods at the Supermercado, and then Dari went to visit a local relative while we had lunch near the plaza. I had excellent beans and rice with a so-so cheeseburger, the only entree on the menu I could understand and was willing to risk. Then we walked over to the plaza to sit in the shade on a comfortable concrete bench, immerse ourselves in the local culture, and let our meal settle before entering the torture chamber on wheels—if he returned. He had enough of our food to stay away for a week, and having to ride fifty miles in that car before then would be too soon. So, I almost didn't care.

The plaza was lovely: walkways of terra-cotta pavers, landscaped areas set off with small concrete curbs, flowerpots on pillars, and multi-globed pole lighting. In the center was an ornate octagonal two-story structure, three highly detailed arches per side, open floor or stage on the upper level over an enclosed lower level—collectively, a very pleasant place for a respite.

Soon after sitting down, I was approached by two local women, who addressed me in a foreign language. I was unsure what was being said. Finally, one stepped forward, stood before me, and distilled it down to a few words or a short sentence that sounded a lot like "Wannafookey?" Subject—implied; verb—wanna; object—fookey?

I didn't know what the hell fookey translated to. I asked Walt and Rocco, sitting on a separate bench nearby: "What is she saying? Can you tell?"

Walt grinned, "I think she wants to have your baby."

Oh, no! Not again. Reflecting back to Nassau, and now on the bizarre sex prop she operated in front of me, it became apparent what she was proposing. Having nothing else to do, no place to run or hide, nor any way to dismiss her from her own work space, I stared quizzically at her like I was Rainman, or too blind and stupid to know a whale when I saw it (just ask Rocco). As a business major, I was curious to see the wage schedule, but didn't want to encourage her, just know how much to make her go away.

To facilitate multilingual transactions, she came prepared with marketing aids, as if that would solve the problem of no demand. While I was grossed out, shaking my head and saying "No, I don't think so," Walt and Rocco, not direct targets of the sales pitch, were laughing, finding the assault delightfully amusing.

We were not-too-soon rescued by Dari, and drove to a nearby oceanside fort with a statue of General Luperon, where we were besieged by various vendors. I took a photo of a local man on a burro, backed by the pretty coastline, in my mind all depicting the colorful native life in the DR. Soon, Rocco got burro-man's message he had to pay burro-man a buck. I had no small bills, and had already turned him away. But Rocco's dollar included getting a photo of me on the donkey, which I would pay a dollar now not to have. Sitting on the midget jackass, my feet were still on the ground. That scene should be the cover of the book, *Oh No, Honey, the Ass Isn't Big Enough.*

Back at the Luperon pier, I observed the adjacent hull of a ship that had caught fire and had partially sunk in a shallow, watery grave. According to Felix, one person had died. The owner had met a lady in town and took her to the boat. She tried to cook dinner on the propane stove while he was at the store getting groceries. Imagine the horror, returning from the store to find your boat and date literally in flames. Truly tragic.

The exhaust repair was successful, the old parts an adequate template for creating the replacement. Now we could head toward Puerto Rico tomorrow, after filling up with diesel—the Commandante, wind, and seas permitting.

Wanting to get roof-top pictures of Luperon, I returned to shore and climbed a hill for a good perspective of the thatched-roof homes. From there, I saw four small boats acting as pontoons supporting a plywood foot bridge over not much water. Almost immediately, I was confronted by a uniformed armed guard of the radio tower on the same hill, apparently questioning my intentions. Using quickly considered sign language, I tried to assure him my intentions were honorable, and not about taking down the tower, but taking only pictures, leaving nothing but footprints, if that. I hoped he didn't think I was saying that when I squeezed off a shot, he should do the same, and put my remains in the small box I had outlined in the air, or spread my ashes over all the land I had pointed out as my scene of interest.

I watched him closely out of one eye when I raised my camera, and when he did not immediately raise his rifle, I felt I might be able to squeeze off a few shots before he did. In beat-feet retreat, I quickly retraced my steps, wondering—*if this is the living standard the free part of their society enjoys, what must the jails be like?* I hoped not to know. The country was picturesque; the U.S. has nothing comparable. Snapping a couple of pictures shouldn't hurt anyone.

We had a calm evening and a colorful sky—ribbons of orange, blue, gold, and yellow, fading to pink—which meant we would be sleeping with no breeze, which meant sweating, but possibly leaving tomorrow. Pasting another page in the scrapbook of life, I'd spent enough time in this village that reminded me of Venezuela, 1974, where the security personnel at state borders were also sporting rifles and speaking only a foreign language, making me feel a little insecure where a misunderstanding could make life uncertain.

After breakfast, we weighed anchor and went to the pier for fuel. With the cesspool-like water in the bay, gloves were *de rigueur* for anchor weighing, preferably not your best ones if you had a choice. The fuel was carried in 17-gallon blue plastic barrels magically balanced on the back of a motor scooter coming from an Esso station up the street. The porter siphoned the fuel from the barrel to the boat, assuring us we did not need a funnel/fuel filter while sweeping aside our efforts to use one between his unassailably pure product and our tanks. Unfazed, or quickly recovered from the indignity, he then went on an errand to get us a bag of hot dog rolls. Still,

I wondered about the fuel. Water doesn't burn well in a diesel engine. If it did, we would use more of it; sells for a fraction of the price—unless it is sold as diesel fuel. Paranoia is advisable for mariners and aviators. Water in the fuel can be deadly.

After long delays, we were finally cleared by Customs and pulled away from the pier at 1130. Walt had asked me to steer to and from the pier to refuel this morning. Coming in went okay. Going out, I went on the wrong side of the channel marker and, yup, ran aground, proving Rocco right to think I'm stupid. Keep the Red (marker on the) Right (when you) Return is the rule: this requires you to know which is the return trip, and what you are returning to—not always clear. We reversed the prop, which pushes water under the boat, lifting us off, and we were quickly on our way toward Puerto Rico, 200 miles away.

The Mona Passage has a reputation for treacherous water currents, is a vital shipping route between the Atlantic Ocean and Caribbean Sea, and lies between us and our next port. We didn't know for certain if we'd go direct, though at 6 knots, there was ample time to decide before our next change in course.

Later in the day, I did the tough work of cutting and coring the first of two pineapples acquired yesterday. In trying to eat my share before the senior staff ate it all, I had too much of the fresh, ripe, luscious, sugar-sweet, juice-running-down-your-chin fruit, and my after-dinner companion was gastrointestinal disaster (big-time fiber). I went below and tried to sleep. The crew may have thought I was shirking my duties; I felt lucky to be alive. We had one more pineapple which, if I didn't peel it, would probably rot; otherwise, I could pick my time. But I got pleasure out of providing these types of treats for my fellow seamen. We would enjoy it, and I less of it, though it was hard to stop eating when it was so good.

Sailing through the night was a romance with nature, even as the seas roughened late in the evening. We sailed east, on the port side a silvery white full moon, and on the starboard side were tall cliffs with trees—thunder rumbling and lightning flashing within them—providing a dramatic and expansive skyscape for our floating, open-air observatory-in-the-round. In the early morning, I was told that we'd had a full eclipse of the moon which

I would have liked to see, sick or not. They said it was blood-red during the darkest, total phase. I imagined it was dramatic, with nothing blocking the view, no ambient light, watching it play out with the reflections on the water and a full-screen sky in our private theatre. That opportunity was lost, unlikely to come again.

Around 0600, the moon was still brilliant, and for the next hour I watched the stars go to bed as the sun rose over the unobstructed horizon, a spiritual, wonder-filled time, every time, with or without an eclipse. There was a palpable sense we were space travelers, riding atop a vast globe named Earth, set in the Milky Way galaxy, the sun, moon, and stars on full display, heading for an endless edge, the world spinning beneath our feet.

I was satisfied with that orientation, but took a moment to get my head around that we were not on top of the globe, more likely riding on the side of it, held there by gravitational forces, and the sun not rising but being revealed by the spinning of our planet, in a universe where up, down, and side, had more to do with presentation than actuality, such as going from the north Georgia mountains "up" to Bar Harbor, Maine. I soon decided I was more comfortable returning to a casual feeling of being on top of the world.

Rounding the Cape of Cabron, crossing the mouth of the Bay of Rincon and rounding the Cape of Samana, we saw volcanic formations overgrown with lush vegetation, including many coconut palms. This was exotic scenery for sailing.

Santa Barbara de Samana:
Honor local Customs; trust me

We decided against proceeding straight across Mona Passage, another 30 hours on top of the last 19. There were things more comfortably done in calmer seas, including dinner. Thankfully, Walt felt we needed more fuel before heading across to Boquerón, Puerto Rico, our next port of call. We turned west and sailed 7–8 nautical miles (nm=1.15 statute miles) into Bahia de (bay of) Samana to a protected anchorage at Santa Barbara de Samana.

Soon after anchoring in the harbor, we were approached by a casual-looking citizen in a motorized dinghy, perhaps offering to take us to the dock. Guidebooks warn about people selling goods and services.

"Hola!"

"Hola! to you, señor."

"Tadasada ata tema lama" he yelled, for all I know.

"No habla Español!" I informed him. "Sprechen ze Deu . . ." no, that's German. "Parlez vous ang. . . ." No, that's probably French. Bah humbug! Foreign languages for tourists: use it or lose it. My hat is off to the multilinguals who can keep it all straight. Ahhh, I may have it: "Se habla Anglais?"

Apparently, that wasn't it either. He said, "Es qui rama lama ding dong," as I translated it. Sounded similar, though I was looking for head movement to see if we had a connection; it didn't come. So far, I couldn't tell what he was selling. Didn't see anything in the boat. Maybe he's selling timeshare condominiums, Casa de No Mea Bia, because I'm not in the market.

"No necessario; no necessario." There, the first one didn't flow but that second iteration sounded more fluent. Just takes a little practice, and Rocco had been no help. He never did word drills with me—not even in English; imagine that! Studying foreign vocabulary is a start, but it's not really grasped until you practice speaking it; understanding it when spoken is harder yet. The señor's words ran together. I was feeling useless, imbecilic.

He persisted: "Hahase quitiempo blahramadiego."

Whatever. Must really be proud of his product. New and improved, Version 4; everyone expects Versions 1 and 2 have more bugs or less features. Even so, Walt would not put up with any more useless cargo on board than am I. "No, not today, gracias señor. Mucho gracias. No necessario." There, I lobbed everything I had at him short of asking about the family, which should have taken care of it, though it would have been polite to ask. He may have asked about mine. Or threatened them.

"Yah yah tormente mi and try my patience hyway on'tde ouye, señorita," he was thinking, if he didn't say so in an articulate manner I could understand. He seemed angry with that last outburst, as though he were saying, "If you don't buy my product, you can burn in Hell in your Speedos, you skinny big-eared jerk."

Well, you dirty rotten, dingy dinghy-driving dingbat, how dare you direct dastardly discourse in my direction, is what I'm thinking, but it's his country and it may be under-civilized to where they lack the polite constraints of our Thought/Speech Police. He had to be done, having given me all the imagined, unmitigated neglect I could endure. I turned my head so he could get the side-channel message along with "Not today, señor, gracias. I gave blood before I left and all throughout the mosquito-ridden Bahamas, and bought my Girl Scout cookies yesterday, so I'm caught up on forced charitable giving." Ha, I can only dream; Thin Mints and Samoas are favorites, but I like them all.

He left, if not gracefully, still looking a little frustrated, as though sorry he didn't take the last English course at the community college. Or maybe he taught Spanish and, when I told him I wasn't interested, he kept selling it. Where have we come across that practice before? I wondered if he, too, had a sex toy and worked the windward side of the plaza.

Looking out from below, Walt asked: "What was that all about?"

"Have no clue; probably selling something, or a dock boy. As insistent as he was, we may have a hole in the hull and we're going down, or a Customs agent from a passed island wants to speak to Rocco. We paid the burro man for the picture, and didn't use the girls' services, so he probably wasn't a bill collector. Seemed a matter of life-or-death, whatever it was."

Walt blew it off, got himself and his papers together, and departed for Customs in the dinghy.

There were a few moments of peace and quiet before Walt returned, informing us the "dock boy" was a representative of the Dominican Republic Immigration office. The crew of *Fantastique* was also there and, having recognized our boat from Rum Cay and South Caicos, they translated for Walt the sincerity and gravity of the invitation and the need to RSVP ASAP by docking the boat. No wonder the señor persisted. He was making an offer we couldn't refuse.

Walt further informed us the Customs folks were currently placing three stools under the hanging tree, checking the ropes. When I was answering "no necessario" the question may have been, "Do you want a jury trial before the hanging?" I switched from sarcasm to survivalism. May buy a condo, after all.

Rocco, who'd been lurking on the bow pretending to stuff sails into a sail bag, immediately became spastic as a cat with tape on all four paws, borrowing cuss words from tomorrow, going through a conniption, all the while looking at me.

"You should have done the translation yourself, big guy. Don't look at me!" I said. "I didn't know what the man was saying. Did you? He didn't address me by name. It was a drive-by, a John 'Rocco' Doe solicitation."

Rocco just knew Customs was gonna get him. We'd almost made it back to U.S. territory; one overnight sail away. If only we hadn't stopped. Would we get a last meal and a final request? I'm a believer in the hereafter, so my final request would be they hang Rocco first so I can be here after Rocco finds peace, and meets the guy he's been shouting to for six weeks—see how that goes down. Perhaps, then, I'd go without too much fuss.

When we took *Godspeed* to the dock, Customs came aboard and was again mesmerized by my oranges, my root beer, and a few other trinkets for the natives. The island of Manhattan was bought, comparatively, on the cheap. The oranges were from their country but getting them from us was preferable to shopping and paying for them. They kept taking my sodas and leaving the beer, which affected my spirit for gift-giving, though Columbus probably fared better going ashore with an armload of goodies than when empty-handed. These portly fellows looked like they'd had plenty of everything, and may have had a written policy of what was acceptable blackmail booty, and what was forbidden: "Take only what you can eat; leave no evidence."

Any foodstuff sacrifice was better than a Dominican jail and a hanging tree. Might these Customs men play on that fear? They seemed adept at it. No wonder the agent was persistent: they were hungry, and we were the next Quik Stop in the harbor. Benign highwaymen, or toll-takers by another name: *"Feed us or we will tear up your boat looking for drugs."* Hey, get that man another orange, maybe a root beer. All for stopping a few hours in the harbor.

While Walt refueled at the pier, I walked out of the marina area to get a look at the town, the harbor, and their jitneys, also called motoconchos, which were motorized rickshaws that could carry up to six passengers. The large bar/restaurant across the street had a thatched roof with gables, overhanging walls of diagonal boards, not of materials I or a fire marshal would pick for a bar, but it was artistic and picturesque, depreciated only by the large concrete structure behind it with a large red and white Marlboro sign on top.

The shaded waterside park west of the pier had decorative concrete benches forming a low wall overlooking the bay. The best scenery of the Dominican Republic was accessed from here, according to our sailing guide: "Samana is the closest you will come to Bora Bora while in the Caribbean." Waterfalls, with hot and cold bathing opportunities, were just outside of town. Bora Bora, by any other name, was not on the captain's mind or charts, so we were not to experience these vaunted local treasures—perhaps another day, another way, bringing more oranges and root beer.

We left the pier and anchored in the bay, fixed dinner, and prepared to set sail, eager to move on so as to arrive at Boquerón before dark tomorrow night and avoid unintentional skirmishes with unpredictable law enforcement. I enjoyed the stop.

CHAPTER
Seven

Puerto Rico:
Who needs a fuel filter?

W e left Santa Barbara de Samana around 2100 hours to cross the Mona Passage, sailing a course toward the southeast, avoiding the dangerous Hourglass Shoals, east of Cabo Engano. Not as infamous as the Bermuda Triangle, the Mona Passage was still treacherous sailing; it just didn't have the disappearing boat count of the Triangle, though, as a percentage, it may have. I took the first watch (I prefer my sleep between midnight and 0800, not that low-level crewmen often have options), coming out of Bahia de Samana in the lee of the southern shore, figuring the seas to be relatively calm there.

Rocco relieved me at the helm at 0045. Around 0300, he was pushing on my arm, asking me to relieve him. I asked if, perchance, Walt, fresh from the States, had been offered an opportunity to further pursue his love of sailing. Sensitive to what was going on in his boat at all times, Walt woke up and took the next watch. Was Rocco forgetful, or trying to push my buttons? Maybe he thought I also was being paid, unable to understand my presence without a financial inducement. Most likely he wanted my berth. I held my horizontal ground and fell back to sleep.

The seas were fairly calm until we neared Hourglass Shoals, then the waves rolled in like mountain ranges on wheels as the waters from the Puerto Rican trench, deepest point in the Atlantic at 25,000 feet, compressed onto the shoals. They were going west, and we were headed east. It would be gracious to say the ride was a bit rough, though the southeast winds were only 15 knots. The reading of 50 feet of elevation we saw on our GPS in Florida would now be correct half of the time. This was the second night in a row we had sailed through the night, so my stomach was rebellious. I stayed away from food in the morning, though fasting as a solution, like alcohol, eventually becomes a problem.

Around 0815, we spotted a freighter coming up behind us, out of the west-northwest. With wind from the southeast, we had a small sail up only to keep the boat from rolling too much and were using the engine for our propulsion. Okay, typical math class question: If a freighter moving at 15 knots comes over the horizon alleged to be 7 miles away (objects on the "horizon" can be seen further away the taller the objects involved) and a sailboat is moving in the same direction at 6 knots, how long before the 34-foot sailboat becomes two 17-footers? For more than two hours, as the freighter closed on us, we spent a lot of time looking backward, speculating on whether the freighter could see us, or whether we could get out of the way, if necessary, at the last moment. All we could see of the freighter was the bow, a sign it was headed directly toward us. Would the fuel filter, that was recently prone to clogging and stopping the engine, do so again, leaving us powerless in the path of the freighter?

As if thinking it would make it happen, our engine sputtered and stalled.

We'd lost our propulsion. The freighter, maybe 200 yards away, was closing on us at significant speed. Sailing magazines grab their readers by publishing stories of boats cut in half by larger boats when the small boat did not show up on the radar screen no one was watching. We had no radar reflector, and the blip reflected from the mast in these deep trough waves was typically looked upon as debris, which we soon could be. We had a life-or-death emergency.

Should we hoist the mainsail, tack, and try to sail off course, fighting the waves? Or should we try to get the engine running again? We only had time for one, maybe neither, and hoisting a sail wouldn't guarantee immediate movement before it would blow us toward the ship. Should we try to radio the freighter? They usually don't answer, you hesitate to hang up, and the time would almost certainly be wasted. Many times they are on autopilot or radar watch only, with no one on lookout, and are loath to make course corrections, since commercial shipping thinks they have the right-of-way on the high seas. We occupied the higher position on the right-of-way list, because we were being overtaken, but we could end up being dead right; far better to self-rescue, if possible.

The freighter continued straight toward us; a collision imminent. Freighters have been known to hit each other, since it can take several miles to stop. If they missed us, we'd definitely feel the wake. The threat was looming large, like a train upon a stalled car at a railroad crossing with no place to run, its doors locked shut, waiting for the impact, death all but certain.

Rocco and I kept the boat from being swamped, watched the freighter, and offered assistance while Walt took off the engine compartment cover, dug around to find a replacement filter, removed the old filter, installed a new one, worked the tickler arm to prime the fuel lines while bleeding the air from the system, jumped out of the engine compartment, put the cover back in place, cranked the engine until it finally caught, sputtered, caught again, sputtered, then smoothed out before he put the transmission in gear and started us moving at a right angle to the freighter, crawling away from the track of doom.

The freighter varied nary a foot, sounded no alarm, changed not its speed—that we could tell—and missed us by less than two of our boat lengths, or 68 feet. Apparently, no one was on radar watch. For so long, it was on our same course and we could have wound up as flotsam in the prop wash. Thankfully, we did not perish. But, let's review: why would we need a fuel funnel with a debris/water filter? For the gasboy! These shore-bound service people should go to sea more often and find out what does and does not work, and why it is important. He sells that light yellow piss at Luperon and never hears any different from the users as they perish, stacking up in the Puerto Rican trench. "Gee! Must be okay fuel: never used a filter, never had a complaint!" So they keep pouring it without filters. Corpses are not loquacious complainers. What if this filter change had occurred at night, requiring more time?

With the freighter off our tail, we changed our direction back toward the southeast and started angling across the mountainous waves. What a ride. Who needs amusement parks when you can easily get sick on a boat with the added excitement of knowing you cannot turn it off, there's no relief in sight, and no guarantee you'll survive. At 1530, the wind suddenly increased, the sky turned black, then dumped a horrific rainstorm on us for half an hour, Rocco and I taking shelter in the cabin while Walt weathered the storm at the helm. Soon after, the air had freshened, and the setting sun lit the clouds between the black clouds and a blue sky to a beautiful peach color. Heavenly, and I was thankful to still be on Earth, able to reflect on the day.

Boquerón:
Oil? Who needs oil?

We arrived at Boquerón, south of Mayaguez on the southwest coast of Puerto Rico, around 2130. This was a fast trip, taking 24.5 hours to travel 144 miles at 6 knots, the best our boat could do, and the best our sailing guide said was possible. And we stopped for fuel! This was our last long, overnight passage. Crossing the Puerto Rican trench, and the Mona Passage, an important shipping route between the Atlantic Ocean and the Panama Canal, was behind us.

There were few lit navigational markers to help locate the harbor of Boquerón and, once inside, no lights at all. We slowly entered the harbor using a dying flashlight to spot other boats, and moved among them to find space to anchor. Eerie, absolutely pitch black, like a floating graveyard, there were no signs of life whatsoever. We crept along at 1–2 knots, eventually found sufficient room, and dropped the anchor, hoping it would hold until dawn when we could reassess our position. We couldn't see stationary objects to gauge our anchor's holding ability, so setting it by backing it down was skipped. If it didn't hold, we would later deal with the consequences, rather than immediately creating them.

Hooray! I was looking forward to being in this U.S. commonwealth. Wanting to visit islands with a higher standard of living might seem superficial, but that's me—for now. The island of Puerto Rico is 35 miles north to south, 100 miles across, and had approximately 4 million residents. There are only a few large cities, if you consider San Juan as including Bayamon and several adjacent areas. Ponce is the second largest. Mayaguez and Aguadilla are notable towns on the west coast.

The next morning we set out in the dinghy, scouting the harbor of Boquerón. We uncovered picturesque waterside taverns and an enticing beach, making us want to stay off the boat and spend time exploring the town—a quaint beach village of well-maintained shops and homes built close to the narrow streets and each other, with balconies overhanging the sidewalks, and cafes with tables and red and white umbrellas to the curb. The place had a European-Mediterranean look to me but for the Caribbean bright colors, maybe more so backstreet Key West or St. Augustine, Florida. This was our first anchorage with more than a few boats since the Exumas. I understood why: the dissuasive long and dangerous passage between.

I was looking for a Puerto Rico Telephone payphone. It seemed I still worked for the telephone company, since the first thing I did on many of the islands was "test" the phone system, to check in on business back home and pick up phone messages from my recorder. The one I found worked, unlike most in the Bahamas.

Last night, as we were approaching port, Walt said we would rest here for two days. Now, he said we would leave tomorrow morning. I cared how long we were here. Being fatigued, I needed rest, but was also curious about this end of the island, having seen much of the eastern half. Around 1300, Walt said if I wanted to see Mayaguez, a desire I'd earlier expressed, this was my only chance to do it.

I took a público (private cars and vans used as public busses) to Cabo Rojo, and transferred to another that went to the Mayaguez mall, where I had a Pizza Hut pizza, my first choice, located next door to a Burger King, a close second choice, across from a Sears—is there something we need for the boat? All the big brand names and comfort food made this feel like home.

My waitress informed me públicos only operate until 1700, and I hadn't time to go into Mayaguez and return to Boquerón before they stopped running. But, but, today was all I had, my only chance, I had to do it now. As

I jumped up, she directed me to the stop for the Mayaguez públicos, where I eventually found an available car. I tried to explain to the driver I wanted to make a round trip with him but he "no comprendo!" A passenger already in the car was bi-lingual and secured my place in the car as well as a return ride home. As we talked along the way, she negotiated with the driver, Roberto Velez, to add on a tour of the town. After the other passengers had been taken to their destinations, I moved up into the shotgun seat and Roberto took me on a tour of the town and the beautiful university campus, then drove me all the way back to the boat, giving me his business card and an opportunity to practice my Spanish, and he his English. Magnifico!

I'd had my long-desired pizza and, at the end of the ride in Boquerón, though close to dinnertime, I bought an ice cream sandwich—my first ice cream on this trip, a daily occurrence at home—and savored it as long as its melting and my pickup appointment time would permit, before returning to the pier, never sure when or what the next meal would be, or how soon I would be on land again. Literally, life was uncertain (I'd left my self-determinism on land when I stepped aboard in Stuart, Florida); so I ate dessert the only time I could, and was feeling good, really good.

At the pier precisely at 1800 for my ride back to the boat, Walt told me of a "no oil to the engine" problem; there was a hole in the oil line running between the oil pump and the cylinders, so we would sail to Ponce that evening. I didn't immediately deduce why we would put out to sea as soon as we knew we were disabled. If we all had a deadly, highly contagious malady, I could understand casting off without being able to ever anchor again, in the interest of preserving humanity. As it was, we'd always anchored using engine power; maybe these guys were better sailors than they'd let on. If they were, it must be due to something they read while I was out frolicking, enjoying my life away.

After a few questions from me about how serious it was (and whether it had possibly broken while installing the custom-made manifold, or in the life-saving rush to replace the filter), then returning to the boat and working on the engine further, Walt discovered the bilge was full of oil and the engine devoid of it. Any use of the engine was out of the question, so he decided we'd go to Mayaguez tomorrow to find a new oil line. We were in more danger of ruining the engine than we knew. More than fatigued, I was exhausted and dizzy.

Starting with Walt's return at Turks, after days of mind-numbing inaction, there'd been a litany of reversals, causing me to question my sanity, if not abandon it: We had salivated over the prospect of a Thanksgiving meal, only to have it devolve into peanut butter sandwiches; we planned to anchor off of Salt Cay and wait for better weather if the waves were too rough, but it was smooth going in the lee of the island so we passed it and, oops, too late, couldn't turn back in such rough seas; "there are no whales here in November, you stupid sumbitch" in just minutes turned into "can't you see there's four off the starboard bow, you blind dummy?" There were none. "I don't much care for pineapple" turned into conspicuous consumption, followed by "We'll just anchor here, not go ashore, so we don't have to go through Customs." Wrong! Hoy no, señor; after being told we don't need a fuel filter, we learned you bet your life you do. And finally, "If you're going to Mayaguez, go right now; it's your only chance." Now I get a second "only chance."

Adding to the many hastily contrived plans with often-unexpected results, when Walt and Rocco pulled themselves out of the hold of the ship and considered their stomachs, they decided on pizza for dinner. In fairness, I didn't object vehemently, though I tried to interest them in delicious native Puerto Rican food, but they would not be deterred; we could get Puerto Rican food in the U.S. Then the pendulum swung back my way—the pizza shop was closed. Yessss! There is a god. We found a little shop that served Mexican food, recommended by a couple who drove us there via a refreshing ride in their open-air jeep. Saved from a two-pizza overdose, I regretted having eaten the peppers. Yes, there is also a devil.

On a sunny, temperate December 2nd morning, we decided to check in first with Customs and Immigration, then find parts to fix the oil problem on the boat, like an old-fashioned treasure hunt. Using what I learned yesterday from Roberto, I easily guided my mates to an efficient Customs office in Mayaguez. Luckily, Orlando, a ship's agent we met on the Customs dock, took pity on us and drove us around town until we found a shop that could replace the oil lines with a new braided hose connection between the two fittings. It took a lot of stops, sign language, and translation by Orlando.

After letting three strangers repeatedly pile in and out of his car, Orlando, only under duress, accepted payment for gas, refusing anything for his time. We caught a público back to the mall and ate at a Ponderosa steak house, enjoying a delicious salad bar with a variety impossible on *Godspeed*. It was mentally comforting and physically fortifying to eat fresh vegetables.

When we arrived back in Boquerón, we boarded *Speedy* and returned to our crowded anchorage, ready to climb aboard and install the new part. Unexpectedly, Walt yelled, "Hey! Where's the boat?"

I asked, "Which boat?" thinking Walt had his eye on a nice yacht or other marker of where we were.

"Our boat. I thought it was right here, next to the blue ketch."

"Hmmm, could there be another ketch just like it?"

"Don't see one," said Walt.

"I've made this trip several times, looks about right. Gotta be somewhere nearby; it won't run. Not long. Not without oil."

Well, damn, that solved the oil problem. Of all the boats to steal, she must have been the worst. No working engine. Thieves probably stole *Godspeed* for the beer and were around the point offloading it on Beer Cay. Must have used a towboat. The thieves may have figured we wouldn't bother looking for it, just file a claim. Remembering most of my money was aboard instantly curtailed my flippancy.

"You know what?" I asked. "We never backed down the anchor, did we? Could it have drifted off?"

We started a worried scan of a beautiful setting-sun horizon on fire with blazing yellows and orange, supporting and backlighting a band of striated clouds and sundry sailboats, their masts melting into the sunset. As we motored further toward the outer edge of the harbor, we spotted *Godspeed*, dragging anchor, leaving Bahia De Boquerón on her way to Mexico's Yucatan Peninsula. Ponce as a destination was not that much of a stretch after all. We caught up with her and used ropes, leverage, and *Speedy* to push her back into the harbor.

In the process of installing the new oil piping, Walt asked me from the engine compartment below deck: "How do you tell when a bolt is tight enough, and what's happening when the bolt's easier to turn after seeming to be tight?"

"Oh no, you're about to strip the head off the bolt. Stop tightening and replace the compression washer. It may already be too late. Another half a turn and you'll be holding your head in your hands."

That was irresistible, and may not have seemed helpful, as he had no new washers, and the oil was still leaking. So he tightened it more, hoping to stop the oil leak with a little more force. Then a tiny little bit more. During one of his little-mores, the head of the bolt came off, the stud still in the engine. Apparently unable to contain his excitement or frustration of having a new oil line that he couldn't make work, he forthwith did the same to the other oil bolt. Two studs still in the engine block, one manly stud in the engine compartment. Alas, he laid down his wrench. He'd sheared the heads off both the bolts available. He may have looked for more. That had to be frustrating! (And a parable for others.) By some logic, why not break them both if you cannot get by with just one? Find out now if you will need two.

That he consulted me beforehand adds depth, or daft, to the story, obviously because I was nearby. Still, a compliment. Or he may have been thinking out loud, and kept his further thoughts to himself: *Hmmm, wonder if Byrd knows what he's talking about? Probably not. Uh-oh! Okay, maybe he was just lucky once. Oh-oh, that's two; now how the hell did B Byrd know that?*

I couldn't shake my head any harder in disbelief without shearing it off, also. We not only did not improve the oil problem, we exacerbated it—or moved the goalpost down the field. Maybe now we would go to Ponce! Or someone, most likely me, would be looking for parts tomorrow, if not in Boquerón, maybe Mayaguez. I did say I wanted to see the city. At this pace, I may soon know it better than many locals. God works in strange ways. Thank goodness for angelic souls like Orlando. We'd met several, and now had need of a few more.

Despite the mechanical challenges, everyone was feeling good that night, possibly from resignation and acceptance of the problems, the lack of solutions, or satisfaction they had broken all there was to break and we would solve it tomorrow. It seemed highly probable, perchance inescapable, we would yet get two whole days here, or at least nearby.

Rocco shared with us it was the first night he had felt content since leaving George Town in the Exumas. That was a long time ago, all but the recent several days spent with just me! *Thanks for sharing, Rocco.* Even if offended, I was glad to hear it; he showed it. Maybe he enjoyed breaking things also, or Walt's bolt job made Rocco feel superior. It was a group compliment. Excuse me for paying attention (or laughing), but there was scant indication his discontent started as late as the Exumas, though I wouldn't ruin his happy moment challenging that point during our "group therapy." Until now, Rocco seemed a person to whom every silver lining had a cloud.

Upon reflection, Rocco and Walt must have talked while I was out sightseeing, because they were totally different when I returned; both seemed like pleasant, normal people. Maybe they remained the same, and I changed. They may have needed a vacation from me, or me from them. Or they enjoyed living on a broken-down boat. It can be low stress when surrendering to there being nothing more you can do. Rocco had to be happy to return the captain responsibility to the owner, though his bunk shrunk. We also had accomplished the dramatic water crossings and avoided death by freighter, so the rest should be coastal cruising; so many possibilities, only a few certainties. I hoped it would last awhile; a full second day would be an anomaly.

Rocco and I encouraged Walt to see Puerto Rico while we were here, and not hurry past it thinking the Virgin Islands were all there was to see. I felt there was much more visible, accessible culture here than on the smaller islands ahead. That was part speculation, but had been my experience. When Rocco and I told Walt of our plan to mutiny, if necessary, to get to see more of the island, he agreed to explore with us. Time would tell, but I was skeptical. This journey of life seemed to have become destination oriented.

Knowing there was dependable mail service, I wrote postcards and could expect them to be received. All of this writing took time, but it gave me something to do while the guys broke the boat down into small, manageable pieces. Despite better telecom service, I could only leave half a singing happy birthday message for my brother before I was cut off. He may know the words and can finish it himself.

Tomorrow's plan, after finding two bolts (if we did), was to explore a hurricane hole and go swimming. But this was not a quest for the average hardware store bolt.

The next morning, having apparently drawn the short straw without drawing any (two wolves and a sheep deciding what's for lunch), I was sent to the Boquerón Marine store to get the bolts we needed for the oil line repair. Possibly because I survived my solo trip to Mayaguez, Walt thought I was the "go-to" guy, the one to go to the store, where two guys behind the counter spoke no English, but made it pretty clear they did not have the bolt, or the washer to go with it. Before giving up, I asked them for their yellow pages phone directory, then to call Pescaderia Rosa (whatever that was) in Cabo Rojo, (wherever that was), to see if they had it. Their ad suggested they were associated with marine supply. One of the clerks made the call then handed me the phone. He probably knew this wouldn't work, but was doing it for me. And him.

I checked with the other end regarding his ability to speak English. When he said no, I said "Uno momento" and handed it back, asking the guy at my end to describe the bolt to the other end, not that my end understood me either. But sign language and an example wouldn't convey over the telephone. You can guess the other end did not have one, and there was no alternative. They probably agreed, in Spanish, to just get rid of me. Had it sold for $22,000 with a 20% commission, they may have tried harder. Otherwise, come back after we close.

I'd struck out on language. When this happens, I don't leave, but hang around to share the pain and the problem. If I owned the problem alone, I wouldn't get anywhere. Even frogs know they shouldn't jump before they have a place to land (according to anonymous amphibious sources). Lacking options, but thinking someone in town must be bilingual, I asked again if there was *anyone* who spoke English, for whatever that might be worth. It was conveyed Ivan would be with me in a minute.

Huh? Are you French? That's what they do: "Ooo, you vant us to speak Anglais, oui monsieur? Okay, how ya doing, whaddya want? Whazzup?" The first thing I had asked was whether they spoke English. They were honest, if not resourceful.

Ivan, the store owner, spoke fluent English and, upon showing him the pieces, said, "We don't stock these, but I can make them."

His answer beat shrugged shoulders and a big smile by a mile. Making this bolt required drilling an oil passageway through the shoulder of a stock bolt, then a centered intersecting passageway the length of the bolt through the threaded tip up to the shoulder passageway. Impressed, I asked "How long to do it?"

"I'll have to go and get the bolts, but I have a machine shop. It would be ready sometime tomorrow."

He's gotta be kidding! Can he do that in just one paragraph? My captain would never stand for that, requiring more than two full days in port! In truth, he and I would both be delighted. Not content with a small miracle, I inquired: "Where are the bolts? Can I walk there and pick 'em up? I don't have much else to do, maybe I can help out."

"The hardware store is close to the post office, where I have to go."

"Can I go to the post office for you? I have postcards to mail."

"We can go in my Jeep," and he started walking toward it.

Wow! We're moving. He knew "mañana," but it wasn't his Bible. In short order, we bought the bolts, a couple new nylon washers, dealt with the mail, and were quickly back at the shop. I enjoyed my second ride in an open-air Jeep—tropical breeze in the face, cushioned seat—and I wasn't walking.

"Now how long?" I persisted.

"Would take some time; maybe by one o'clock."

"You mean today?"

"Yes."

Yessssss!

Fabulous. Hell, that was a miracle, maybe as high as a Class 2 (saving Class 1 for something *really big*!). We found the bolt and knocked a day off the estimate. Walt should be delighted, but that's a stretch. I could have made the problem the captain's, but had he gone to sea with no engine, hoping to find the bolt sooner in Ponce, we all would have been fully vested. Not that sailors haven't gone to sea for roughly 5,000 years without engines, I think they may have, but not these sailors. And a lot of those old sailors haven't lived to tell about it.

We worked on other boat things until it was time to pick up the bolts. Ivan had to shorten them, run the threads up higher on the shoulder of the bolt, and drill the holes. Practically hand-made, and they looked great!

Three-and-a-half hours after asking for the bolts, we had them. Three bucks, including the original cost of the bolt! His drill bits alone must have cost that much. We would have paid any price—we weren't going to sit here until they went on sale—one of the marvels of the trip. In providing marine parts, most suppliers have no shame. They'd charge that much at home to look at the bolt. Ivan was a miracle man, another angel, who probably only charged for supplies.

Being oil bolts and well lubricated, the old studs came out easily, though we still had leakage problems after installing the new bolts: the old copper washers had been compressed to match the old fittings. Before he could break the new bolts, I presented Walt with the nylon washers I bought as a just-in-case backup option, and we were soon back in the boat delivery business.

Later, I glanced at the captain's brief version of the story, written in the ship's log and lying open on the chart table. His version was gracious, since he had his hands full of bolt tops at the time: "After installing the new oil line, we still could not get the engine to run because Captain Walt broke a bolt off by tightening it too much. At this point I was resigned to spend the rest of the winter right here out of total frustration, but Bryan, having other ideas, took over and found a machine shop to make a new bolt and off we went . . ." I understood his reluctance to document that he sheared off both bolts, and it's not important except that true science and learning (as well as inquisitiveness) required replicability. He would recognize that feeling if it came again (at which point it is too late). I confess to knowing it too well, having done many more than two, and it's a setup—the bolt's strength is weakened by the holes drilled through the shoulder so the oil can flow through it; any minor leak is cause to tighten it a bit more. Only a torque wrench, experience, or no leakage would inform you to stop.

Having now an engine to burn it, we refueled, had dinner, and made plans to leave around 0300 for Ponce. So much for the beach and exploring hurricane holes, or spending "the rest of the winter right here." I should have let the bolts cool in my pocket for twenty-four hours. That was a strategic blunder. If I'd kept just the washers in my pocket, we'd have needed two more bolts made, and stayed here another day. In college, I signed up for a class in Deception, but it turned out to be a misprint, or I misperceived what was actually a class in Perception. Tough course, too. Deception may have been less technical and more useful, but it wasn't offered. Not openly, anyway, as the name would insinuate. Perception was deceptively useful, though, teaching the benefits of slow hands and a soft touch when a bachelor, or when flipping wrenches, ending the practice of stripping oil bolts.

If I were to undertake a similar trip, there would be many new things to see, since we were missing most of it. But it was still undeniably an adventure! We were having a wonderful time doing what men do—fixing stuff: testing circuits, fixing speedometers, brazing oil lines, installing them, building exhaust systems out of galvanized plumbing parts, and performing occasional miracles. What do others do in Paradise? We went swimming several weeks ago, and we got to sail, as a means to an end. I guess we were avoiding boredom by breaking the engine, then starting out on what seems to be a treasure hunt destined to acquaint us with the land and its people. It was working. Were it not for our travails, the interior of the islands we passed would still be a mystery. Our motto should be: "Don't worry, be happy. Something good will come of this mess. Gotta be a pony in here somewhere." I went to bed, knowing 0300 would come all too early, bringing something good, hidden inside another mess.

Ponce:
What are they doing out here?

*U*pon leaving Boquerón to head east along the south coast of Puerto Rico, leave your anchorage . . . early in the morning so that you round Cabo Rojo at dawn when the wind is light and hopefully still out of the north. Heeding the advice of our sailing guide, we weighed anchor by 0325 for a 40-mile trip to Ponce, our first passage in the Caribbean Sea. I went back to bed when my two mariners were safely away from land and past the first two waypoints. They'd had their coffee, so they couldn't sleep anyway, and shouldn't hit anything. I took the helm around 0800. All was good; land was visible off the port side, as it should be.

A few hours later, as we were nearing Ponce and I'd been relieved of my watch, I verified by the charts and GPS we were on track to arrive at our next waypoint. Dead-on! Gonna be a good day. Casually looking around while enjoying the cruise, I noticed that between us and the channel we would take into the harbor for anchoring was a beach full of sunbathers. Other boats were using the channel, but we had sand and bathers to deal with before we would reach it. Damned inconvenient. Not an ordinary day of sailing. I checked the charts again and verified we were certain to run aground, full speed ahead, boat on autopilot, in just a few minutes. Unworkable, if not inconceivable; obviously, it was conceived.

Walt and Rocco had kicked back on their watch, relaxing after a change to the usual cool, bubbly beverage of choice though still well before lunch, looking backward until our arrival at the next waypoint. I was reluctant to disturb them and receive their aggravated stares, but safety won out over a potentially tragic collision of plan and reality.

"Hey guys! Is this Houston? 'Cause we may have a problem."

"What's that?" asked Walt. Rocco just looked irritated, likely thinking, *What the hell are you up to now? Can't you shuddup for a few hours?*

"Well, the way I figure it, those boats going into Ponce Bay are in the channel."

"Yeah? So?"

"Are we on the course you want to be on? Did you plot the next waypoint?"

"Yeah!"

"Well, we'll soon run up on that beach dead ahead and the bathers will either be pissed, or amused. Try not to hit the bambinos, or we'll be strung up like piñatas and beat until our candy falls out. Looks like they're already clearing the beach."

Walt was skeptical, thinking I was punking him, giving me time to finish that long setup. When he had his feet back on the sole, had slowly turned around, and could see forward over the dodger, he gave a facial expression I would have loved to record, his eyes wide. "Whaaaaa?" He lunged toward the controls, slowed the boat to a crawl, checked the charts, then changed course, turning back and going farther out to sea.

Our threat to the bathers' safety laid bare, Walt said I'd passed the test— of common sense. *Well, good for me! How 'bout you guys? Any other scholars aboard?*

As a result of our serious near-miss, in broad daylight, no less, a wiser Walt suggested all waypoints should be verified by one other knowledgeable seaman. My hand shot up. Though not sure I qualified, I didn't want to leave it in others' hands. When it came to planning to go aground, maybe die, I would cherish being involved in the organizational phase, not just the execution. I'd wanted to be "The Master of my fate, the captain of my soul" since twelfth-grade English. For a whole year of study, that was all I remembered. That's not quite true—I also remembered Poe's *Raven*, which I'd been doing here a lot—never more.

In Bahia de Ponce, we anchored at the Ponce Yacht and Fishing Club in the midst of boaters getting ready for a big offshore racing event the next day. We were surrounded by lots of big, husky, straight-pipe, cigarette-style power boats. Engines were being tuned up, with an ear-splitting, deafening ruckus bombing the marina—boys and their toys, high on testosterone.

After doing our required maintenance activities, Rocco and I broke away to check out the town, knowing this island could slip away from us if we left land-based discovery to the captain. Rocco spotted what he thought was a público. Hey, he was coming alive. I waved it down and ran after it when it slowed, then stopped. I asked for a ride into town and immediately learned it was a senator with a driver. Nice catch of the big fish, Rocco. They'd give us a ride, but could not show us around. We could live with that. In Washington, D.C., I can assure you, they won't even slow down for you.

I was a bit embarrassed by the mistake, but feeling embarrassed and stupid while riding was better than feeling embarrassed and stupid while walking, so we climbed into the car. *What the hell? He was going our way, might as well share. When we arrive at our destination via free, luxury car, I can convince myself that feeling stupid is not always bad. Yup! If you can control your mind, you can control your destiny, and we will arrive at ours motorized. Feels smart to me.*

The senator might have been thinking (also) to himself, to share later with his driver: *Got to do something about the wharf rats. Third time this week I've been flagged down like a público. Especially bad during race week. Need a better place to hide and still be seen as part of the action. I can use the votes, but these guys don't live here. Maybe they know someone that does, and will put in a good word.*

To fill the awkward silence, Rocco conducted a hard-hitting interview of the Senator for his opinions on the pros and cons of being a 51st state of the U.S. Hah! I wish—Rocco never says a damn word. I never thought of it, either, but did try a little name dropping from my business contacts at Puerto Rico Telephone. The senator gave me his card and said to call him if there was anything he could do for me. Whoa! That was gracious. The people here had been fantastic—from Mayaguez to Ponce, mechanics to senators. Would that call go through? It might, you never know.

The senator dropped us off at the meticulously restored Parque de Bombas, Ponce's first fire station (1882), now a museum. Before pulling away, he instructed the docent to give us a first-class tour. It was a kind gesture but, from what I was able to observe, you could look at the station from the left balcony, the right balcony, examine the trucks, and leave by the open bay doors you came in.

First, though, Rocco and I went to lunch nearby at Café Tomás to prepare for such a tour with a first-class meal. Fortified, we took the first-class firehouse tour, snapping pictures of the first-class engines and the unusual Gothic/Moorish building of large red and black horizontal stripes, and reading plaques about major fires. If they served drinks on the first-class tour, the docent overlooked the senator's instructions, or caught the secret wink. The tour was short, like a first-class speech, and pleasantly worth the time.

Next, a self-guided tour of the adjoining Plaza Las Delicias, the Lions Fountain, and the Cathedral of our Lady of Guadalupe, also named Ponce Cathedral. We caught a trolley ride of the town (two-plus hours) visiting the Baldorioty De Castro National Mausoleum, Puerto Rico's first national pantheon (1842), from which we could see the palatial home of Serralles Distillers owners (Don Q rum) named Serralles Castle, with the Cruceta El Vigia, a 100-foot-tall cross, standing in front of it. The cross served as a watchtower back when enemies prowled the coast. Now they had only to beware beach-breaching boaters.

Nightfall and a brief tropical rain shower set up a complicated but first-class photo opportunity in town—the colorfully lit Lions Fountain reflecting off the wet pavement. When culturally sated, I inquired how to get back to the boat, and was directed to a hole in the wall where we could request a cab or bus. In trying to talk to the attending young lady in Spanish, she discouraged me a bit by laughing in my face, saying my Spanish was not intelligible. At least she thought it was Spanish! It helped us get an island tour in Caicos, and after studying diligently in Turks for several hours, how could it not be elegant? Will it get us back to the boat? My ignorance was humbling, and the interaction brought her and me closer, trying to solve a common problem—communication. We were both laughing through it, both getting practice. It was her island, though, and I needed a ride. If I wanted to speak Spanglish, she would likely advise me to go to Mexifornia.

After much pointing and animated sign language, Rocco and I were in a cab headed for our anchorage, directly in front of La Guancha Promenade where they were playing loud music that would last most of the night. It was similar to Baltimore, Maryland's Harborplace in appearance, but smaller in scale and without stores, only refreshment stands selling beer, beer and chicken, beer with beef on a stick, and beer and pizza. Beer was the blue blazer that went with everything. The Promenade was colorful and brightly lit. Lots of people came out later in the evening. They ate and drank as they talked and looked at the boat people, as the boat people looked back at the land people.

This was the first time I had not been one of those land people, and I knew what they were thinking: *bunch of gypsies, have no anchors, can't stay home. Running to (or from) something? Must be nice to be rich, not have to work. Who are they? What do they do for a living? How can I get on that boat, or one like it? Wonder what that's like?*

It had been another great day. Walt's approach to seeing more of the island was to send Rocco and me. Next, a recurrent wishful theme—sleep. On a boat at anchor, you never know what you're gonna get.

We left Ponce at 0925 to sail to Isla de Caja de Muertos. The name translates roughly to the island of the box of the dead, due to its coffin shape. En route, Walt let me practice tacking, an upwind change of course, something I'd not done before. The first two attempts were overdone; I had no experience in how far and how fast to turn. The third was good enough. Class dismissed. Walt took back the helm. While at Coffin Island, we visited the 1887 neo-classic lighthouse, Caja de Muertos Light, unique for its unusual Cross of Lorraine, a double-arm T-type structure, then went snorkeling. Underwater life was sparse, but it was a pretty island, and the local party scene was entertaining.

Around 1500, we sailed to Salinas after retrieving Rocco's hat from the sea. Unusual, as we'd sailed many miles on this trip in strong winds and, using no hurricane straps, his hat had never left his head unintentionally. Having used my hurricane straps several times, I was envious, suspecting he had a magnetic hat band and metal plates in his head. Why didn't I think of that? We arrived at Salinas after dark, which made getting in difficult, with a plan to leave tomorrow, before light, to sail to Palmas Del Mar. So much for Salinas. Our sailing guide suggested you could spend the winter at Salinas. More evidence we were just ship shipping.

The next day was a long one spent daring the sea to keep us from Palmas Del Mar. Street's guidebook warned us if we were to try and reach Palmas Del Mar from Salinas in one sail, it would be miserable, apparently not to be missed. It also advised to leave the night before, be sure to avoid the confused seas offshore, and be a mile off of Point Tuna to avoid more confused seas. We left at dawn, sailed all day, doing everything we were not supposed to do, the confused seas beating us badly and occasionally joining us in the boat. For those thirty-five miles, we were heading directly into the wind almost all the time, as we had been for the whole southern coast, validating the guide's advice.

On probably the toughest daytime sail yet, to keep from getting seasick, I practiced "Peter Piper picked . . ." and other voice and diction exercises, sang every popular song I knew, from "Jesus Loves Me" to "The House of the Rising Sun," then switched to Christmas carols. My, what a lovely voice! Nobody really knew, though, because we motored all the way, and no one could hear a thing over the engine noise. I made up a song to the tune of "I left my Heart in San Francisco" (long version). It was, well, you'll see. Using your best Tony Bennett or Frank Sinatra voice, you can sing it with me:

"I had the urge to roam but now I'm missing home.
The heat of the Bahamas roasted my pajamas.
The tankers o'er the trenches and Boquerón's avid wrenches,

Drove us to Ponce for a day, by the way.

I left my ship in Puerto Rico,
Upon a rock, too hard and high,
The waves came pounding down on we, and washed us out to sea,
And we may ne'er be seen again, I can't swim.

I left my ship in Puerto Rico,
Amidst the wild and stormy sea.
If I come back again to Puerto Rico,
T'will be a plane that carries me."

Great art can come from boredom, just not this time. Nothing else to do when it is impossible to read without throwing up. I took a shot at solving all of life's thorny problems but, due to the complexity of the task, arrived first at Palmas Del Mar around 1600 only half done.

Palmas Del Mar:
Resorting to first class

Palmas was as pretty as when I left it—on a business trip five years ago, adding a weekend to bask in the luxury of the resort. Along the marina's edge were well-maintained two- and three-story homes, several with big boats tied up in front. Guest boats anchored in a lagoon close to the marina entrance.

To avoid the hassles of eating on board, I recommended we have dinner at Chez Daniel's, a familiar restaurant at the marina. The guys balked at such a pricey food palace, so I offered to treat. We had tablecloths, linen napkins, real glassware, wine, delicious food—altogether a splendid evening. I was full, clean, happy, exhausted, ready to sleep, looking forward to a leisurely day at Palmas.

Perhaps inevitably, it turned out to be a rough night. Don't know if it was prompted by the rough seas, the roughage of breakfast and lunch, or the high-fat sauce on orange roughy at Chez Daniel's. The last attack was between Luperon and Samana, in heavy seas after a granola bar and probably too much fresh pineapple. This otherwise little annoyance was more than that when the boat was heaving and I was about to. Granola and the fiber in pineapple, and oranges when I eat the membranes, seem to be in evidence when the attacks occur. All such occurrences seem to be during times of stress or angst. Inadequate hydration may be involved. Diarizing is helpful.

Otherwise, I loved Palmas del Mar—the lavish landscaping of flowering plants and trees, the cool relief in the shade of the palm trees, curving sidewalks leading to "let's-check-it-out" sites, staff members treating you well if you will just dress nicely and, one of my favorites, working telephones. Oh, and flush toilets.

In the first several days of December, I was advised Rocco would be leaving the ship on December 17, and Walt would be going home for Christmas near that time. Walt asked if I, an apparently homeless wastrel having no connection to civilized society or religious holidays, could stay with the boat to keep it afloat until he returned in January.

"Only if I know how, and am allowed, to sail it."

"We can arrange for that," said Walt. "You already know well what is hardest—anchoring to stay put. The rest is not so hard, and you've been learning all along."

While I had access to a phone that would accept my calling card, I considered who I would invite for this special treat in the Caribbean. Now that the hard work was all but complete, the best was yet to come and too special not to share. Topping the list were my two sons. They'd be game, and each could probably get a week off. Nikki dives frequently, is or was engaged, and running a shop that requires her to be there daily, more or less. That's an easy cross-off.

I called Nikki anyway, just to talk. Though I felt the chances were slim to none, I told her the setup of having prime time to share.

"Oh, that would be a dream . . . realistically, there's no way I can get away. Where would I say I was going?"

"I can't answer that but wanted to ask, in case you had the answer. . . . Has your grandmother died yet? I have a difficult tenant whose mother has died three times, and yet still lives and votes in Detroit. Could something like that work?"

"Grandma is still alive and, unfortunately, doesn't live in St. Thomas, so, probably not."

"And 'in failing health' wouldn't work if she lived in Texas, would it?"

"No, she's in good health, thankfully. She does live in Texas. Was that a guess?"

"Does she really? It was, and I'm not surprised you didn't throw in with the unscrupulous. It's nice to hear your voice. Are you doing okay?"

"Guess so. Relationship with Raul is worsening, maybe because I now know what's missing and what I overlooked. Thanks for the advice in our last call. It's quite obvious after taking a few steps back."

"I can relate. Many can. A change in vision can change things, if not immediately."

"It's a start. Look, in the meantime, I have a friend, Julie, that I work with in the evening a couple days a week, helping her set up a business. I could receive calls at her place. Want the number?"

"Absolutely, though I have nothing to write with. Can you call my home phone and leave the number . . . and the dates and times I can call? Is it a fixed schedule?"

"Yes. Great idea. Are you able to pick up messages remotely?"

"Yes. Bahamas was ridiculous, fruitless, but in Puerto Rico it works."

"It shall be done. Now, I'd better get back to work. Sorry, but thanks for thinking of me, dreamboat."

"Oh yeah? That's funny. You should see what I'm wearing."

"Oh no, I'm serious. I've got you in a white T-shirt and jeans."

"Oooh, you little . . . okay, I can do that. If it's working for you, it's working for me."

"Yup! . . . Uh-ooh! Gotta go. Thanks for calling Dixie Dive."

Next, I called my two sons. Neither answered, so I left messages for them to coordinate with each other and that I was paying—their Christmas present, dockside pickup included. That should help make it happen.

Though we hadn't spoken since the night at Walt's, Megan was self-employed and could make it happen if she chose. We'd been to the Caribbean three times, so she was a good prospect. Give the son to the ex-husband, and he'd take her to the airport. We'd been able to get along even when the candle wasn't lit—maybe better. My inability to find my way to the altar was my most glaring incompetency. But we traveled well together, and I held her in high regard, deserving of a special trip if she wanted it. She'd be good company if she was available.

I should have taken more time to plan the call, but the first response usually changes the course anyway. Luckily, she answered.

"Hello, Megan?"

"Well, helloooo! Surprised to hear from you. How are you?"

"If you've ever been where I have, I understand your being surprised. But I'm happy to be anywhere."

"Where is anywhere today? How's it going?"

"Puerto Rico. Today is great. Up to now, not so much. It's a dichotomy. One minute, actually hours, we are at death's door, then we sit in a beautiful bay, dead-still for the next 36 hours, blowing bubbles. Or there's no conversation for days, then I have to talk my way in two languages into someone saving our butts in an emergency. We lost Walt early in the trip, and later got him back. Waves, weather, and life seem to come in bursts. How are you?"

"Getting by, working. Nothing that exciting. Doing a new café and a country club, bidding on a hotel job, so . . . keeping very busy."

"Well, then you may be too busy or not interested, but Walt has asked me if I could sit on the boat for a month while he goes home for Christmas. I'm at Palmas Del Mar, heading to St. Thomas, both places we've been. I hope to get Ken and Chris to join me for a week each, but that leaves two weeks, if you are interested. I think the ass-kicking part of the trip may be behind me."

"When will the boys be there?"

"Don't know. Left a general message at Ken's. First one to choose sets the schedule. I don't know what's in your head right now, but it's a fantastic opportunity, and we get along well, so thought I'd make the offer. And you can come as just a friend."

"Why would I want . . . I was interested until you said that."

"Oooo-kaaay! . . . We'll have time to discuss it. Know anything about sailing? If I take the helm, can you handle the anchor?"

"I think I can raise the anchor just fine."

"That's pun-worthy. Ever done it before?"

"Sure. You just need to know which buttons to push."

"What do I say next to keep the puns coming?"

"I dunno; gimme more material, I'll see what I can do. So far, you've made it easy."

"What if I said the boat doesn't have a power wench?"

"I'd leave that alone, fraught with perils."

"Can you handle the sails?"

"Of course, you know I love a bargain . . . but I need to stay here through Christmas with family and for business, probably New Years, then demand drops off for a while. That'd be a good time to get away for a couple weeks."

"Terrific. Let's book it. Start doing your anchor-raising, button-pushing exercises; pack a bathing suit and your pearls. I'll tell the guys to come before the end of the year, work on their schedule, and I'll call you in a couple days to get your schedule. If there has to be a small overlap, there's room."

"Bryan? . . ."

"Yes?"

"I do . . . Never mind. I'm getting another call. Later. And thanks. I look forward to it."

I found a beautiful palm-lined crescent-shaped beach, where an attendant gave me a chair and set me up to relax and enjoy lunch by the sea. I took every opening offered to talk to someone new. Ultimately bidding my short-term acquaintances and the restful beach adieu, I used the magical indoor facilities of Palmas once more and headed for the dock to yell at Walt for a pickup.

I hate to mention flush toilets so close after lunch, but they're related. If you have ever had to, in a small space, use a manual toilet on a small boat, especially for months, you, too, would love flush toilets. Next time you push down that little handle ONE TIME, or, in something akin to a dream, encounter one of those totally automatic infrared flush-a-matics, take a moment to appreciate it.

In minutes, Walt was at the dock. Once on board, I started reading, appropriately, *A River Runs Through It,* by Norman Maclean. Early in the evening, cleaning up for dinner in resort fashion, more or less (less), I took a bath on deck in a brief rain shower, and collected two buckets of runoff, one of which I used to wash my Tilley hat, best sailing hat in the world, guaranteed forever. The Tilley company tells stories of their hats being so durable as to survive passing through elephants, and the hat being returned to its owner. I guess that book would be *A Hat Runs Through It*, penned by NormaLee Clean? As everyone's friend, Dr. Seuss, might say, "If you find my hat, in elephant scat, please don't bother, I'll buy another." Or send it straight to Tilley, and ask them to return a new one.

We planned to depart at daybreak, so I was off to bed—to dream exotic dreams. The songs were sung, body was relaxed, hat and body were clean. Today was a paradise-nice day, although my leg still hurt from squatting in the dinghy on a ride to shore at Boquerón for bolts. Probably a strained medial meniscus. This approach to paradise isn't for sissies or without risk.

Morning came before I was ready; the boat was dancing badly, even though our "lagoon" was almost entirely enclosed. A strong surge coming through the inlet created irregular subsurface waves from several directions. I didn't thoroughly understand wave theory, but the lagoon was a defined space where wave surges in strong easterlies could deflect off concrete retaining walls, having no place to play out, making an early departure welcome. If you were going to bob, it was better to be at sea where you could anticipate the wave patterns.

As was the custom, I had to weigh the anchor, since it takes two to stare mindlessly at the helm, but the hook was not ready to leave the lagoon, seeming to have put down roots. Coaxing it otherwise provided a much-too-early morning upper body workout. To pull in the anchor rode I pulled the boat to the anchor, as usual, though it was a much tougher process for all the wave action. When the boat was directly over the anchor, determined by the taut, straight-down angle of the anchor rode, the twenty-five-foot length of chain started to appear, but the chain only came up a link or two at a time. I had to wrap the anchor line, then chain, around a cleat, and each time the boat pitched with the waves, I advanced another few links on the dips and re-cleated, akin to using the boat as a 34' crowbar. Stooping down, head almost between my legs, trying not to lose a finger or a hand in the thrashing of the chain against the boat deck, I was becoming exhausted and frustrated.

Up to this point, while I sprouted inguinal hernias left and right, the rest of the crew waited and wondered what the hell was wrong with me that I could not pull in a measly anchor, and why the bow was pointing down into the water with the stern rising in the air, Titanic-like, while my buddies sat, holding on tightly, singing a resonant bass-only rendition of "Stuck in the Muddle with You."

That was not completely true; neither one could sing worth a damn that I know of. With perseverance, and too-late help from Rocco, who came sliding down the deck toward me, the problem was revealed. The anchor had hooked a large section of iron scaffolding, roughly eight feet by six feet, made of interconnected pipe, deeply buried in the muck. Jettisoning the scaffolding for future use by the next mariner for his secure anchoring and aggravated departure, we were belatedly on our way.

After I'd established the undistinguished record for the biggest catch of any day and a personal best, we headed east into another dramatic sunrise of scattered black clouds gradually lightening to gray to pink and robin's egg blue, offering the promise of another pretty day. Once the anchor was up, the sails set, and the boat was making way, any good weather became more delightful. If it was a Caribbean sunrise, it was thrilling. When clear of the rocks offshore, we turned north. Along the way, we were "escorted" by a Navy helicopter carrier, which anchored south of Roosevelt Roads, a U.S. Navy base on Puerto Rico. We watched them do their high-speed business as we seemingly dawdled our way north to the marina at Puerto Del Rey. There was more boat, fighter jet, and airplane traffic today than we had seen thus far. Keeping track of it all kept us busy, not knowing from which side we might be approached, hoping we would not be overrun.

The Puerto Del Rey marina was a top-notch shipyard from what I could tell. I took a picture of a sleek Broward yacht named *Britannia*, out of Norfolk, VA, and was reminded of Balzac's "Behind every great fortune is a great crime." I am now a man in search of a great crime. We were to see this instantly recognizable ship again.

SURVIVING *Paradise*

Isla Palominos:
Heaven's gate

After doing laundry and eating another pizza, we sailed east to anchor and snorkel at Isla Palominos. Then we took *Speedy* south to Isla Palominitos, a small island, gorgeous and inhabited only with sea grape and palm trees clustered in the center of a wide, inviting sandy perimeter of beach, all of it surrounded by light-blue and aquamarine water—the brochure paradise. No pizza though, and no flush toilets, which I'd remember next time I saw this island on TV.

On the larger island of Isla Palominos was a first-class beach club, operated by the La Conquistador Hotel on the mainland of Puerto Rico, near Fajardo, directly to our west. They operated a shuttle to the island for the guests, which appeared to run every hour. A refreshment stand on the beach had a wait staff to serve the loungers and swimmers. Appealed to me! It beat macaroni and cheese, no ice in the drinks, and fix-it-yourself. While I admired their circumstances, they may have been dreaming of being where I was. I had news for them, who may have had news for me. The grass may seem greener elsewhere, but I would stay where I was. Things were looking up.

We picked up a mooring at Palominos, where we would spend the night. The scenery was gorgeous, the sailing easy, and Walt and Rocco finally had the pizza they'd been craving. My spirits were rising each day, as we neared St. Thomas, while my family made their plans to join me here. I was importing Christmas, hoping this was what my sons asked for in their letter to Santa. I could buy everyone duty-free perfume or lace tablecloths in St. Thomas, or give them airfare and a week on the boat in the Virgin Islands. Not a tough choice.

When I wasn't fighting the weather, mechanical problems, terrorist mosquitoes, starvation, groundings, or interpersonal imaginings, I could appreciate that this place was exotic. On deck after sundown, looking at the magical lights that surrounded our anchorage, I could see Fajardo to the west, a marina and a few houses directly to the west-southwest, Roosevelt Roads

Naval Base to the south, Culebra off in the distance to the east, and a few lights southeast at the beach club on Palominos. A lighthouse stood nearby, adding a flashing, seafaring touch of safety to life on the water. The velvet breeze was temperate—absolutely perfect—probably 72 to 75 degrees. There was the smallest sliver of a moon, the land dark and indiscernible, allowing the glistening lights of the islands that surrounded us to converge seamlessly with the vast display of twinkling stars stretching to every horizon. This was Heaven. Who wouldn't love it? Should I linger and let my pulse continue to drop, or go to bed and try to sleep? The view was of a fairyland, too beautiful to look away.

Early the next morning, we left Palominos, planning to sail on to St. Thomas afterward if Culebra could be explored in less than a whole day. At 1110, as we neared the entrance to Ensenada Honda, we had our first sighting of Walt's primary objective—the U.S. Virgin Islands, straightaway to the east, about 22 nautical miles. Walt was curious about Culebra, so we motored through the channel, noting the carcass of a ship that failed to find the channel, and anchored in the bay. We mounted the outboard engine on *Speedy* and headed for shore, giving a disabled speedboat a tow along the way, which must have been a sight to see—a dinghy that does well to carry the three of us, slowly towing a slightly larger boat with seven more people, both boats nearly under water. It resembled the Cuban Mariel Boatlift gone adrift, and may have been a newer version.

We took a short walk through town, observing the housing and islanders, inevitably ending up at a grocery store (our favorite kind of store) at the ferry dock. We shopped grocery stores like others shop jewelry stores and cosmetic counters: "What do we need to keep us viable?" While preparing and enjoying lunch back at the boat, we decided to head for St. Thomas immediately afterward. Boredom sets in easily among adventurers and outdoorsmen. To nauticalize a familiar proverb, our roaming hull gathered no algae.

CHAPTER
Eight

U.S. and British Virgin Islands:
I see virgins everywhere

We had great weather directly overhead all day, though afternoon showers appeared behind us and to both sides, as if escorting us to our destination. A good distance ahead, Sail Rock came into view, a keystone of Walt's dream. He had read that when you see a lone rock mistaken for a boat's sail, you have made it to the USVI. The sun was over our shoulder, making the rock glisten brilliantly like a white gemstone. Walt's excitement was only discernible through his intensity of focus—both hands on the wheel, looking straight ahead, at the pinnacle of his sailing career. A dream was close to fruition after all that he did to prepare the boat, acquire and study the books and charts, install a wind generator, solar panels, autopilot, water maker, and GPS among many other items, then beg and buy sailing assistance, sail part way, leave to take his wife to the hospital for surgery, care for her before flying back to Turks to continue the journey, make repairs and constantly re-provision. Sitting quietly behind him, watching it play out, I admired Walt's tenacity and appreciated what the sight must mean to him, like a victorious commander returning from battle, his perseverance and faith having made it happen.

There are events in life that seem to be of a divine origin. A brilliant, robust rainbow, the marine equivalent of a ticker tape parade, was bestowed on us with perfect timing upon our arrival—an appropriate icon for the treasured destination sought by these sailors. Walt must have felt he had reached his pot of gold. I was not feeling so bad myself, uplifted for having helped make it possible, however unskilled I may have been.

St. Thomas:
To Chase, or pursue?

We set two anchors close to shore in Honeymoon Bay, amusing for an adventure requiring such a major commitment. Why two anchors? To restrict our swinging since the anchorage had many boats in it. When all was set and done, it was 1800 on December 9, the 49th day of our sail from Stuart, Florida, to St. Thomas, USVI. It was too soon to assess the whole adventure; I was obliged for five more weeks, four of them as captain. For now, there was great relief and satisfaction that three guys, still in good health with modest financing, had the ability to spend this amount of time doing what few ever dare experience.

In celebration, we opened a bottle of Sangria and drank a toast to a successful trip. This was worth celebrating, and I wasn't driving.

Walt said, "Well, here's to a great adventure! Thanks, guys."

"Congratulations to you, Walt. Most folks wouldn't have endured what you did to make this happen," I said. "You had several chances to call it off or postpone it."

"Good job, Walt," said Rocco.

"It took a lot of planning, but I've wanted to do this for a long time. The trip wasn't so bad for a little sailboat, not too uncomfortable. Of course, Felicity's health was a major challenge, but here we are, guys."

I waited to see if Rocco would join in on the "not too uncomfortable" statement, tempted to blurt out that Walt couldn't have timed his absence to avoid the life-threatening mayhem any more precisely if he'd had a working crystal ball and an atomic clock. And if he was planning on sailing home someday, not to be lulled into insouciance, just double up on life insurance and don't call me. But Rocco was quietly taking it all in, enjoying the weather and lights of the town. *Was he secretly an ambassador of something, nonplussed, or comatose?*

Unable to resist, I said, "Well, you missed a few things . . . I bet one was your dog."

"I do; I miss Samson. Wish there was room for him, but he's not well enough to make a trip like this."

"There were other things you missed."

"What's that?"

"Some major ass-whippings. I had to tie Rocco to the wheel to keep him in the boat between Rum Cay and Mayaguana, lash down the sails, then go back to the cockpit and tell him Fairy Tales to keep him calmed down after I was almost washed overboard. Isn't that the way you remember it, Rocco?"

"That was some rough goddamn water. Roughest I seen."

"And we took another death-defying whipping from Provo to South Caicos where, thankfully, there were mermaids."

"I'll remember the crossing; there's no damn mermaids anywhere," said Rocco.

"Bryan, we're cutting you off," said Walt. "No wonder you don't drink."

"Heck, if Sangria brings mermaids, I should've started in Stuart. That seascape gets nauseatingly monotonous when there are none. . . . Sangria does double the number of Christmas lights on shore, though, kinda pretty. . . . So this is why folks drink. Walt, you may see what we experienced if you ever take the boat home."

"I expect I will, but don't know when. There's nothing like this at home. We could be here awhile, lots to see . . . might decide to circle the Caribbean. You both are always welcome."

There was no need to remember the mosquitoes, the Bermuda Triangle, the small berths and refrigerator. No one was lost at sea—not quite. We had mechanical challenges, but all were quickly conquered and became highlights of the trip. There was a lot to remember, all of which looked better when viewed under the gracious and forgiving light of retrospection.

We awoke where we anchored, ready for our first official day relaxing in paradise; rest assured, there were mosquitoes. It would have been unbelievably comfortable without them. We went to bed with them, a few stayed over, and they would return.

After breakfast, we took Speedy into town, along the way passing a bazillion boats of all sizes, shapes, and conditions—from "cost more than the Louisiana Purchase" immaculate to "how does it stay afloat? Must be sitting on the bottom" hulks. I kept the watch of *Speedy* at the seawall, fighting off the "you can't park here" admonishers, while Rocco and Walt bought their airplane tickets home. When they returned, Rocco and I stayed ashore to shop for groceries and get a yogurt cone for me and a haircut for him. I'd decided to hang on to my seven weeks of curls and look the part of a vagabond a while longer.

Rocco wanted to stop and see Kirsten, a family-connected friend working at Bluebeard's Castle, an in-town hotel. While we waited in the bar for her to appear, Rocco bought a gin and tonic; I had a Coke for five times the cost of the same in a vending machine outside that would have come without the barkeep's generous air of arrogance. He must have mistaken us for having just washed ashore and, wanting me to feel comfortable with being classless, didn't fuss with a glass and ice. When Kirsten arrived, she and Rocco exchanged hellos and a handshake. It didn't surprise me that I had to introduce myself.

"Are you gentlemen hungry? Can I treat you to lunch?"

"Oh no, no, we're gonna get something to eat a little later," said Rocco.

Damn, Rocco, you ARE crazy. "Actually, that'd be terrific, very kind," I said. "We weren't sure where to eat. Do you recommend the food here?" Of course she would. Or get fired. "That will give you time to get reacquainted."

"Well, I, I . . ." stuttered Rocco.

Good God, man, get hold of yourself. "Would it be better to eat here in the bar, or you probably have a restaurant in the hotel, don't you?"

"Oh sure, let's eat there. It will be quieter and service is better," she said. "Follow me . . . do you have enough time?"

"Yes, ma'am. Rocco would love a good, solid meal that I didn't cook." I hoped service would be better, and that they'd have glasses. Habitually, I was ready to rip my can in half and throw it overboard. Rocco and I had previously discussed eating lunch next, and the best way to improve on that was to share it with her, when I could practice the suspended, if not lost, art of conversation and witness Rocco talking with someone other than Walt. She may later have to call security for help in having us removed. I'm ready to sleep in the damn lobby if they don't have an empty room, though I'd like it better if the hotel would stop rolling.

We settled around a table where there were better chairs, higher ceilings, far more attendants than we had on the boat, and linen napkins. *Good move, last-mate-almost-Captain Byrd.*

"How's your mom, Kirsten?" Rocco asked.

"She's just fine. She complains about her knees. How's your wife doing?"

"She's okay, having trouble with her back, but she has good days," said Rocco.

I let them converse without butting in, happy to learn something more about Rocco if only his relations, though I did add detail to his sailing stories. Rocco had a word vault where he was saving his adverbs and adjectives; probably nouns and verbs, too. Kirsten was doing most of the talking. Who could see that coming?

A lunch of broiled fish, steamed fresh vegetables, and water with ice in a glass was served on a table that wasn't moving, and we didn't have to do the dishes—so far, so good.

Observing the conversational exchange reminded me of how, when we stepped ashore on a foreign land, there was important information to gather quickly about the nation, its people, and availability of goods and services (pizza and waitresses). Against the pressures and backdrop of World War I, the U.S. acquired the Virgin Islands from Denmark for $25 million to keep them from falling into enemy hands. The islands were renamed and officially became a U.S. possession on March 31, 1917. Inhabitants became U.S. citizens ten years later and, unlike islands like Allan's Cay, the occupants on this island were friendly. We just needed to know where they shopped, and how to get there.

After lunch, Rocco and I sought out a Pueblo food store that Walt had inquired about earlier, then told Rocco it was up the main street "a little ways." The two of us walked up the street a long ways, then asked for directions and were advised to take a bus for an even longer ways. At the bus stop, I asked waiting riders how to use the system. Eventually, our bus came, we took it, got off when the driver said to, and found the store. If we had tried to walk, we'd have thought Puerto Rico was nearby. Rocco started shopping with me, then wondered if there was a dock closer than the one back in Charlotte Amalie, opposite the Chase Bank, where we were to meet Walt (albeit late, at this point). Rocco headed to the restroom while I proceeded with the shopping.

I checked out, looking around the store for Rocco, then stepped outside with the groceries; no Rocco. Surely, he had a plan, but what? I waited. . . . Still no Rocco. He didn't have to go to this length to keep from picking up the check. Was he powdering his nose in the restroom? The temperatures inside and outside my head were rising, unspoken words were turning foul. My mind was in a cul-de-sac, going in circles wondering how to find Rocco. Was he somewhere waiting for me, or was he coming back?

After waiting and pacing far too long, a local man standing outside asked if I was looking for someone. Assuring him I was, he described Rocco in detail—"is he white?"—and said someone of Rocco's description (there can only be one white Rocco in a Caribbean world) had jumped in a cab and headed downtown. If that was true, what should I do? Holding eight bags of groceries, including milk and other perishables already getting warm, I shouldn't spend the night. But should I leave, or stay? I didn't think I was near the water, and it didn't appear I was near Rocco. Oh hell, let's play chase; Rocco was in a cab, I was on foot with the groceries.

I hailed a cab, in effect saying, "follow that cab," albeit one long gone—a retiree's relaxed form of hot pursuit. When I finally arrived at Chase Bank (it was Friday rush hour on THE main street) I found no Rocco and no boat. Had he and Walt taken the boat in pursuit of me at the store? Knowing, in such confusing times, someone had to stand still so they could be "caught," I decided against rushing back to the store with the load of groceries, only to miss them coming back here after not finding me. I was where I was supposed to be, if not when. I wanted to be licking a soothing ice cream cone, since Baskin-Robbins was nearby. Give me enough pralines and cream in a waffle cone and they can do whatever the hell they want for as long as they want. After a long and principled wait, I was discovered, like Columbus discovered the natives, here all along, waiting. The roundup at Chase seemed poetically apt.

As Walt approached, slowly lining the boat up with the seawall, Rocco on board wearing a sheepish grin, Walt said he couldn't wait to hear the other side of the story. I couldn't either, but would I? It was tempting to be aggravated, but I assumed Rocco had done his best to get the boat closer to the store. The fly in the ointment was the elephant in the room—Rocco's poor communication style—so I didn't challenge him for an explanation I might not get. (Sorry about the double cliché; the 800-pound gorilla made me do it.)

After jumping on the moving boat with both hands full of groceries, stowing the perishables, and marveling at, while passing, a cruise liner more than eight stories tall that made us feel like a guppy in the ocean, we continued out of the harbor of Charlotte Amalie, put up the sails, and turned east toward St. John, ten miles and two hours away. The sun, wind, and views were delightful, leaving the confusion behind, which, on the scale of Big Deals, soon failed to register. Being a captive is a relaxed state of mind.

St. John:
If I had to choose just one

We pulled into Hawksnest Bay close to dark, and anchored. Sent out by the local blood bank like a bevy of Red Cross nurses on wings, the mosquitoes were there to welcome us. I had to finish my anchoring task and make the deck clear of ropes, including installing the chafing guard on the anchor rode. Having done most of the shopping alone, I was able to acquire fresh fruit plus a few extras, thinking I might yet keep these guys healthy, against their will. Is that considered torture? Based on questions of astonishment coming from the cabin below—"What the hell? Yogurt? Who eats this? Why so many bananas?"—I would guess the fruit was now being discovered! Ha ha! That will teach 'em to abandon me in a supermarket.

The anchorage would make an exquisite place to live for a couple days. No rolling of the boat to speak of, and the temperatures were moderate, the usual 70-75 degrees at night. We would sleep well. No alarm tomorrow, but Rocco would still awaken at 0630, the rest of the crew at 0730.

The next bay over was Trunk Bay, where we snorkeled in the morning over an underwater interpretive trail of pictures and descriptions of the native fish swimming among us, mounted on the sea floor possibly three to ten feet deep. I'd done this 20 years earlier; this time I had a prescription lens in my mask, which made a big difference. We went back to the boat before lunch, and on the 51st day, Saturday, December 11, 1993, God created . . . wait for it, I sure did . . . manners! It took only seven days to create the whole universe, but the really tough jobs take 51. Rocco said, "excuse me" three times before 1130, only the first, second, and third time for the whole trip, as we bumped passing in the narrow aisle below, done many times over 50 days without comment. If that wasn't stupefying enough, while I was hoisting and lowering the jib on the foredeck for maintenance as midday drew nigh, he brought me two Ritz crackers with peanut butter on them. It was scary and totally unfitting. Penance? An apology? I had no clue! Many unnatural, otherworldly phenomena remain unexplained, but this and seeing those February whales in November put the Loch Ness Monster and Puff the Magic Dragon in play as possible dinner dates. Maybe one would even take us for a ride. Just put the anchor line between his teeth, and . . . poof, magic draggin'. Paradise and Rocco's conversion will make you think all things are possible!

At first feeling faint, then afraid to eat the crackers, I thought Rocco had read my diary and was sharing his emergency hemlock. It smelled and looked like peanut butter, maybe I would try it. A sudden wave would have put me into the water, I was so caught off guard. I considered jumping in, believing the cool water would be an antidote to my shock. It was complicated. What to do? It had to be a trick to get me out of my protective shell so he could towel-snap me before we stopped showering together. Did Walt, an infrequent practical joker, pay him to do that? "Here's cab fare to the airport, Rocco, if you'll take these to Bryan, rattle his cage for buying all that fresh fruit." Being a sucker for peanut butter and Ritz crackers, and always hungry on this trip, I was an easy target. Undisciplined at times, I couldn't help myself. Puzzling, but delicious!

Afterward, we snorkeled Hawksnest Bay, finding most of the interesting animal life among the coral reefs along the sides of the bay. At the posh Caneel Bay resort, which shared a beach on the bay, life looked interesting as well, though it was doubtful any single women on the beach were interested in a swimmer with size 36 blue webbed feet, a curved orange pipe emerging from the side of his head, a face-distorting oversize dive mask, and a penchant for peanut butter and Ritz crackers. Oh, what they were missing—a kinky, easily-resistible package.

Back on the boat, the weather was perfect and dinner was pretty good. I took a shower with few observers. Without my glasses, I couldn't see them, so I assumed they couldn't see me either. It's a child's technique. Being a private person, bathing in "public" requires adaptation since it's not frequently done in the U.S. without conviction. I hoped I didn't appear in the background of a couple's honeymoon pictures taken from the balcony of the house on the hill, though the guests' "Wow!" over the scenery could be heard.

In our after-dinner discussion of life among the Virgins, Rocco's opinion was surprising: "When we got to Puerto Rico, I was glad, for the first time, that I came; now I'm really glad I came!" While he contended the snorkeling was not as good here as in the Bahamas (e.g., we had yet to see any sharks), he did admire the topography, the climate, and the quality of life in this paradigm of paradise. His unusual demeanor today paralleled his expression of gladness, though I wondered how long his exuberance would last.

The next morning, December 12th, Rocco was back to silence, his metamorphosis short-lived. I read last night, "Silence is the enemy of friendship." It is hard to decipher, hence warm up to, silence. There is no ability to bond on common ground. I heartily agree, after spending 52 days with this sphinx. Nothing has happened, no calls from home, no news reports. Was it all in the mind—his or my own? It has been a long-lasting conundrum.

Today would be my first official lesson in sailing, *and* the final exam. Not an accredited course, this sailing trip had certainly been a valuable learning opportunity, and my charge was to "captain" us from Hawksnest Bay to Cruz Bay, my first solo challenge. Asking a few questions, I was told to also provide the answer. I verbally laid out everything I planned to do, in case I was devising a disaster. Given a quiet nod, I gave the commands:

"First mate Rocco, go forward, weigh and secure the anchor. Captain Walt, when he's done, hoist the jib."

Captain Walt asked, "Aren't you going to start the engine?"

"I don't think there's a need. We'll have the wind push on the jib 'til the wind is on the port side, then we'll flip the sail to starboard and go out of here on a beam reach. We may get blown back a little, but I think we have room. Go ahead and hoist the jib."

When Rocco returned from the bow and Walt had the foresail aloft, I commanded, "Rocco, pull in the sheet on the port side and let's get out of here. When it turns enough, I'll give the command to come about."

Rocco looked at Walt as though he was unsure if he should follow my orders, but pulled in on the sheet as the sail continued to whip loudly. This was their game, and I'm playing it.

"Tighten it up and hold it, don't need to cleat it," I ordered. "Walt, man the starboard sheet and, Rocco, prepare to come about . . . okay, guys, that's abooout right, COME ABOUT!"

Rocco let out his sheet at the pace Walt was pulling his in. The sail swung across the bow, putting us on a port reach. I didn't have to tell Walt when and how to set the sail. We left the anchorage under sail, which we had not done on this trip, free to roam, feeling the snap of the sail, the roll of the boat, the splash of the waves, just us and nature, pure and free.

When my crew had secured the lines, stowed the winch handle, and returned to a relaxed state, Walt looked at Rocco and said with a grin, "Well, Rocco, doesn't that beat all; looks like we'll be crew and passengers for the rest of our time."

Rocco replied, "That's alright by me; I could use a vacation."

Their wide-eyed look throughout was either astonishment or fear of what could happen. It may be safer to have the engine running; in case of an unexpected wind squall, you won't be smashed on the rocks. I got away with it. Actually, without the engine running, Rocco had to pull the boat to the anchor—not intentional on my part but, well, it's good for him.

This was the best way to learn—to have full responsibility and feel I was on my own. Soon I would be, preferably safely, and wanted Walt to relax while at home. I'd done the piece parts over the last 51 days—most of the sail handling and all of the anchoring—but was always told what and when. We reached Cruz Bay without incident. Finding room to anchor, I did an upwind turn, gave orders to drop and set the anchor, then furl the sail. After closing up the boat, the three of us squeezed into our two-man dinghy and went to the dock.

Standing on the pier, Captain Walt brought his right hand to his right brow and said, "Congratulations, Captain Byrd."

I returned a snappy salute: "Thank you, sir!" . . . Well, yippee, skippy, I'm a skipper. A license to drive, free to roam, alone, on Earth's wet 70%.

The National Park Service exhibit center in Cruz Bay acquainted us with the island culture and history, reef fishes, and coral before we had lunch at the Texas Coast Grill, a place that felt like home. Better still, there were working telephones nearby! With plans being finalized for my guests, coordination was crucial.

Returning to the boat, Walt said. "Okay B-Byrd, science must be replicable to be valid. Can you get us to Trunk Bay?"

I looked around to observe the location of other boats, then told my crew, "We'll do what we did coming over, but there's more swinging room on the port side, so we'll first sheet the jib to the starboard side. Alright, let's be about it." In no time, we were sailing again. No engine! No noise. Magical.

Anchoring outside of Trunk Bay's protected underwater park preserve, we took the dinghy to Johnson's Reef, a half mile out in Pillsbury Sound, anchored, and slid eagerly over the side. In places, the reef was a foot or less below the water's surface and too shallow to boat or even snorkel over. I kept looking up, though, lacking confidence other boaters of my skill level were not heading our way. From above water, it looked like an inviting, wide-open boating playground, and in this exotic, movie-like setting, I could imagine James Bond attempting a getaway in a fast boat with gorgeous women in black bikinis, chased by gunmen in black wetsuits on jet-skis. I could not imagine Bond worrying about staying in the channel or running over snorkelers. Still new at this, I kept looking up.

The reef had stunning underwater scenery and a wide variety of fish— angelfish, blue tang, butterfly, porgy, snapper, parrotfish, the strangely shaped drum, and many more. A three-foot-long barracuda looked ferocious but was just hanging out, like a thug on a street corner.

After such fantastic snorkeling, would Rocco be inclined to change his opinion? If this wasn't the best site, it's a top contender.

Our becalmed evening anchorage in Trunk Bay—blue sky, blue/green water, the verdant hillsides, and golden sand beaches—had to be one of the most gorgeous and peaceful places on earth. But we would keep looking, just to be sure. Tomorrow, we'd visit the Baths at Virgin Gorda, reputedly spectacular. Being the designated helmsman pro tem, I needed sleep. As long as I was alert and did not wreck the boat, I would gain experience, and the others had someone to sail them around the islands.

It was fun being captain, to connect with the soul of the boat, enjoy the serenity, and be able to say: *Alright, Rocco, weigh the anchor! And Walt, hoist the main; we'll go where'er she blows.* I suspected Rocco was not enjoying the game as much as I (never knew anything for sure about him), and I had other commands to use tomorrow he would recognize but may not like any more than I did: *Don't drop it until I say so, you blankety-blank,* and *Not here, you expletive!* Being a rapt student, I remembered all his lines, and would clean them up a bit, if I needed them at all. Yeah, I could do this, and enjoy it.

Virgin Gorda:
The Bitter End

Someone remembered it was Monday, so we were up at dawn getting an early start. I took my camp shorts out of the corner where they stood last night—salt spray was as stiffening as starch, but clammy—to dress for a quick breakfast, and another sailing lesson as we headed toward Virgin Gorda. We were going to the Baths. It took only three hours to go 18 miles, because we didn't go aground. Saves time when you travel non-stop.

The world-famous Baths were formed by volcanic activity, and feature grottoes and crevices carved into boulders. Many boats were there when we arrived at 1020. Mooring away from the island, we snorkeled to the beach, a considerable distance. The snorkeling was dramatic; you could navigate through channels between the massive boulders if you dared. There were also sheer drop-offs covered with coral and abundant fish. With heavy waves bouncing us up and down, snorkeling over those submerged boulders was an exhilarating experience, as was the trip back to the boat due to an unexpected storm whipping up the water.

After lunch on the boat, we sailed northward to Gorda Sound, and therein to the Bitter End Yacht Club, metaphorically named using a sailing term. The bitter end is the loose, dangling end of a line, as we mistakenly had on an anchor at Mayaguana, and the club/resort is the last location in the Virgin Islands chain, heading east, before you get to St. Martin, a hundred-plus miles. This seemed to be a popular area for people to go ashore and eat, though we would not. So I hoped to come back with one of my cruising guests and enjoy the area more leisurely.

The day's sailing lesson was using the jib, reefing (reducing the size of) the mainsail, sailing close to the wind, and tacking. I was gaining confidence! Keep your eye on the telltales, I'm told. Telltales are pieces of yarn attached to the sail surface to indicate how effectively the sail is trimmed. If the air currents are passing over and between the sails efficiently, the telltales will be flying horizontally; swirling yarn is evidence of disturbed, less effective air currents.

That evening a giant display of shooting stars lasted all night and into the morning and stimulated much discussion on the vastness of the universe and the possibilities of others, the speed of light at 186,000 miles per second, and stars that still shine but are not there anymore. All of it was overwhelming when we tried to imagine the magnitude; speeds, light years of distance, number of planetary bodies, all in motion or long since evaporated, even though still "visible." If we can still see them, how can they be gone? All contemplated from the deck of a 34' boat with an insignificant top speed of six knots. Quite the juxtaposition.

We woke in a leisurely fashion the next morning, sailed to Peter Island, and anchored in Deadman's Bay. On shore, there appeared to be a true tropical island resort (Peter Island Hotel and Yacht Harbour) with palm trees on the beach. Their water sports included windsurfing and ocean kayaks. I snorkeled ashore, walked the picturesque beach, and was tempted to chill out in one of the enticing hammocks suspended between palm trees, which looked peaceful, relaxing, and romantic. Not sure how that would be received nor having anyone to ask, I sat on the sand and watched a few windsurfers falling off their boards and wondered, if I offered to give a few lessons, could I use a board for a while. Again, no one to ask; they were in the water up to their chins, and pretty far out, so I enjoyed the ambience and the view until I swam back to the boat.

After lunch, we sailed to the Bight (a curve or recess in a coastline; a cove) at Norman's Island, and snorkeled at Treasure Point. The fish were all around us, the largest fish we've seen in one place. Awesome! You can also snorkel the caves. Having already been slammed into a coral island riding on a surge of water, I passed up going into the caves, but spent delightful time observing the underwater life along the coast, including many yellow jacks. There was plenty to see. I was mobbed by fish when a tour guide close to me fed bread to the fish for the amusement of her followers. I later dropped bread from the boat and watched the fish swarm and hit the bread, roiling the water.

Too soon the time came to weigh anchor and sail west for an evening in Salt Pond Bay, on the southeast corner of St. John. Not a long sail, not much traffic on this side of the island, nor was there much wind in the bay. When we picked up a mooring, we were eagerly greeted by mosquitoes. It took a while to exterminate the critters in the cabin. Installing the screens would have to become an important step in the "sail down, anchor down, screens up" sequence. I also got a sense dinner would include more onions with fried potatoes. If onions had a citronella/repellent effect with the mosquitoes as it does with me, I would have been more accepting of their predominance in our diet.

Salt Pond Bay is a well-protected, picture-perfect anchorage tucked deeply behind Ram's Head with sandy beaches bordered by shade-producing sea grape trees, a few picnic tables, and scattered homes on a distant, gradually sloping hillside; a settled place to spend a comfortable night after watching the sunset through the southwest-facing entrance to the bay. In the morning, Walt and I went ashore and hiked, first to Drunk Bay, where there was enough beer can detritus washed ashore to justify its name. It was on the other side of a peninsula toward Coral Bay. Climbing the peninsula southeast took us to Ram's Head Point, a mile-long steep hike and 200' of elevation change. The views were outstanding. On that cloudless day, no vegetation blocking the view, you could see St. Croix, 35 miles away. At that height, the sea looked smooth; the boats in the coves below were miniatures, the sailors hardly discernible.

After lunch, Rocco and Walt went snorkeling around Booby Rock in the bay's mouth, while I dove from the boat and contemplated what I might need to know when I had the boat alone. We were in awe of the beauty surrounding us, and spent a lot of time bathing in it, soaking it up. Rocco was a short-timer, so he was trying to pack in as much as possible. Walt, leaving as soon as tomorrow, was no less appreciative of the natural beauty.

When we completed our various adventures, we sailed around the southwest corner of St. John and anchored in Christmas Cove, off Great St. James Island between St. John and St. Thomas. We were instantly rolling; we'd likely not get much sleep. So far, though, it had been another outstanding day in paradise. I finished my greeting cards, such as they were. Greetings from Paradise postcards, found in a magazine store in St. Thomas, became a Christmas greeting by adding a few words.

We left Christmas Cove early the next morning for Charlotte Amalie with the engine running to charge the batteries. We topped off the fuel tanks, left Walt ashore to reserve an earlier flight, then anchored. I went to pick up my son Chris in the dinghy. How great it was to see him, and to hug someone, especially Chris, a rock-solid armful. We did our errands in town, went back to the boat, then I left to pick up Walt. Rocco could have left today, but he did not want the hassle of changing his existing arrangements. Customs officers had depleted his hassle tolerance, had he any. Secretly, he may have wanted another day with me—a very well-kept secret.

St. Chris:
Is it the head, or is it stinking thinking?

In a few hours, I took Walt ashore in the dinghy and helped unload his luggage. He gave me a gripping handshake, saying, "Thanks, B-Byrd, you did great!" picked up his luggage and went to the street where a cab was waiting. Then I returned and worked on mending the seams in the dodger (a vinyl and canvas "windshield-equivalent" to protect the companionway and front end of the cockpit from sea spray and other elements) and tried to replicate a meal Walt did well—ham steak, sweet potato and (gratuitous) green beans. The corn starch balled up, the ham sauce was not as sweet as I preferred (the pineapple was in its own juice) and the sweet potatoes needed more butter and brown sugar. Canned beans are canned beans. I missed Walt's cooking already and he was probably still in the air. Thankful that I'd practiced sailing, I should have practiced cooking his specialties. True to form, Rocco didn't comment on the food. Not knowing what he was *really* missing, Walt was eating airline food and probably missing the boat food—unlikely he was having fried onions with a garnish of potatoes.

After dinner, we retired to the cockpit to drink in the lights of the town, harbor, and heavens. For sleeping arrangements, I moved up to the V-berth and let Chris have the salon sofa, my perch for the past two months. I admit to having a little nervousness, being responsible for this floating environment. Chris had no sailing experience; he was a motorboat lover, liked the power, and had no time for the details of sailing, so I was now on my own. His biggest task would be accepting the pace of sailing, which he must unless he was one hell of a swimmer.

In a few days I'd feel much more comfortable. I could cook and sew, after a fashion, and probably sail. Chris would help. A strong guy, he should have no trouble raising the anchor, haha! Even motorboats use anchors.

Around 0200, Chris and I went up on the foredeck to be quiet and away from Rocco, and talked about Chris and investments until we'd cured our insomnia. When we retired, the lights of St. Thomas were still beautifully ablaze.

I wasn't eager to get up with the sun, though I wanted to finish sewing the dodger and re-secure it before Rocco, a man who makes his own sails, left the boat, should I have questions. His estimated time of departure was 1000. I was curious how that would go down.

When Rocco was ready, I learned he didn't want to take a cab from the marina, he planned to put his bags in an airport locker and tour the town until boarding his 1645 plane. With his direction, we took him close to the airport in the dinghy and beached it on the sandy shore of Emerald Beach resort. Chris and I took his bags ashore, taking pains to keep them dry. Rocco was in bare feet, long pants rolled up, making his way through the water too shallow for the dinghy. Once ashore, he sat on the slope and put on his socks and shoes. We stood by in case he had forgotten something or we could be of any more service. *This was the moment; would he let bygones be bygones, let whatever's be whatever's, would we hug, just shake hands, or would he remain unto himself?* His unique personality had been the cause of my constant unrest and ongoing introspection. Perhaps he would reveal a clue to his inscrutable behavior.

He unrolled his pant legs, stood up, brushed off, and straightened his trousers, picked up his bags, turned around and, with the affinity felt when stepping off an escalator, started up toward the resort. Unfazed nor surprised, I eventually blew kisses to his back.

Chris and I—Rocco's butler, chef, and coachmen—watched him climb the slight hill, then simultaneously turned to each other. Chris, looking more quizzical than I could have and thinking I had the answer, was driven to speak first: "What's wrong with him?"

"I don't know . . . but I'm not really surprised. What's in the well comes up in the bucket. His well is in deep disrepair, for unknown reasons. Let's get back in the boat. You, or anyone else, will never believe how strange it's been, like an arranged marriage only held together for the sake of the kids. In a one-room hut." Had I been retained to render a professional opinion, I'd likely opine he was nutzo, uncivilized, and wonder if he might be sociopathic.

"Did you guys have a fight?"

"Not that I know of; he may have had one in his head, but he's been the same since day one."

"That must have made for a long trip. Did he ever tell you anything?"

"Only that I wasn't his problem. I forced that out of him. Walt knows him better; they had conversations before Walt left mid-trip. Rocco's dad was a stern man, pretty rough on the wife, and when the kids tried to intervene, they got their dissuasive comeuppance. I got the impression alcohol was involved. A pretty common story."

"So far, it sounds like my life," deadpanned Chris.

"Oh sure! You had it good. If alcohol was involved, it was yours. I may have been a bit stern; I cared how you turned out. Nothing else was similar. Although . . . I was only there for your first five years, then missed the next eight. There's a lot I don't know about the years you lived with your mom.

Still, your interpersonal skills are excellent, and you have a great sense of humor."

"Well, it was all your joke-telling at the dinner table that gave me a sense of humor. I still remember most of them."

"That's surprising. Single parenting was so challenging, I was afraid you thought it was all bondage and discipline with the occasional plate of bread and water slipped under your bedroom door. I'd have shared my gruel, but the door was too low for a bowl."

"What's this about Walt leaving mid-trip? Didn't he just leave yesterday?"

"He missed a part of the trip, the worst part. There're a lot of stories I could tell."

"I can't believe Rocco, what I just saw happen. You two spent two months on top of each other—you know what I mean; it's a small boat—you two should be hugging, teary-eyed that he is leaving. You probably went through hell together. I sailed in this water when I was in the Corps; it's not always kind, especially the Bermuda Triangle, even on a massive ship—our anchor gear was bigger than this boat—many of us puked our guts out. Many people have disappeared. Damn! Don't you get over your childhood, whatever it is?"

"That would be a 'no;' a 'maybe, if that was all that went wrong. Childhood is crucial, and life is long, during which stuff accumulates—who knows what else was going on. It's a long time to explain in a few words without many clues. Anyway . . . he's drastically different. Maybe he can't help it."

"Can't he be whatever he chooses?" Chris suggested.

"Well, he is, we all are, but are they good choices? It's a complex question. Life comes at you a decision at a time. Without encouragement, someone who cares, or a vision, something else happens. Good discussion topic for an insomniac: 'Why are you you?'"

"I am, because of you."

"Wow! I'd bet most parents never get any credit. It's a nice, short answer. Hope you're okay with it. Consider a person being like a car; it starts out shiny and new, and over time its care and environment determine whether it becomes a short-lived rust bucket or a timeless, valuable classic. That's a rough analogy—whoa! Before we become two sunken rust buckets, spin around and push us away from those sharp rocks will ya? Spare the inflated rubber bolsters."

"Good idea. Do you think he might have an illness; depression or bipolar?"

"I guess he could, but his solemn nature was pervasive, unipolar, never saw him smile. For a long time, I took it personally, as if something about me may have tripped a switch in him. He may not always be that way."

"I think he may be depressed."

"Could be, he depressed me, but his appetite and sleep patterns seemed normal. Regular as a dog at his dinner bowl. He'd look at his plate, and I had to fill it. . . . Wait. That's not true. I didn't have to fill it, I just did. Nobody ever said, 'Bryan, you're the cook.' Wonder what would have happened if I'd cooked for myself and said, 'Rocco, the galley is yours! Have at it.' But he never missed a meal, and I could count on him to be asleep by seven every day . . . saved my social life one day."

"Social life? At sea? What kinda—"

"Bleak. One date every two months isn't too often, is it?"

"Well, yeah, no, but how was Rocco involved?"

"That's just it. He wasn't. Another story. We supported each other probably more than once, even without knowing it. Had to. It was a kickass trip. It's pleasant sitting here, just drifting, no supervision for a change—damn, just realized I'm back in charge of my own life—let's start the engine and take a celebratory tour around the area, enjoy this freedom, blue water and sky, and nice temps. We'll put a breeze through your hair and a cool spray on your face . . . might get a little wet."

"It's possible he's depressed. I've treated a lot of people for depression."

"Really? In your role as doctor, boyfriend, or bartender?"

"Bartender."

"So, that's how you netted more money than a doctor; large volume, no overhead, and patients are drunk when they leave your tip—can't do math. I'll give you the last word, but I'm twice your age, met a lot of people, read every good psych book, textbook, and magazine, never seen anything like it."

"You didn't specialize in depression like bartenders do."

"True, and had no actual patients, but to a hammer, doesn't everything look like a nail?"

"You said I'd get the last word." He smiled.

"Eventually. Didn't say when. . . . Alright, what is it?"

"He's depressed."

"Hmmphh. That's certainly the last word. For now. But with your curiosity, I bet you want more than that. Wouldn't you like to know why? I would."

Rocco left as ungraciously, and almost as unknown, as he'd arrived. I couldn't speak for Rocco, nor did he, but it would have been impossible to not wave or say something were the situation reversed. Throughout the trip, he'd offered no "thank you's," essentially no "excuse me's," no response when a meal was placed in front of him. I'd been feeding a machine. He could have at least turned and said, "Screw you! You son of a bitch, you took my bunk!" if that were his issue, or flip me the bird, or give any indication of what I meant to him and how much he enjoyed the magical mystery tour we'd shared. Over two months, we'd spent twenty-four hours and three meals a day together. We'd almost died together. Should I have expected him to treat me any differently than he would a guy lying face down on the beach? Maybe we didn't have time to bond, or we should have planned more team-building activities; a survival course across an ocean. A guy who could have become a friend for life after what we'd endured was nothing but a bad memory. If I could have spent more time with him, I might have become . . . more nutzo. Small strides may already have been made.

Some cause happiness wherever they go; others, whenever they go. I wondered if he was as happy about his leaving paradise for the ice-encrusted northeast U.S. as I was, or dreading it. He gave no clue.

How different could the journey have been with a "team player" personality, one curious and excited about life, a "Let's try this!" type of person who might consistently share observations like, "Did you see that bird? What kind of plant is this? Did you notice the boat is sinking?" (He did point out a shark and lobster.) It was too late now, and you only get to choose partners, whether for sailing, marriage, or otherwise, from among those with whom you cross paths. My three guests would be of my own choosing, two of my own making who, I was happy to say, would be quite cheerful to hilarious; the third, a wild card.

As a sailor and captain, I was on my own. What I didn't learn but needed to know would be learned the hard way—hopefully not as hard as coral, a dock, or another boat. Chris and I went to Crown Bay Marina. While I was gassing up *Speedy*, Chris went shopping, and returned with new music for my ears and soul, sliced turkey, and ice. *Ice? What in hell is ice?* It was his idea; hit me like a ten-pound block of frozen water. It hadn't occurred to me ice might be allowed on the boat. But then, all of the "proper authorities" had left, so why not? Chris was a breath of fresh air and should not, would not be denied. We put the ice in a small cooler found in the bottom of a locker and there were iced drinks on the boat for the first time in two months! The bartender was paying off, as liberating as adding ten feet to the length of the boat, or cleaning out the garage, finally parting with the 8-track tape player. A lunch of yogurt and fruit as well as a sandwich with lettuce, tomato, and chips was outstanding. Who knew about this stuff?

Chris did. He knew how to enjoy life. I'd accepted the mentality of the crew and adjusted to the confinement and limitations of the voyage; now Chris was stimulating me to snap out of it. Having been parked in survival mode for so long, I needed help shifting into Thrive.

We pulled up the anchors and sailed to St. John, arriving in Trunk Bay in time for a snorkel along the underwater nature trail I'd visited with Walt and Rocco a few days before. After snorkeling, we took a shower, then a dinghy cruise-by of Hawksnest Bay at sundown, the secluded cove with high verdant hills sloping down to white sandy beaches, or all the way to the water, scalloping the shoreline, sporadic palm trees shading the beaches, and just a house or two in view. Absolutely beautiful. Chris heartily endorsed the environment and the day. Once back at the boat, we were in for the night.

Uh-oh! We weren't in for the night, only in for a night of it. The weather had picked up, and we swung around, maybe dragging anchor, and started bump, bump, bumping into the marker buoys for the swimming area that say, "No anchoring." We were being washed ashore. That's how sailboats get converted back to their individual parts. There was "I screwed up" money in my locker, but it was too early to lose it, and it may not have been enough.

In the black of night, I put another anchor and line in the dinghy, took it well away from the reserved area, being extremely careful not to puncture the inflated bolsters, dropped the anchor, then returned and drew the boat toward it, spreading the pull of the boat over both anchors. If we were dragging the first anchor, it may have been due to not using enough scope. Being exposed to Pillsbury Sound was okay for a few hours, but not a good plan overnight. Maho Bay would have been a more protective anchorage, but we couldn't reposition after dark for fear of making things worse, just add anchors as necessary.

Tortola:
If you had only one life

We rocked and rolled all night as I worried about going aground. It was a relief to pull up the anchors early the next morning, vaulting the void between feeling helpless versus being in control, and headed for Virgin Gorda and the Baths. The seas were high at the Baths, the waves crashing thunderously on the shore. Studying the situation for a while, Chris and I decided to anchor, dinghy in as far as permissible, tie up on the mooring line and swim to shore. As it turned out, the closer-in moorings were reserved for charter boats. I felt qualified, having already been here and probably destined to return twice again, but it was a foreign country. I stayed with the boat; Chris swam ashore. Considering the agitation of the water versus my swimming proficiency (love of breathing, really), I'd decided not to suffer the anxiety created when breaking waves unexpectedly filled the breathing tube. My sailing insecurities may have been permeating other areas.

After Chris finished exploring, I saw his signal, picked him up, and we sailed back to Road Harbor on Tortola, British Virgin Islands, to clear Customs. They charged $7.71 for a boat and two people for six days—cheaper than camping, no bears, and the scenery everywhere was beautiful. Immigration charged twenty cents. Not a profit center, maybe they just wanted to know who was here. Checking in was voluntary, but if you were caught in BVI territory and hadn't checked in, allegedly they would take your boat—or fine you, which was easier. The Customs officers and the few people I'd encountered were rude and unfriendly. Since not all tourists are ambassadors or angels either, one may beget the other.

We had dinner at the nearby marina at Village Cay, bought groceries, and returned home with a pint of Ben & Jerry's ice cream and ten pounds of ice. While enjoying our ice cream under a brilliantly clear, star-studded night sky, I told Chris: "You're as liberating as a regime change. You've a history of challenging the way I do things, usually for the better. Your brain is always engaged. You always insisted I use lots of real butter to season whole-kernel corn. Not healthy, but a risk worth taking. Now you come along with ice and, of all things, ice cream. It was a great trade, swapping Rocco for you."

Chris, pensively staring at the heavens, said, "A bartender in the U.S., if he's out of ice, he's out of business. Or close to it. My head's shaken, maybe stirred over Rocco's departure. You couldn't have been his problem. Had to be something else. I wanted to run up that hill, tackle him, and say, 'Hey, pal, you forgot your manners.'"

"Awwrightt! So, we send in a Marine to break things and kill people. If you could just make him talk, we might learn something. People organize their brains through conversation, as we're doing now—it's fundamental to psychotherapy, a pressure-relief valve. If people don't converse, they lose their minds, which I almost did, because Rocco and I talked so infrequently, and there was no other way to know him. He was a headcase—in my head. I know he had a tough childhood, then 54 more years to get through. By the time someone is 72, they may not suffer fools easily, and he could have done without me, who had the better bunk and may have caused his palm to burn up. Every morning he used his burnt hand to slither out of that coffin, his hate may have been reignited and his resentment set ablaze. Or maybe he had folks in his life who stole his joy, he had a bad job, hell, a bad marriage could do it. Relationships can be our greatest joy or worst nightmare; sometimes one is both. I would guess anyone his age is carrying at least one major burden, possibly several."

"Well, I've had guys come and sit at the end of the bar, order a drink, look around, and all night say nothing but 'yep.'"

"Really?"

"Yep. If I said 'the usual?' or 'want another?' or 'had enough?' they'd answer 'yep.' Some didn't even say that much, just kept pushing the glass toward me. Wasn't sure if they were psychopaths, or playwrights; they were smoking, drinking, and thinking about something. Others wouldn't stop talking about their troubles. Proud to be depressed."

"Yep—chronic pain, abuse, depression and all of its causes—it's endless. Personal choices can bring on depression."

"Dad, your friends seem to be . . . have well-balanced lives."

"Probably. You might think. Though one of my best friends of many years, and I didn't know this until recently, was tortured by his mother, wickedly mean to a precious-looking young boy. Unimaginable, except she was an alcoholic. He's highly functional, more than anyone I know. So functional, he may be dysfunctional. But we have the deepest conversations about psychology and relationships. He's so adept at it, preachers and psychiatrists come to him for their own counseling."

"Are you talking about Jerry?"

"Yeah, many degrees, prestigious jobs, well compensated, he made everything run on time at a profit—all with abuse in his background. I may not know anyone who's not carrying a burden."

"Okay, so how many are you carrying? What are they?"

"Oh, Chris. Probably more than even you think."

"Like what?"

"Nothing too serious; depression isn't one of them. It lived in the neighborhood, but exercise was my solution, or one of them."

"What's your best solution for depression?"

"Off hand? Stop doing what's depressing you. Most important, in my opinion, is doing the right thing. If you don't, and you feel bad about yourself, destructive habits can crop up. It all goes to hell right there. If you don't like yourself, neither will others, or you'll think they don't. So, do the right thing. Good things will happen."

"After that?"

"Well, stop thinking about yourself and do nice things for other people— altruism is a great cure. Come over and mow my yard sometime. . . . Nah, I'd rather you mow Ms. Thomas' yard instead; it's usually taller than my grass, I'd help, and we'd all three feel good—sunlight, exercise, we're not snacking in the kitchen, dopamine's flowing for all. But you are doing that kind of stuff already."

"True, I'm just asking for a friend. Got another?"

"Sure, and maybe this should be number one: Be thankful. You've been given life; the rest is up to you. If you think someone owes you something, you may have a hard time collecting. What if the person you are waiting for doesn't show up? Take whatever blessings you have and joyfully run with it. . . . Going back to dopamine and sunlight, an important one, I take a vitamin D supplement, said to ward off depression and keep the cold and flu away. It's a miracle vitamin/hormone. Look it up. Being sick all the time is depressing by itself, okay? Hey, here's something different . . . buy yourself a set of dinnerware you really love and use it, so every time you eat a meal, it'll give you pleasure. I've never seen it mentioned in a study anywhere. It's zany, but I have a set I really like and, when I reach for a plate, I think things like, 'Let's use these plates and make this a special day; you're worth it; this could be my last day, so live it in style.' And it's good for entertaining."

"So, paper plates are out?"

"For entertaining? Preferably; certainly don't let them stack up in the sink. That's depressing. Throw 'em away, just keep the silverware. And buy a quality set of that. Eating is an act of reinvigoration; nourish the mental side of it."

"Does that tie for second?"

"Chris, potentially everything is second to number one—altruism, dinnerware, playing upbeat music, sports, education, money in the bank, avoiding addictive habits. As long as I was making progress, growing in some area, doing the right thing, I had hope for the long term. There are always down days. If you stumble, remember that what you do next makes the difference. . . . On a lighter note, you probably know I carried one cross since forever that kept me humble and the object of frequent derision . . ."

"Yeah? . . . I'm waiting. Let's hear it."

"Uhhh, as a kid, I was the spitting image of Alfred E. Newman, probably drawn to look like me, my first and last unpaid modeling gig."

"Oh yeah, I saw that picture. Actually, I thought he was better looking," chided Chris.

"Well, he still looks the same; at least I lost the freckles and, unfortunately, the curly red hair, which I'd pay to have back."

"Too late. Even hair dye wouldn't help."

"Hey! I admit I was never confused with Paul Newman, alright? He had blue eyes."

"So you're happy?"

"Chris . . . yeah, most of the time. I am happy with where I am, happy with my choices, especially the choices about alcohol, tobacco, drugs, and diet. Those are four horsemen of a personal apocalypse. If you become addicted to one or more, life will be wretched, for you and those around you. Addicts on drugs or alcohol have less than a 10% chance of ever getting free of it. The best thing is to never start. The evils of tobacco are well known, primarily cancer, I guess, from lip to lung. Obesity makes life hugely difficult and unhealthy. Manage those and you have more freedom and latitude in so many ways, which got me here. And I am thrilled this trip with Rocco in such a small space and a constant mental challenge is over."

"At his age—the way he just walked away, that was weird—he should have worked through his problems by now."

"It depends on the person; most have the ability, if they so choose. You infer he can because you did, to a degree. One can learn helplessness or optimism, some have birth defects, concussions, things you can't do much about. In his case, he stayed with the parents too long, still is, abusive parents at that, didn't learn self-reliance, never felt independent, could be angry about it, who knows? Torturous childhoods with dysfunctional parents produce both high achievers and lost souls—Jerry rose to prominence and personal fulfillment, is pursuing transcendence, his sister dropped out of life, his brother committed suicide. But loving, supportive families also get mixed results, and may have a low achiever. A child could despair about a parent who did the right thing, though it wasn't what was wanted at the time. Or if a parent says something unkind, like 'You're stupid,' don't let it ruin your life, consider if it was said by a neurosurgeon who has done a brain scan. If 'no' to both, dismiss it as a forgettable, baseless, maybe emotional opinion. If 'yes' to both, then you may be stuck on stupid, so wise up."

"Can you divorce your parents if it's not working?"

"Asking for a friend again? . . . Sure you can, depending on your age and how co-dependent you are. That's what Marco did. His dad wanted him out of the house and working when he turned 18, but for good reason he had only finished the 11th grade. Fortunately, he found new 'parents' after sleeping in a bus shelter awhile. Now he's college-educated and thriving, set himself up for a great life."

"That must have taken guts, and a vision."

"Yup. Eighteen years is long enough to become responsible for yourself. Parents aren't perfect anyway; they didn't train for the job, especially not the first born because it's frequently unplanned. If you make it to 18, you've won the lottery; the odds that your egg was fertilized were minuscule. So, forgive their failings, recognize you won't be perfect either, thank 'em for the gift of life, and get on with yours. If they offer advice, don't discard them just because you don't agree. Consider it."

"Isn't parenting more a condition than a profession?"

"It's a lot of things, but not a college curriculum. Most do the best they can. It's kinda important, a basic sustaining principle of mankind and a wonderful condition—right now I'm enjoying it but you know you were a handful. Was it worth it? Much depends on what you do with the life you've been given. Today, I say 'yes.' We'll see what tomorrow brings. I am enjoying our collaborative conversation, clearing my head after my solitary confinement. We can stop, talk about you and the weather, but before we do, let me mention one more thing."

"What's that?"

"Parents can divorce their children, if holding them close is ruining an otherwise good life. Some people are best avoided, no matter the relationship. If you are a raving asshole, your parents may not frequently fete you at the country club. If an addict, you may be divorced from their will so as to not make your life worse. Or they may just stop inviting you for dinner. A parent's love may be strong, but not insuperable."

"Trying to tell me something?"

"Hadn't thought that far ahead, Chris. Might consider it. But if you strive to be the best you can be, you will have a better life with many more options than if you don't strive, and have to accept hand-me-downs, be it clothes, low-paying jobs, or life partners. A guy on the beach at Palmas Del Mar, when I told him about this trip, said I should write a book. If I do, I may include the thought and you can show it to your kids. Or I'll show it to mine."

"Kids? I still feel like one myself."

"You do have a creative, youthful spirit. I hope you can keep it alive. . . . So, how's the weather, Chris? Meet your approval?"

"It's great. Perfect. The Baths were awesome. How did those boulders, as big as a large house, show up to stand alone on a sandy shore? Never seen anything like it."

"Wondered that myself. Geologists theorize the granite rocks were an upchuck from volcanoes. Weather eroded softer rock from around the granite leaving rounded boulders. Where else could they come from? They weren't trucked in. Did you wade or swim among them, see the streams of light, the reflective pools and angular shapes?"

"Yep. It was sublime. Hated to leave."

"That's how I felt. Shall we go back, or see something new?"

"Like what?"

"We could go to Norman Island, also called Treasure Island, visit Robinson Crusoe and his goats. Has excellent snorkeling. Sound good?

"Let's do it."

"So, Chris, are we done with Rocco?"

"He's interesting, and it's about more than Rocco. Unlike you and Jerry, I don't have someone to share this kind of conversation with, and you're curious too, right? Why waste your one and only life?"

"We think he should think as we do. The mind largely determines how things work out; your thinking determines your future, but he's coming from another place. Ever hear the maxim 'where you stand depends on where you stand'? Rational, logical thought comes from training and practice, and having the initiative."

"Guess so. Life can be tough."

"Very, under the best of circumstances. That's why a good education, with emphasis on teaching virtue and morality, is important—so you can make good decisions. You're a man of charity and good will, right?"

"I guess so, try to be."

"You definitely are. Don't doubt it. You stood up for your country when you enlisted in the Marines, and you put your body and wit at risk as a bar bouncer to bring order out of chaos. You're kinda amazing, really; a stand-up guy. You've seen guys at stoplights with signs asking for money, still have their legs and arms, just down and out. Ever wonder what their life story was, what caused their fall? Could it be their thinking, about the events that affected them? Every time I was tempted to say 'screw it!' at work, I would think about them, and decide I was not going to jump off the ladder to success only to climb back up again. Too much work. Whatever their situation, it reminded me to be thankful, a feeling of 'that could have been me.' It still might, who knows; life is fragile."

"That puts Rocco in a different perspective. He's obviously functional."

"Pretty much. As a sailor, he's highly functional, absent one near-catastrophic decision. He got us here. Something's a big issue for him, but there's so much we don't know, and so little we do. . . . Look at that bright star just above the port side spreader; is it still there or did it die out and it's so far away we're still seeing light it sent out years ago?"

"I don't know. Speed of light being what it is, that's hard to imagine."

"Hmmm, is it analogous to what someone might have said to someone years ago, good or bad? You still see or hear it years later? Something even a now-dead parent said still hurts? Or helps—my mom called me her prince; never said anything negative. I must have been a perfect kid. At least it made me want to be—if it wasn't too inconvenient."

"Awww, c'mon. That's harder to imagine, especially since we know better."

"Dad took the opposite approach to my wanting to be better. They both work. Mom saw a prince after Dad switched my behavior to a higher level of performance. I was usually late for dinner, wanted one more time at bat. The forsythia bush he used for switches had bad symmetry. He wasn't a landscaper, more of a scorched earth kind of guy, but sensitive, since he usually said 'This hurts me more than it hurts you,' to which I thought, *If it did, you'd quit,* but didn't dare say it, just got my little smartass home. Someone would drop off my ball and glove later."

"So follow your mom and only say good things?"

"It feels better, worth a try. If it works. If something negative needs to be said, it is wrong to not say it, just say it the best way possible. . . . Somebody apparently said something nice, because, well, turn around, and tell me if what's happening on that boat just off our port bow is what I think I see?"

"That one? . . . I think . . . Damn! Really? . . . Do you see much of that down here?"

"It's pretty sexy here—swimsuits, nudity—first time for anything that carnal. We're downwind, they don't hear or see us, so we don't see them or they don't care. They may have no privacy inside. That's been my approach to taking showers in the cockpit. For two months, when I took off my glasses I felt no one could see me. No harm done if they did. I wasn't going to not take a shower. It's likely the same for them. I don't need the stimulation, gonna hit the sack. You?"

"I was. Not so sure now. I may stay up awhile. It's a beautiful night."

"Well, sweet dreams. Hope she doesn't pull a 'Natalie Wood.' If she does, take the dinghy and offer a hand. Wake me if you need me."

Road Harbor was relatively settled that night. We slept soundly, which was much appreciated after two nights of little sleep caused by poor anchoring—a complex necessity for a novice sailor and a daunting task when the anchorage is crowded. The length of your anchor line, the depth of the water, and the quality of the ground beneath determine where you can anchor, as does the room between boats and the length of their anchor lines. The direction of the current, of the wind, the proximity of the shore, all play a role. Amid all these exigencies, you do not want to hit another boat, easily done in the middle of the night on a wind or tide shift. Hence, achieving a good night's sleep requires planning and can be rare. Even the moon gets involved.

Chris and I intended to go to the Bight and Norman Island, but first had to investigate a diesel smell and an oily discharge discovered the prior evening. The bilge discharge was caused by a water leak, probably from the packing nut on the stuffing box; I would leave that for Walt unless we started sinking. (Technically, any water intrusion is a start, but the bilge pump automatically handles small amounts.) The oily appearance was diesel leaking from a fitting on the fuel pump into the bilge. For environmental and safety reasons, this needed attention. Being Sunday, the likelihood of finding a compressible copper washer, which is what I thought we needed, was not high. When we needed two for the oil leak that developed in Puerto Rico, we couldn't find any, but an alternative sufficed. Checking the Tortola Yacht Services by VHF radio, I learned I would have to wait until Monday.

Never content with being patient, and having the whole day to snatch a victory from the jaws of defeat, we jumped in *Speedy* and puttered around to the Moorings Charter Company, which had a vast fleet of boats. With millions of dollars' worth of boats in the water each day, if one needed a washer on a Sunday, I doubted they would go anywhere but to their own depot. Looking helpless and desperate, a frequent feeling of late, I appealed to the first person I saw by explaining my plight. They found the washer I needed, and gave it to me. Bingo! It worked better than the aluminum electrical connector I tried first, and was immensely better than twisting off the head of the bolt.

With the fuel problem solved, we sailed over to the Bight and the caves. The number and variety of swarming fish were astounding, many swimming eye to eye, inches from our faces, bumping into our legs and arms. We had a clear water scene of boat hulls, snorkelers, fish, and underwater growth. It was hard to smile in a snorkel mask, but it couldn't be avoided; delightful. We later headed for Salt Pond Bay, which Rocco, Walt, and I had found to be a beautiful, calm anchorage with permanent moorings. Our mooring procedure was our second of the day, both accomplished without error.

We swam until late, then fixed dinner. For evening amusement, I cleaned the head because Chris said it smelled. I didn't smell anything. My nose had adjusted to reality. The first home I owned had a serious mold problem due to standing water in the crawl space. I didn't smell it unless I went away for a week or two. When I returned, it was awful for an hour or more, until my nose made the adjustment.

Chris brought a fresh nose, as well as a fresh outlook on life.

We read books in the cockpit and I told him a couple stories previously alluded to, until

Chris said, "I've wondered why you retired so early. Did you secretly get fired? You don't have to—"

"Oh hell no. I was at the top of my game, but my boss, in essence, said I could quit working so hard."

"What kind of boss does that?"

"She was unusual, for sure. She was the first person I'd ever heard use the

F word in the boardroom. Then she inquired about how I liked my women. When I asked why she was asking, it was because her sister wanted to be dating, and that I might please her. I told her I didn't date anyone at work, and dating the boss's sister was an even worse idea. What could go right? Of course, once she had asked the question, I was in a no-win situation. A rejection for any reason was still a rejection. To the boss, her sister was special, and I should take notice."

"So, she fired you for rejecting her sister?"

"Well, I'm not sure, since she went on to tell me I was number one for being promoted next, but it would be years coming because Affirmative Action was requiring other genders and races be promoted to the smaller number of jobs at that level."

"Did they need to be qualified?"

"I can't say, and I didn't see the list. Maybe she wanted me out of there if I wouldn't date sis. Her attitude toward me changed after that."

"What'd you do?"

"Well, you can't successfully stop in the middle of the road—you'll get run over. I was never enamored with work for its own sake, so I reordered my investments, preparing me financially for a reduction-in-force buyout several years later, which I accepted and became an emancipated man. You work; I play. With aggregate marginal tax rates likely over 50%, it was a no-brainer."

"Did you feel like a victim? I guess you would."

"That's something to purposefully avoid. It's hard to think of yourself as a victim and not suffer the anger and depression of victimhood."

"Still, in one way or another, that must have pissed you off."

"Well, here again, how well you think determines how well you live, and I'm not going to sit here on a boat in paradise with a jingle in my pocket, free to roam, able to carry a tune, and pretend to be mad about it—though I had been training for my career for 20–30 years, then got my legs cut out from under me not because of merit, but racial and genetic differences. It would be better if promotions were based on merit; otherwise, a lot of talent is lost. Nevertheless, forced changes are sometimes good for you, if you make the best of it. We can watch to see who gets hurt later that loves it now—nothing works forever, which is why we should be tasteful in our words, for we may later have to eat them."

"Sounds a lot like reverse discrimination to me."

"Possibly, Chris, and one day, there will only be women and special categories working. They will have accomplished their goals so thoroughly, they'll have swindled themselves into doing all the work, while the last men will be meeting for leisurely lunches, chatting on the phone, playing golf, taking boat rides to the Caribbean, and flying around the world, maybe living longer, even longer than women. Or we'll be somehow euthanized for lack of a purpose in life."

"Are you, we, the last men?"

"Well, you know, they're not making 'em anymore."

"They're not?"

"Not as many. Young boys are being given drugs and participation trophies to subdue their competitive proclivities. Testicles are shrinking; boys are growing up without fathers. In two generations, society will implode, replacement rate births will be insufficient, and we may be speaking a different language. . . . Just saying. Hope I'm wrong."

"I know what you're saying. I told you when I graduated from Parris Island that I was disappointed qualifying was so easy."

"I remember; we were standing on the parade ground. It was the next thing you said after 'Hi Dad.' Guess it was so the Ritalin-participation-trophy kids could qualify."

"Definitely, but weren't we talking about your issues?"

"You asked me why I quit, no, if I got fired. Did I?"

"Guess it depends, certainly encouraged. Okay, so you turned lemons into lemonade. Leave you with a sour taste in your mouth?"

"Everything has an impact. We all suffer or thrive based on 'stuff.' I may be wiser or more sensitive for having walked in the shoes of those treated unfairly before me, and I paid a price, other than the small amount of money I received from a class action suit because men at my level were being paid less than women. But it's not just me. Any government scheme to benefit one part of society will penalize another part to pay for it, whether they give field advantage or economic redistribution. Replacing one discrimination with another undermines the chances of equality, as there will be enough discrimination to go around to eventually everyone. What have you gained if you elect a President in your preferred gender or race and lose your country, living your life in servitude? In most cases, everyone loses. And who gets to choose which is the good discrimination du jour?"

"Guess so. There're no angels in government to assure those created equal are treated equal. . . . Any issues come from your experience?"

"I don't think so. Awareness, maybe. Wait, I do remember, shortly after retiring, having a couple dates with a woman who had a job with my company at the level denied me. After two dates, I decided I couldn't continue, for no reason other than what we just discussed. I can still see her look of bewilderment, standing at the threshold when I left early in the evening. She was almost certainly thinking *tonight's the night.* Her hugs were warm, through her blouse she showed signs of being cold in August or stimulated, soft music was already playing, and it's possible the bed was turned down, candles ready to be lit. But I wouldn't kiss her and couldn't any more make love to my abridged career than I could have to my ex-wife after she kidnapped my kids. Is that an issue? I've occasionally wondered about it. . . . She was a nice person, we had a lot in common—biking, travel, ice cream . . . was it fair to her? It wouldn't have been fair to start a relationship with a built-in, unanswerable question. Better to avoid it. She had no clue. What could she do about it? So, there are two issues for ya. Now that we're reminiscing, I kinda miss her, though memories of ex-friends improve over time."

"We're getting in over my head. Bartenders have easier clients than you, typically addicted dysfunctionals or vice versa, and they eventually go home, one reason bars have a closing time. I bet most people have issues."

"We all do. Like bubbled paint on an old car, if you rub hard enough at the right place, you might discover their pathologies. Don't feelings of insecurity, inadequacy, or resentment predominate? Life is evil, full of suffering; it's hard, and humans are fragile; terrible things happen. Accidents, sickness. Almost everyone is taking a prescription drug for something, not to mention all the suffering incels. I hate to think about it."

"The who?"

"Oh, involuntary celibates. Folks who want love, and can't get it—most of us, at one time or another."

"That's not you."

"Sometimes it is. In any case, we're sitting here in paradise but, when we return, we'll be run over by the manure spreader of life on its inevitable passes through the neighborhood—or even before we leave. The key is to focus on the goodness in life. Like, well, we could talk about the inspiration and motivation of growing up poor. It surely motivated me."

"Oh, I know all I want to know about that. Got that down."

"To some degree, maybe . . . did you know it's a blessing?"

"I'm not buying that. Why so?"

"You have no guilt. And, what you achieve is all to your credit. How about the benefits of having good parents?"

"Don't know anything about it. What's that like?"

"You laugh, but there may be some truth there; depends on your perception. I had a good experience . . . mom was fantastic, because Dad was the disciplinarian and I always deserved it. He kept me in line. . . . Here's my question. . . . You and Ken were in your mother's custody and kidnapped, is my word for it, when you were seven, ripped out of your home with no notice, within a day after we came home from our cross-country vacation. Took me three months to find you. That had to be traumatic. Heard you cried for days. Ever think about how that affected you? Wanna talk about it? Can you?"

"Uhhhmm . . . yeah . . . I guess so. I've always wondered how you found us. Glad you did."

At that moment, as if a warning shot from above, an exonerating soft rain started to fall. We picked up our books, retreated to the cabin, secured the portholes and hatches, then went to sleep, cocooned and listening to the pitter patter of rain on the cabin top. Chris did not try to restart the conversation. Men are usually protective of their mothers. I let it lie.

An early morning dive off the boat deck for a hearty swim in crystal clear water provided an invigorating wakeup. I loved mornings here, sitting in the cockpit sipping a glass of orange juice before breakfast, watching the pelicans dive-bombing the bay, emerging with their breakfast of fish. A soft morning breeze in the mid-70s, sun coming up over Ram's Head, surfaces heating up, it was heaven on earth. Any future sense of a similar morning would cause me to reminisce back to this paradigm of what constitutes a Caribbean morning—the light, action, temperature, and the slight scent of materials microscopically surrendering to the forces of ultraviolet assault—a memory for all time, and a reason to take notes for later reflection.

Island Perils and Pleasures:
Man over-bored, you name it

His week almost over, Chris and I stayed in Salt Pond Bay until Ken's arrival, giving us time to finish a week of deep conversation, sitting in the cockpit with a wake-up drink of choice.

"Chris, I had time to think last night, and I'm gonna share my last thoughts on the Rocco enigma. You may not be aware, don't need to be, that children must be socialized by the age of four."

"Rocco is older than that."

"Well, you woke up firing on all cylinders. Brilliant observation. The reason is, if your child cannot get along with others in the sandbox, they get excluded from social activities which are essential for learning behavior on the long path of life. There, if people can stand to have you around, when you exhibit behavior, you will either get approval or pushback, which could be a roll of the eyes or a punch in the nose—mid-course corrections."

"I see where you're . . . damn, did you see that pelican hit the fish? He's got breakfast. So, if you don't have the social nudging, shall we call it, how do you learn what is good behavior, right? You don't."

"Well, the "loners" don't; they go off, forced off, on their own and become troublesome, or at the extreme, insane. But let's keep it short. Besides having bad parents, Rocco had what? A job as a postman. You don't see a nudging crowd of people on his route with him, not like the Pied Piper. Heard the term 'going postal'? And what did he do for a pastime? All I know about is sailing. So, there's little socializing as you might get if you work among others, and sailing is a minimal-crowd sport. That's a lot of time to think without having anyone to talk it through. Bad thoughts run amok, and they are the easiest to come by."

"That's good enough for me. Perhaps a bad start in the morning, it cooks in the brain all day, you're ready to cuss someone out by bedtime. No wonder he didn't have anything nice to say. It may not be the answer, but it's a possibility. How much time do we have?"

"It's about time to move on. But I'd say, if he had all that working against him, he did a pretty good job with it. Rocco was pretty normal when Walt returned. If he resented my presence and what it meant to his comfort, it may have been a big part of his issue. Ever read *The Gulag Archipelago*, by Solzhenitsyn?"

"Don't think so."

"You'd remember. While he was in the Gulag, he pondered why he was there, concluded it was resentment, a prison of its own, and knew he had to rid himself of it before he would ever be free."

"A lot of my bar customers seem to be resentful, Dad."

"Probably why they were there drinking. Earlier in the week, we were thinking Rocco was depressed. Could that stem from resentment? It's a heavy burden people impose on themselves, which they must conquer to prosper."

"What's a good way to do that?"

"I'd say take responsibility for your condition. Then change it. Blaming someone else gets you nowhere, and keeps you there. . . . We should leave to pick up Ken, but to wrap it up, if Rocco had resentment, and we *are* speculating, did he negatively impact the trip for himself as he did for me?"

We made things secure, then headed for Charlotte Amalie on St. Thomas. During the hours we were sailing, Chris had one last thought. "Hey Dad, before I leave, tell me your secret for getting rich, though I'm well known for not asking for advice."

"Probably because I too willingly provide it."

"You're right, I'm usually trying to avoid it, but I've found fascination with this lifestyle."

"Well, if you mean financially independent, then let's call it that. Rich is a relative term, easy or difficult to achieve, because it is impossible to define to universal agreement. You can be rich in many ways, and still be broke. Your question is about being able to meet all of your current and future financial responsibilities, right?"

"Yeah, good point."

"With a small annual retainer for your advisor, of course."

"I guess if you earn it, you deserve it. I remember you telling me something like 'free advice is usually worth what you paid for it.'"

"That's right. If you pay for it you are more likely to use it. I can think of many times when free advice was expensive. So, I've already told you I was poor when I was young, but after many years of hard work, I was no longer young. . . . It isn't a matter of how hard you work, but how well. Create more value than you consume, by not consuming so much, and/or providing what others are willing to exchange value for, usually goods or services, which may require education or training on your part. Earn more than you spend, save the balance, and put it to work earning more than inflation so that someday your money can work and you can relax. That's how it's done."

"If it's that easy, why isn't everyone rich?"

"You mean financially independent; it's not easy—my words are easy; the work is hard—and they don't really want it. Life gets in the way. Every minute, hour, and day, life throws challenges and opportunities at you that require choices. For example, choosing to avoid habits that keep you poor, and we already discussed the four horsemen of personal apocalypse. But if you will spend a few years doing what others will not—delaying gratification—you will someday be able to do what others cannot.

"You may remember I had an employee, Craig, who asked me how I could afford to be looking at Porsches when deciding what car to buy. He was an amiable guy, so we sat down and estimated his expenses for alcohol and tobacco for a decade—or less, don't remember, exactly. The number came to within ten dollars of the cost for the car. He was stunned. I soon would have the pleasure and value of the car. For the same price, he had the burnt home furnishings, stained teeth, bad breath, and ashes—to be repeated each decade over a lifetime, along with health risks. He had no DUIs, or I could have upgraded to the turbo. One of his but-but-but's was a car is only a way of getting from Point A to Point B. When the car was delivered, we went for a ride at lunch time on a little-used, new road, quickly taking it to 110 mph, followed by high speed, sharp turns. When he caught his breath and quit choking his seatbelt, he said, 'Wow! There IS more than one way to get from Point A to Point B, isn't there?' He could accept reality, one of his good points, and had started cutting back on the smoking habit before I moved on. Though once you're hooked, quitting is really tough. By comparison, after four years, I sold the Porsche for about what I paid for it, to a beautiful girl who also wanted companionship. That's called 'winning.'"

"I remember Craig, tall guy, red hair. Didn't we borrow his K-car to go skiing at Lake Placid, New York, one Christmas?"

"You've a good memory, Chris. I wanted his car for the front-wheel-drive traction on snow—and the space, since Ken wanted to bring his girlfriend— so I asked if we could trade cars."

"You traded the Porsche for the K-car?"

"I offered it. He didn't want the responsibility, or wanted to smoke while driving; he took my truck."

"One of our best vacations. The Olympics bobsled ride was awesome, the hotel was Christmas decorated, and the food was farrrr superior to our cross-country trip in '76 with Uncle Wayne and his two sons. Nothing but tuna helper, as I remember it, right?"

"Close to it, but edible; it had dried peas and carrots in it, just add water from the Virgin or Merced rivers. Remember, we didn't go that far for the food. And there were other choices, like peanut butter and jelly, the only thing your cousins David and Michael ate the whole trip. Nobody died; all of you are alive and healthy today. If you want, I'll add a few other points that I think are worth mentioning before you leave. There's more to life than money and fast cars, if you can believe that."

"Oh, I don't know. I'd be happy with those two."

"Short term, but what if that was all you had, and no friends? Let's look further ahead, avoid going aground.

"One, believe in people. Your best and worst experiences will likely come from people. Know there are people of all kinds. Humans are the highest order, right above animals, but from my experience, the Venn diagram overlaps. Having housed thousands of tenants, and been around awhile, I think it's no accident that pig parts can be transplanted to humans. Most people are good, just be careful; trust but verify. At the same time, great relationships absolutely require that each be trustworthy.

"Which brings us to number two—be someone others will desire, whether friend, mate, or employee. Don't be the last chosen for anything. Be the best you can be, and you will get to do the choosing. You've only one life; don't waste it. It's better to be among those at the top than those living under a bridge. Think about it early, and prepare accordingly; education will be your wings in life."

"Didn't we cover that earlier?"

"Maybe, partially. . . . One more?"

"Go for it. We have the time. Plus, I don't have a dad at home."

"Not recently, anyway. So, believe in something higher than yourself, and it's not the government. You're a smart, clever guy, but when at wits end, it is a powerful solace if not a physical solution to believe you are not alone. You can usually solve your own problems, given inspiration from God or wherever it comes."

"That's a lot to remember. Guess I can call you if I need help?"

"Always. I should be home in three weeks unless something better comes up."

"It's hard to reach you on a boat."

"Yep! . . . Oh, wait, Chris, I may have saved the best for last."

"What's that? I'm already pumped; feel like a kid with a new bike."

"What are two of the most powerful words in the dictionary?"

" . . . I give up."

"That's three words, and possibly the weakest."

"I dunno. That's two words."

"Thank you."

"You're welcome, but why are you thanking me?"

"No, 'thank you' are two very powerful words. Use them every chance you get. You and the recipient will gain much from it. Doesn't cost anything, and pays big benefits. A mark of civility."

"Thank you?"

"Well, if you give someone something and they don't thank you for it, how many times will you repeat it?"

"Probably none. . . . Hmmm, good point. Thank you."

"You're already getting the hang of it. Good for us. . . . Oh, and thank you . . . for being a good communicator this week. Sometimes that is what it takes to keep someone from committing suicide. Of the two I know, one by gunshot and one by alcohol, I do wonder if there might have been something I could have done to prevent it, and regret I didn't have or take the chance."

We arrived at Crown Bay Marina around 1430, washed clothes, bought groceries, greeted Ken, and had an excellent meal of fish and chips at Tickles, the marina restaurant. Back at the boat, Ken unpacked his homemade cookies. These guys were rescuing me, a Man-Over-Bored with the same food. After taking a vote, the Tickles meal was considered our late lunch, the cookies our dinner. Might as well; couldn't quit on the cookies, and nobody was watching. This left us with a full evening to converse in a close, intimate environment. I couldn't remember when the three of us as adults had ever had a similar opportunity, and it probably would not occur again. It was a father's dream. Usually someone had to get to work, either on a job or a relationship, good excuses to limit time with a parent who might look askance at tales you would enjoy sharing with your brother for the sake of a good laugh over audacious bravado.

"Ken, bring us up to date on what's happening with you before Chris leaves."

"Well, let's see, where to start . . . did I tell you about my heart fibrillations?"

"Ohmygosh, no. What's that about?" This was startling, coming from a guy who ran 10K's without training, and had annually biked the Assault on Mt. Mitchell, a 102-mile ride with an elevation gain of over 5,000 feet, as high as the Grand Canyon is deep, done in several hours.

"Well, they started occurring just after my bike crash. Did I tell you about that?"

I was beginning to numb; one more stunner and I wouldn't feel a thing. "Nope, didn't know about it. What caused it? Who hit you? Were you hurt?"

"Well, I ran into a car that had stopped. I was thinking so hard about my tax returns I hadn't filed for several years that I wasn't paying attention."

That's it. This is why alcohol was invented. I start drinking tonight.

Chris, until then sitting back, assessing the carnage, hoping not to be complicit in whatever might surface next, jumped in, "You haven't paid taxes for several years? You gotta be kidding. They're gonna get you, boy."

"Well, I didn't make any money, not a profit, so I didn't think I owed anything, had nothing to give 'em."

I suggested, "You may not, but you would do well to do the math, and know, not just guess based on no money in the bank at year's end; that's commonplace. Anyone working on that?"

"Yeah, an accountant has all my receipts and income. He thinks I might owe a little."

"If you want to sleep in your own bed, I'd bring those accounts current," said Chris. "Otherwise, the IRS might arrange food and shelter for you elsewhere."

Ken told a short story about the divorce and remarriage of close friends before Chris followed with a few stories and jokes of his own and kept us laughing for several hours. We caught up on current events at the same time, many of which prompted more jokes, not the least of which was the Michael Jackson affair. Arkansas jokes were popular, as were the Clintons. As a bartender, Chris served as a storage and distribution hub for humor on all topics and perspectives.

Ken and I would plan an itinerary after Chris departed. Windsurfing was his first priority, sailing his second. He expected to fly on his board if his high-wind hopes materialized.

Breakfast on December 21 included scrambling of the eggs broken on the way back from the store yesterday. Chris wanted to take a hot shower at the marina, so Ken joined him, possibly giving them a chance to finish the stories they dared not tell in my company. Not liking the public and cold shower using a handheld showerhead arrangement on the boat, Chris hadn't showered since he stepped aboard. Being in and out of the water several times a day and a quick rinse afterward kept the dust down. In that way, he had almost not been here, but he could make an impressive paw print in the liquid and food supply, as could Ken, like most guys aged 24 to 29.

We went back to the marina to store Chris's luggage while he shopped for import-tax-free deals on booze for his friends, uh-huh (probably true, though). After dining on comfort food at McDonald's and an ice cream favorite at Baskin-Robbins, Chris retrieved his luggage and caught a cab to the airport. I hated to see him go. Would we ever be able to do this again?

Ken and I returned to the boat after calling a few windsurfing shops. The best deals were in the Red Hook area, so we weighed anchor and headed there. En route, I noticed that the alternator was putting out zero amperes, so we anchored in Christmas Cove west of Great St. James Island and looked for the reason, quickly obvious. Yesterday, what sounded like we had run over an anchor chain was the alternator belt shredding, ensuring we had at least one mechanical failure per day. Feeling the same dread as when reaching the bottom of a Cheetos bag, we searched for a replacement belt, and found one. Alas, too long. But wait! Ahhh, yes! A box with a replacement alternator and a belt. Should be perfect! Nope, belt's too short. Why were they here? Like the Virgins, to tease?

I installed the longer one, adjusting the throw all the way out, and started the engine to recharge the batteries. At a low engine speed, we could generate 15 to 20 amps without the belt squealing. During dinner, we charged the batteries up to 12.6 volts, a level with which we could live comfortably through the night and not have to hand crank the engine to get it started. Tomorrow, we would navigate Current Cut, try to find the correct belt in Red Hook for a permanent repair, and then rent windsurfing gear.

The moon was beautiful, waxing, almost full, lighting the tops of the hills, and dancing on the tips and facets of the diamond-like water. Great ambience for conversing with Ken and catching up on his recent activities and holiday plans. Regardless of our location in Christmas Cove, it was difficult to engender any appreciation of the approaching holiday from here when we were used to snow, reindeer, and sleighs, as well as crèche scenes and holiday music.

"Ken, tell me more about Charlie's divorce. I like him. We've played tennis together and ridden bikes with you. He's a good athlete, nice guy. Do you know what happened?"

"He and his wife didn't agree on politics."

"Wait, he lives on the Isle of Palms, a place I wouldn't mind having a home—except for the mosquitoes— and doesn't he have children?"

"Yeah, two."

"So, they probably had to sell the home, arrange custody, and miss out on raising the children together, split everything, and it's all over politics?"

"Yep."

"Someone had to be pretty rabid in their beliefs, with stick-it-in-your-eye behavior. Is Charlie dating anyone I might know?"

"No, they got back together. Decided to just not talk politics."

"Smart move. Hmmm, wonder why that didn't come up sooner in their discussions. And ours! Still together?"

"Think so."

"How is your relationship with Jenny?" I asked.

"It's okay."

"Just okay? Are you short on adjectives, or enthusiasm?"

"I guess, of those two, enthusiasm. She plays sports I like, biking mainly; she plays tennis better than I do, but something is lacking."

"Figured it out yet?"

"Well, this may sound funny, or too critical, but . . . she has never called me by name, any name—dear, darling, jerk, never my given name. She talks, we have good conversations, but she could take 'em to the guy next door and not change a word. I never hear a name, feel like I have no identity, no relationship to her, no status. I didn't identify it for over a year until we were having a party at my place one Saturday. I was cooking on the stove, and she was behind me fixing drinks for everyone. When she said, 'What do you want to drink?' there were guests in the kitchen, so I didn't respond, happy she was serving the guests, figuring I knew my way around the kitchen and would fix my own. When she asked again using a higher volume, I turned around to see which guest she was abusing, and she was looking straight at me. I got angrier than I probably should have, but that's me."

"Awww, man," I lamented, "I'm sorry. That's corrosive, dehumanizing. Something's wrong somewhere. Have you discussed it?"

"Not yet, been busy, it took a while to even notice, wanted to think it over . . . what do you think?"

"My reaction may have been strong, because I've been there. It's weird. First, I think you owe it to her to confront, or discuss, the issue. Find out if she knows she's doing it, why, and whether she wants to try to fix it. You have something to say and should say it. Problems don't get better with time."

"I've been meaning to, but it seems easier to just talk about it later."

"It is, but quality of life suffers, the players get tired, the relationship never thrives. You can discuss it without it being a do-or-die situation, but it may come to that. When I studied how to be a better salesman, I learned the customer likes best to hear his or her name. They can hear it above the din of a room full of people like no other words. Well, maybe "erotica" and words of that ilk would be easily heard. . . . Veronica would hear that. And any fricatives with a strong F sound, maybe."

"What do you think it means? Is she afraid to establish a relationship that would have a name?"

"I have no clue, Ken. I thought my problem was unique. Now you have it. I wonder how many others are suffering the same fate and may not know what is not happening, why the relationship has no depth, no sense of intimacy. Doesn't it seem standoffish, a lack of a buy-in, like sitting in the back row in church, hanging on the periphery where she can make a quick getaway without being too hurt, each term of endearment an investment she may not get back or want to make? I really don't know. You'll have to ask her."

"Okay, I'll look into it when I get home. She may not know either, but we could discuss it."

"I wouldn't wait too long, Ken, though it's easy to do. It may be an early sign that things aren't working out, and you need to attend to it soon. Don't let your lifeboat rot until it sinks; catch defects early. Everyone hurts when it doesn't work out. There's more eagerness to make an effort early in the relationship, like having the energy to wax a new car versus a rust bucket. It makes a difference—black and white versus Technicolor. Oh, and in the bedroom? It's nice if you use the name of who you are with. Maybe a couple times."

"Yeah, I hear that . . . so, how did yours work out?"

"I told her about it, encouraged her, but she couldn't do it, ignored it. We eventually parted ways. She thought we would be together forever. Paid a therapist to tell her what I told her, and the therapist didn't really know but took her money anyway, probably blamed it on me, which didn't help her at all. If you want to see the future—she married a year later, they lived separate lives together, until they divorced. Why? 'He was unresponsive.' What name did she use for him? She couldn't remember ever using one. . . . Bingo! He was unresponsive—to what stimulus? No small, recurring motivators or rewards, his was a life in a desert."

"Wow!"

"Now, it's hard to say it was cause and effect; could have been many things, but it couldn't help. Imagine someone writing love letters without an addressee; you could sell a bundle . . . except, they already do it—greeting cards. Thoughtful folks usually add the name of the recipient. You might want to try, before or after discussing the subject, giving her a flattering card with no name anywhere. If she likes it, tell her you're not sure who to give it to, you just wanted her opinion, then take it back; later, put her name on it and don't just give it to her, but mail it to her, giving her time to reflect, alone. You might make a point, and may not need to break up with her . . . she may do it. In either case, sending a card is a nice thing to do. Or try leaving a Christmas present conspicuously in the room without a name when you get home. Do you have a gift for her?"

"Yeah!"

"Take the name tag off. . . . Don't tell her who it's for; if she asks, just say names aren't important, or that you don't remember, doesn't have a name. If she asks how you could not have a name on it, you have a conversation starter. Something to think about. If she doesn't come around, find yourself a Waffle House waitress; they throw out terms of endearment like candy and beads at Mardi Gras."

"I can dig it. It's kinda nice; southern hospitality. Love their pecan waffles."

"Me, too, and you can earn a "darling" or "sweetie" just by walking in the door. When you use a name, for that moment, you isolate, actually captivate that person, more or less, depending on your tone of voice. Imagine the positivity of having names thrown at you like "handsome," or "dreamboat;" and what would you do for a "cutie pie"?"

"I'd swim to shore right now for a pecan pie."

"Oh, wow. Nice thought. So would I, Ken. So would I. You want it warmed, with whipped cream?"

"Hell yeah! Dad, you're killing me."

"You started it. Coulda stopped at cutie pie."

There were enough other life events to discuss and work projects to share that we whiled the night away until sleep consumed us.

When we awoke and looked out of the companionway, we had swung around to a completely different view, not uncommon. Feeling dangerously close to the rocks, we didn't waste time preparing to move on.

You cannot dawdle in Current Cut without risking being crushed on the rocks when the wind gets blocked, so I removed the loose, squealing belt and we powered through the Cut and into Red Hook, tied up at American Yacht Service to buy diesel fuel, and water, of all things. With water costing $.09 per gallon, it was cheaper to buy water than use half a gallon of diesel fuel to generate a gallon of water by reverse osmosis. A Yanmar dealer was located at the end of the dock, where I bought the right-size belt and copper washers for the fuel and oil lines. Ignoring all signage prohibiting it, there being no current demand for the space, I installed all fixes quickly while at the fuel dock, wishing I could anticipate the next problem before leaving the parts dealer.

West Indies Windsurfing in Muller Bay had the gear we were seeking. Ken and I each rented a board package for four days. He rented a high-performance board he may not have enough wind to sail; mine was one I could handle, with enough flotation and sail area that it could be sailed in light winds. Ken had done his homework and discovered there were "Christmas Winds" in these islands. Being a man of great acumen and planning, he had them scheduled for December 25. It may not work out that way. (They are winds out of the northeast at 25–30 knots, occurring sometime between November and February; afterward, the wind moves more southeasterly in time to bring us hurricanes, starting in June.) We weren't feeling anything ferocious yet, but had a few more days. Without the winds, he had a "sinker" on his hands—insufficient flotation to hold him above the water without significant wind and forward motion to plane out. It'd be like water skis without a boat—nice to have but useless.

Ken's windsurfing history went back to the late '80s, possibly catching the bug from me. He lived on an island off the coast of Charleston, SC, and had ready access to water and wind reports. It could be sunny or raining, cool or hot, preferably with small hurricanes off the coast, and he'd be out sailing. When he and I took a trip to the Pacific Northwest to bicycle and windsurf the Columbia River gorge—considered the windsurfing capital of the United States—he nailed it and has been a major fan ever since. That was the first venue I'd sailed where they gave you a helmet with the sailboard due to what could happen, including flying masts and bodies. Getting big air and achieving record speeds became his ultimate thrill. On the Columbia River, a special channel had been created, surrounded with wave-deadening floats, for timing speed-record attempts. I couldn't expect him now to commit the crime of low aim and be thrilled at the prospect. Were the Christmas Winds to arrive, I'd be overpowered with sail while he'd be living large.

We strapped our gear to the life lines and headed for Leinster Bay, a lovely location on St. John. After anchoring, I rigged my board, then took a quick turn on it before Ken sailed it across Sir Francis Drake Channel to Tortola territory while I followed in *Speedy*. At Tortola, we changed rides, Ken taking the dinghy, and I the sailboard back to Leinster Bay, running out of wind as I came within the wind shadow of land, making the last 300 yards difficult, requiring delicate balance and patience to get through the cut between Waterlemon Cay and St. John to the boat. The fear of falling into a visible shallow bed of sea urchins kept me attentive to every wisp of wind. A circling great white shark would get the same respect.

Only a few hours passed before the next equipment problem appeared. The dinghy motor was cutting out and hard to restart. I hoped it was a clogged filter and we'd have a replacement onboard—something simple. This was to be another new experience for me. Two months before, I could hardly spell outboard motor much less operate one; now I had to diagnose and repair it.

A near-full moon that night gave the mosquitoes light to body surf. Ken was tired and had a sore throat; hopefully, it was only the sun, saltwater, and excitement. We'd had an enjoyable day playing with the windsurfer and *Speedy*, and the next day should be a typical day in paradise—fix the toys, use them until they break, fix them again. It's tough, but everyone should try it.

The next morning, I took apart the motor, examining and blowing out the fuel screen to no avail. Towing *Speedy* across the channel behind *Godspeed* to Soper's Hole, Tortola, we hoped to find a mechanic, but were told to find Randy at Nanny Cay (another idyllic site), who had the motor running smoothly in less than ten minutes, then spent five minutes telling us how he adjusted the carburetor mixture. Relieved to have it running again, we had lunch nearby at Peg Leg, mostly to enjoy the priceless views of Sir Francis Drake channel, then crossed it to Norman Island, arriving in time to snorkel the caves at Treasure Point and anchor in The Bight before nightfall.

Our evening entertainment was watching the patrons quietly go to, and later loudly leave the William Thornton Floating Bar and Restaurant, deducing that alcohol is an amplifier. It rained sporadically through the night, and I spent much time opening and closing the portholes and hatches while Ken slept, secure on his father's watch.

Could the strong wind that brought last night's rain and little sleep bring the Christmas Winds? It brought an earlier than planned start toward the Baths on Virgin Gorda. The easterly winds put high waves on the nose as we motored east, making our progress to the Baths uncomfortable and slow. However, the lee side of the island provided wind protection for a good anchorage and smooth snorkeling to the island where we visited the grottos, seeing many fish and tourists.

Afterward, we sailed north to Gorda Sound, bought groceries at Leverick Bay, and dropped anchor near uninhabited Prickly Pear Island. *Speedy* seduced us out of the boat for a little exploring but was frigid about getting us back. The fifteen-dollar fix didn't last long, leaving us without a dependable dinghy again. The alternator belt on *Godspeed* was squealing, which would have sufficed for the repair of the day. I was hoping to adjust the belt and take a holiday.

The 10–15 mph wind in Gorda Sound provided for decent board sailing using the larger sail in the afternoon, an excellent venue due to its sheltered water between Prickly Pear Island and Virgin Gorda. We took turns with the board, sharing it and enjoyable conversation with a couple from Montana we met on Prickly Pear. Dinner was topped off with Ken's famous cookies, which went well with the Christmas music on the radio, resonating with the reason for the season, though it reminded me that friends and family were out of touch, a time of the year normally used for getting back in touch. Having Ken here was my saving grace. No snow, no tree, no red and green decorations, Ken and I would celebrate the holiday for its original meaning. We had everything else; it was like paradise. It WAS paradise.

Planning ahead, I asked: "What should we have for Christmas breakfast, Ken?"

"What do we have, I dunno, eggs? Cereal?"

"How about banana, pineapple, coconut, and blueberry pancakes topped with whipped cream and fresh raspberries?"

"Oh, hell yeah! That'd be killer! Can you do that?"

"Oh, heck no! I can do banana pancakes. We don't have the other stuff. I just dream about it. . . . Be nice if we did."

"That's okay, Dad. Banana pancakes would be great."

"We could go to a restaurant; Pusser's, get whatever you want, if they're open on Christmas."

"Probably not. And we have a better view; this is like living on the front of a travel brochure."

Then it was off to bed to chase sugar plums, blueberries, and coconuts around in my head and give Santa a chance to come down the mast. What else could he do?

Our Christmas was unusual. We enjoyed morning boardsailing in light winds, especially because we could wake up, put on a bathing suit, jump in, tune the sail still lying in the water from the night before, untie the board, and take off. Five minutes from eyes-open to launch—a wake-up like none other—and I was singing with joy all the way across the sound. After breakfast, Ken gave me Robert Fulghum's book, *Maybe, Maybe Not,* followed by a card from Megan; how apropos the combo. We then launched into what was required to keep our little "eco-environment" operational and afloat, which included adjusting the alternator belt on *Godspeed,* checking its fuel line repair, then pulling *Speedy's* fuel line and pump to find out why it refused to run. I had no luck with that, other than concluding there was too much air in our air-to-gas ratio and I could get it to run by choking it, which was how I had come to feel about it anyway. Cathartic.

Taking our chances with the moody motor, we packed a lunch and went to snorkel. To mitigate any misfortune, we took oars, life cushions, and extra drinks. We soon had lunch on the nearest beach because we forgot necessary details from our guidebook, nothing looked like we expected, and we didn't know where best to snorkel. We defied a myth about males by asking for directions, and a local directed us to a buoy in Eustatia Sound marking excellent reefs. Though we never found the buoy, we found magnificent coral and fish in extensive reefs that were stunning and beyond our expectations. There was an incredible, totally different world lurking mere inches below the water! The price of admission? A face mask and a snorkel tube.

"Dad! Did you see it?"

"Fee whaa . . . see what?" I said, looking up while taking out my tube—my ears were available, but my mouth was taken.

"The octopus! It's in that coral. C'mon, follow me." We dove down, Ken showing the way, and he pointed out my first octopus. Yikes!

The site was teeming with action: octopus, moray eel, many hundreds of fish grouped by color and size, like shrimp in a seafood market, obviously a breeding site, a fish nursery. A school of bright yellow juvenile blue tang by a patch of seaweed, a school of intermediate phase blue and yellow blue tang to the left of a beautiful coral garden—grade school, middle school—then a high school of larger, deep blue fish, adult blue tang. In waving flags of vivid color, they moved like a drill team, all turning in unison, their lateral line enabling them to swim so precisely. This may have been the most varied and prolific dive site so far.

For the rest of our snorkel, we held the ropes from the dinghy and drifted alongside. This had its attractions; we didn't risk damaging coral with an anchor, could float with the current and not have to return upstream, and safety was, literally, close at hand. I didn't feel the need—seen one shark, you hope you've seen 'em all—but when starting this adventure, I was not as confident. Now unafraid, but still wary, I could be out of the water fast as a flying fish if the need arose, but had to be sure I didn't knock myself out and back into the water by hitting Ken in the head doing the same from his side, like something out of *The Three Stooges*, though precisely what occurred earlier in the voyage. A head butt with that force dazes, leaves you vulnerable.

Relaxing in the cockpit after dinner, enjoying a near-full moon, clear sky, and tropical breezes, it was amazing how quickly the repairs and other little hassles are forgotten. If it isn't electrical or water, it can wait until morning. Living beneath the vast sky, most sailors cannot avoid thinking about the cosmos: If the cosmos is considered all matter and space, and it is expanding, where does it acquire the additional space? What is outside the unending boundaries of the cosmos? Is anything faster than the speed of light? When a wormhole takes you to the other side, where are you? What happens when the Milky Way galaxy collides with the Andromeda galaxy? Of course, we won't be around in our current form but, of all that, we have no clue, just astonishment and incomprehension, so we lay face up on the cockpit cushions, gazed at the sky, and enjoyed the peace and quiet.

"Hey Ken . . . see any stars you recognize?"

"Heck yeah . . . I have a telescope at home, but you can easily see Orion's Belt almost straight up. The two bright ones above and below it are Betelgeuse and Rigel." (Beetle-jooz and RYE-jel)

"Those names sound familiar. Were they stars in *The Sound of Music* with Julie Andrews?"

"It's possible they were. Been around for over a billion years. You may remember when they were born."

"Hey, hey, respect your elders, though as a ratio, we're getting closer in age all the time. We could pass as brothers now."

"We already have. Remember the hostess in the Half Moon Saloon? Oregon? That was funny. . . . Now, over this way, maybe southwest, that's Sirius, brightest star in the sky. And this time of year, we might be able to see the Little Dipper to the north. . . . Yep, there it is, near the horizon. If you have binoculars handy, I can show you a couple star clusters."

"I'll get them; Walt's 10x50s, should light up the sky. Wish we had two, we could spend the night out here." When I returned, "Here, Ken, try these. Maybe you can see Heaven."

"It's likely my only chance."

"Me too, I fear."

"Right here is like Heaven. How much better could it be?"

"I suspect it might lack the toughness of life on Earth. Would that be good, or not so much? Reminds me of a great story. Do you believe in God, or a greater power?"

"It's hard not to think a greater power created all of this synchronicity of . . . what would you call it? Stuff? But I cannot imagine it."

"Ken, I took a course in college about how to assess risk. One case study was whether believing in a God was a sensible risk. Best I remember, it was a binary choice, with more outcomes in your favor. If you believed, lived a good life, died, and there was a God, jackpot! If you believed or not, lived a good life, no God, you won in life, afterlife was the same for both. If you were a non-believer, and there was a God, oh baby, that's what you don't want."

"Do you think most people give it much thought?"

"God only knows how much. The U.S. is predominantly religious. And if people believe, they more likely follow the teachings than those who never heard of them. History reflects the debauchery in a society that doesn't believe, and the order and civility in one that does. Be glad others believe even if you don't. The uplifting story of William Wilberforce, UK slavery, and the song, 'Amazing Grace,' are about the shift from debauchery to civility—a life of amazing grace."

We spent much of the night outside, then woke up early to perfect weather with light breezes, sparkling clear, blue water, green islands, and a rich blue sky. On some mornings, I'd slip quietly outside to sit, watch, and listen to the sounds and the silence as the world awakened. It's a different world, and every tender, aware moment is cherished: moments to observe, thoughts to contemplate. The flat water promotes a calmness of spirit and questions of how did all this nature, so perfect, so beautiful, get here. Did this idyllic orchestration of loveliness happen by accident?

The air was pure, unobtrusive, and I searched for life—a songbird, a pelican diving for a meal, a ripple from a jumping fish, a turtle poking its head above water—each movement of nature a singular and noticeable event. Other boaters were in a world of their own, showering on deck, storing or making things fast in preparation for getting underway, or relaxing with a cup of coffee or tea, watching their world come to life.

After breakfast, we de-rigged and pulled the sailboard out of the water, secured it to the lifelines, and headed out of the sound. Clearing the shallow channel, we put up the foresail and mainsail, then Ken took the helm, having the best time of his sailing life. After a spirited, successful sail, we went into Road Harbour to clear out of BVI customs.

We were unable to tie up at the dock or find ample space for anchoring in the harbor, plus the wave action had become very rough. Since the Customs process here was convenient and quick, I took our passports and, as Ken passed by, I jumped onto the end of a large concrete pier, like a getaway scene in cinematic train robberies. Ken stood off, keeping the boat in motion until I returned. When he brought the boat around, he passed by the end of the pier, but too far away for me to safely make the leap aboard. The middle of the boat (the beam), being wider than the stern, passed close enough, but there was no break in the lifelines at the beam, nor anything to grab hold of to keep from falling back into the water and being caught between the boat, the pier, and the prop. The stern tapered away too far to risk a jump at the speed he was traveling. I realized then it was easier to jump onto a large, stationary object from a small moving position than vice versa. This was perhaps why outlaws first run or ride alongside the train they intend to rob.

"Try to get closer . . . and slower," I yelled.

On his next pass, he brought the boat a little closer, suddenly veering away to swing the stern toward the pier, since the boat pivoted on its center, but he swung the stern too sharply. Not wanting the hull to hit the pier, he left the helm and placed his bare foot outside the boat, trying to push off. The surging of the water and the rising and falling of the boat caused his foot to get wedged between the boat and the pier, and the many thousands of pounds weight of the boat and surge crushed his foot.

"Yeow!"

Holy crap. I have to get on board. Just do it! I jumped. He couldn't have brought it around again.

He collapsed in the cockpit. "Take the helm, Dad. I can't stand. My foot is crushed."

"Think there's anything broken?"

"Every damn bone in my foot, the way it feels. Ohmygod! I'm about to pass out."

He was bleeding, writhing in pain. His foot was still attached, but we had a health crisis on our hands in an inconvenient location. The thought of his injury made me nauseous. I was captain, doctor, and nurse, not well-trained at any of the three, but experienced at crisis management, having had a lot of calamity cross my path, even of my own making. We were still moving, so my first priority was to avoid further catastrophe by ensuring we did not hit, or get hit by, another boat while wondering what kind of attention his wound would require. His pain was intense, and the swelling was increasing. How many of those tiny bones in the foot were broken? Could he wait for medical attention until he arrived home tomorrow, as scheduled? Could he get home? Where's the nearest doctor?

I was too busy to panic. We were in foreign waters on a slow boat, had no ice, and never needed to use the first aid kit, which was hopefully on the boat somewhere. A cold pack I'd brought in case of strains was in the refrigerator. I steered my way among the many boats in Road Harbour and back to the wide-open Sir Francis Drake Channel. If we needed a hospital, I'd rather it be in the U.S., and St. Thomas was within view, maybe ten miles and two hours away. I sat Ken at the helm with his foot up, pointed him on a course toward Red Hook, cleaned his wound with towels and water, stopping the bleeding, then applied the cold pack, hoping to reduce the pain.

Any dream of more sail boarding now thwarted, we headed toward the shop to return our equipment before they closed. We'd used my board several times, but less than if we had both rented the same level of equipment with large, 6.5 sq. meter sails. The Christmas winds were a no-show, so Ken didn't have the wind-power required to make his smaller board plane. His sails and high-performance board never left their bags, though I couldn't fault him for low aim. He favors his dad in aiming for the fences, knowing you have to swing to hit a homerun.

In the seemingly interminable time it took to get to St. Thomas, I reflected on how Ken's youthful exuberance is part of his charm. His attitude is so positive; he gets enthused over almost anything. He was always eager to share his excitement by sending me envelopes of pictures of his last accomplishment or the rare gift of a handwritten letter, wishing I could be more involved in his life than was practical over the distance put between us. His excitement of building a spud gun was explosive. On my last visit to his home in Charleston, SC, he insisted I see it.

"What is a spud gun? Anything like a salad shooter?"

"Much more fun! It's made of PVC pipe. Just give it a dose of gas, jam a potato in the barrel, hit the igniter, and it comes out like a rocket. Can't give it too much gas, though, you'll get hurt. Let's go try it; it's downstairs on the porch."

Looking at it, I said, "That's pretty clever. How's it work, and what do you use it for?"

"It's pretty simple. Put the fuel in here—I use this old Windex spray bottle of gasoline. You can use hair spray or starter fluid, but a few sprays of gasoline give you the most bang for your buck. Then screw this cap back on. Find a potato that's pretty round and bigger than the barrel—this is a nice one—and jam the barrel on it like a cookie cutter so you have a tight fit in the barrel. Now we jam it in further with this smaller pipe. That's like the compression stroke of an engine. Put it up to your shoulder, aim, and hit this button."

"Okay, obviously you get instant French flies. Can it do cheeseburgers? I love cheeseburgers."

"You get French flies, you get mashed potatoes, and I make hash browns out of what didn't fit in the barrel. Everybody wins."

"What do you aim it at?"

"Usually that metal door of the pumping station across the street. It goes 'WHUMP!' and the potato explodes all over the place. Instant chaos."

"So, you do it for the chaos? AND the instant mashed potatoes?"

"Hell yeah, man, isn't that cool? Watch this!" . . . clickBOOM! . . . Bamm "Nailed it! Did ya see that?"

"Pretty neat. Nice rig. When the revolution comes, you'll be ready, if the potatoes don't spoil, which may be even better. A rotten potato is repellent, sent strong men running to the toe rails in the Bahamas, eager to jump in. You've reinvented the musket. If the Patriots had had gasoline and PVC, the Red Coats wouldn't have known what hit them, since you could put anything in the barrel. Unless they'd invented it. Then we'd be speaking haughty English like those bloody ol' blokes and they'd be chuffed."

I wondered about the cost of his "bullets," but knew, myself, thrills like building a gun and not getting blown up. And I shared his enthusiasm for setting hang-time and speed records on a sailboard, a bike, the environmental finesse of the sports, and nature in general.

The rental shop was on the water in Red Hook but had no pier, so I tied up on the closest mooring. Water conditions in the area are always rough, due to being open to Pillsbury Sound and the ferry traffic to the other islands, so getting equipment that was larger than *Speedy* off the boat and onto the dinghy in choppy water, then back on land and into the rental shop without Ken's help was a challenge. I bought ice, returned to the boat, and tried to contain the swelling.

"How ya feeling, Ken?"

"Hurts like a sonofabitch. I can feel my heartbeat in my foot, throbbing—boom, boom, boom! But the sting of the antiseptic has mostly gone away."

"Well, I can't visualize it without getting that shiver running through my chest, but here's my assessment of where we are. Getting you off the boat, climbing down into the dinghy, is problematic, as would be climbing a ladder to get out of it and up on a pier. You could take one step, but probably not the second. Then you don't know what will happen in the ER, might catch a malady worse than you now have and, of all the folks I have trucked into an ER, including myself, doctors seldom set any broken bones the day of the accident; they let the swelling go down first. If I'm wrong and the medical care here is not great, they might set it poorly and you'd be screwed up from now on. OR we can continue to work on calming down the foot, take ibuprofen and use ice for the pain and swelling, and wrap the foot for your scheduled flight home tomorrow. Is anyone able to pick you up at the airport?"

"Yeah, I got a ride."

"Or, there's a third option: I could saw you off at the ankle, tape it up, put a coffee cup on it that has a catchy slogan, and make you an attractive pirate."

"If I could get something for the pain right now, I might go for number three; otherwise, I'll take what's behind door number two."

"That's my boy, you're no sissy, and humor in the face of tragedy means you're gonna live. If you can fill a PVC pipe with gasoline, put it beside your head, and ignite it, you can handle a major case of what we hope is just, well, let's call it Road Harbour rash."

After dinner, we examined the foot for any excruciating pain indicating a broken bone, found none, then bandaged the foot and considered how to shoe Ken for shipping back to the States. His mobility was near zero: we needed an air-conditioned shipping crate with a recliner. We also needed diesel and water but that could wait. Meanwhile, having tied up to a private mooring, I stood watch until late in the day; no one showed up by dark, so the mooring was mine for the night. Significant sets of waves, likely to diminish after the ferries stopped running, came through all too often and severely rocked the boat until 2150, when I passed out.

The waves and his pain kept Ken awake all night. I had no clue. Tired, stressed, and secure on a mooring, I'd slept soundly. We went directly to the Crown Bay area, anchoring off Water Island between Ruyter Bay and Elephant Bay. I took the Johnson outboard to Crown Bay Maritime to have them fix the fuel problem, then we hailed a cab. At the airport, I served as Ken's crutch and handled his luggage until a Customs officer processed his papers, then brusquely told me I should not even be in the building.

"Then how about calling for a wheelchair."

Blank stare.

"That's okay, Dad. I think I can make it from here."

We had a hugging contest, said our goodbyes, and Ken hobbled toward his gate. Ahhh, Christmas in paradise. What could be better?

(It was years later when I realized that, in the islands, a gratuitous stimulus must precede their response. Pavlovian.)

The outboard was ready when I returned to the shop, so I remounted it, glad to have it fixed at any price, then returned to *Godspeed* to make things shipshape. I reveled in the thoughts of the rarity, value, and joy of having a week of exclusive, private time with each of my sons and nothing to do but have fun making memories while getting to know each other. It was priceless.

St. Ursala comes through:
Now it gets interesting

Later, with past events settled but feeling restless and wanting to be out doing something to celebrate the fixing of the outboard motor, I thought of ice cream, the foundational slab of my food pyramid, and developed an urgent desire for it. I took *Speedy* to the Baskin-Robbins store on the main street by the seawall for a treat impossible to come by at sea. The store was empty except for the woman behind the counter.

I ordered a cone of pralines and cream, having a more than pleasant encounter while doing so, wished the woman well, then retreated to the door.

Walking slowly back to the dinghy, I finished my ice cream while contemplating the previous exchange. Nothing wrong with a little flirting, lifting a mood or making someone feel attractive. My schedule was already full, so I'd given her all I could offer—a pleasant exchange and a good sense of herself. And she returned the favor.

The Sugar Reef Cafe came recommended by the lady in the Johnson repair shop. I headed there at dinnertime in my revitalized dinghy before the sun disappeared. Unfortunately but predictably, the outboard still had traces of its original problem, which showed up when I had returned to the boat earlier and now while docking at the cafe. Embarrassed to be driving a jalopy, I quickly tied it up and shut it down.

The meal was excellent. Boating would be more compelling if I could dine like this every night. When back at the boat, I put the laundry away, made the bed, and went out to the cockpit. A brilliant full moon was making the tips of the tiny ripples sparkle like a sea of diamonds. I felt like roaming; feeling the tug of adventure, I wanted to be in the middle of it, to drink it in. Prudence suggested it would be much safer to stay aboard. The motor did idle upon arriving at the boat, but for how long? Being adrift in an unlit dinghy at night with no power and no one to miss me was not a safe situation. I could drift to St. Croix by morning, if lucky, more likely out to sea. I decided to pass up the romantic joyride and pursue the engine issue tomorrow, living to enjoy another day. Hard choice though; I have an abiding love affair with nature.

The next day, reaching out to touch someone at home, I learned from Walt that Felicity was improving, though still had no use of her arm, their weather was cold, Christmas was okay. Ken's foot was still tender, nothing broken, just needed time to heal. He was still amped, "Oh hell yeah, man," about the fun he had. Megan sounded excited about her trip here. Caught her in her car, where she always sounds more delighted to hear from me than she does on the home phone. Unable to delve into her mind to achieve a better understanding—or relationship—I could only wonder, and ascribed her mood to her love of cellular technology or multitasking. It surely wasn't me, a known constant.

The morning was spent cleaning in anticipation of Megan, arriving at 1315. She was my wild card—hearts and diamonds, or spades and clubs? Her flight was held up in Cleveland due to snow, frozen stuff that seemed foreign at the moment, my only comparable here being ice cream. While waiting, I went into town again and bought reading material. Being among smiling people was novel and enjoyable.

Deciding another ice cream cone would not be too much of a good thing after two months of a dessert desert, I headed back to the Baskin-Robbins store and pushed open the door.

"OHMYGOD, that's him."

"It can't be!"

"It is! It is! I swear it is!"

Hmmm, had my new movie been released early due to overwhelming demand? Did I commit a crime, my picture hanging in the post office? Maybe it's my hat. Or the nickel tip.

By this time, I was well inside the store, walking toward the back counter where my server of yesterday was huddled with another store clerk. The public space was not vast, just big enough to display 31 flavors and sherbets, and handle a few of the crowd from the cruise boats that came to Charlotte Amalie and disgorged tourists by the thousands.

"What do you mean, 'Oh my God, it's him'?"

"I can't say!" said the blushing clerk familiar to me.

"She had a dream about you last night," said her younger co-worker, in a contrasting, monotone, "Duh! Whatever" style. She could have been knitting a sweater and delivered that line without dropping a stitch.

I gave it a try. "Oh really! That's interesting. Was it a good dream?"

My now beet-red-faced dreamer would only say, "I can't tell you."

"From the blushing taking place, I would guess it wasn't a nightmare. . . . What's your name?"

"I can't talk. I'm too embarrassed," she said tersely.

"Well, your name shouldn't embarrass you . . . just your first name?"

"Dawn. . . . What's yours?"

Gimme a break; makes my forearms ache. Dawn brings memories of Abraham Bay and rug wringing when the Dawn soap bottle spilled while crossing from Rum Cay.

"Bond. James Bond," I declared in my most assured, strong voice.

"Oh sure, that's a good one. What is it really?"

"Byrd. Bryan Byrd. Four-letters, both start with a 'B,' five-letter first names. It's an alias. You're the only one that knows. Pretty close, isn't it?"

"Kinda."

"How close does it have to be? We both travel in exotic cars and fast boats, rescue damsels in distress, same number of letters, five and four. That's no meaningless coincidence. Now, damsel Dawn, your dream that is making you blush, if you lived it out, would that be a good thing?"

I was feeling rather confident and, having established myself as a near-equivalent to James Bond, the words were flowing, surprising me if no one else. Amazing what confidence does for verbal fluency. I knew too well the opposite, when my bilingualism shows as I speak gibberish. In her timid but connected way, she was encouraging.

"Ahhhh?" she took in a quick breath of shock or surprise. "What kind of ice cream—pralines and cream?"

Ah-hah, she remembered. "Sugar cone. One scoop. Big one, though, you know size matters." I watched her turn beet-red again, then: "Dawn, would you believe I had a dream about you last night?"

"Did not! . . . I don't believe it . . . You didn't! Did you?" she only halfway insisted, sounding more and more like she wanted to believe something more improbable than winning the lottery.

"Then what drove me back here today? I had to see you again. Ice cream is just a cover. Want me to tell you about it?"

"Heck yeah!"

"What happened to 'Ladies First'? Show me yours, and I'll show you mine. Was it as good for you as it was for me? . . . And isn't it about time to meet the parents?"

She giggled. "I'm not talking. I can't tell you about my dreams," she persisted in a high pitch. "I'm too embarrassed." Turning to her friend, "Why did you start this? Look what you got me into!"

"I didn't get you into this. You screamed first; you didn't have to . . . say . . . a . . . thing!"

"Well," I inserted, "okay, wanna hear about mine?" A slight nod yes. "We met at a party in a friend's Mediterranean-style mansion in Mission Hills, Kansas; do you remember that? You had been seated across the table from me during dinner and played with my leg with your foot, especially during dessert. Remember what we had? . . . Ice cream, and the way you were tonguing your spoon, only sucking half of what was on the spoon off at a time, slowly withdrawing it, was suggestively oral. Then we danced in the large foyer with a pianist playing. When the music stopped, we kept holding hands, looking into each other's eyes. I asked if you'd had a tour of the home yet. What did you say?"

"Oh, no!"

"Exactly, you had not, so we went exploring upstairs and passed a window in a short hall between two bedrooms that overlooked the vast, sloping front lawn, the statuary, fountains, and reflecting pools beautifully lit. The window was low and open, so we knelt and put our elbows on the windowsill and stared into the night. You wiggled to get your hip closer to mine. We looked at each other and lightly kissed, then turned toward each other, still on our knees, and kissed hungrily. You rubbed against my thigh, obviously excited. We looked for some privacy, entered a bedroom, locked both doors, and then you, well, should I go on? Lucky it's just the three of us. Wanna hear the rest?"

"I DO!" interjected the friend.

"Holy crap. Uhhhhh . . . No, I don't think I can . . . not right now. You made that up, didn't you?"

"Well, I've knelt at that window with a woman that looked just like you. Is your dream different?"

"Oh my God, I can't," she whispered, then exclaimed: "I don't even know you!"

"You don't know me? After last night? Dawn, you know everything. C'mon, you have to either tell me, or your priest. I'll give you dispensation at a discount and my phone number, no penance. Priest may not be as cheap, and he will surely want all the details. It's what he lives for. You may even have to pay up for a dream that good." I'd made my best offer. It had been fun thus far.

"I can't, no way . . . almost wish I could," she said, glancing toward her friend.

"Then you're not Catholic. That's a deal you shouldn't refuse."

"But it's not a substitute; I'd still have to pay."

"Probably. Church has been in business much longer than I've been in town."

Her adamancy seemed certain, then she sounded like she was weakening. By now, I was worried about the dinghy, so I didn't have all day. Almost wished I had paid to park so I wouldn't miss the ending, but one, maybe both were unavailable.

"Well, that ice cream cone you've been holding is melting; can you drop that scoop back in and get a new one? It's hot outside, like it seems to be in here. If I can't get the story, I'll settle for the ice cream. They may be impounding my yacht as we speak."

I had tied up in a space where it said to not even think about it, so I tied up as suggested—without even thinking—feeling that would suffice as compliance for the short time I expected to be there, not at all expecting to star in a young lady's dream. That may not hold up in court, but it should be a plausible defense. Hopefully *Speedy* was still there. It would be hard to walk back to the boat, anchored in Honeymoon Bay. I was going to need it, any honeymoon here being held at bay.

"Can you tell me how it began, or if it had a happy ending?"

"Uh uhh," she uttered, still blushing. She handed me the cone, touching my hand in the exchange, then used a towel to wipe up the counter absentmindedly.

I gave her two bucks and started for the door. "You may never know, but I guarantee it's better in real life, and you can take as long as you like. See you in your dreams, my dear. OH! . . . Thanks for last night," I smiled.

Pausing in the doorway, I turned and made the telephone hand sign next to my ear and said, "Call me," then walked away. She may be driven to torment, or it may have been a nightmare for all I know. Surely she got relief seeing me go, her later thoughts perhaps another matter, like it often was for me—what-if's can last for years. I wouldn't have made so bold a bet if I hadn't felt I was holding a good hand. After all, we had spent the night together. Doing what, I didn't know, though curious. I was relieved when I saw *Speedy* was still mine.

Megan finally arrived around 1500. As she walked toward me from the taxi, I had time to admire her appearance—a great smile, girl-next-door fresh face, sexy body dressed in a denim skirt and multi-colored geometric-design blouse, coordinated accessories, green eyes, and long, curly, auburn hair (that will soon disappear under a ball cap after proper re-introductions are made), looking so good I was amazed at my luck and questioned my own thinking. She hadn't wanted me to make this journey, but her presence and the magnitude of her smile confirmed she was happy to be here. It appeared our on-again off-again relationship was, for the moment, not off-again. I'd give it time and another try.

Looking at this beautiful woman and concluding there's no finer designer than of the feminine form, I was, once again, unsure what to expect. Would we enjoy the next two weeks, or spend it composing and singing our swan song? We went inside Tickle's on the marina and ordered settle-down, get-reacquainted drinks and appetizers.

"You look great, Megan—as usual. Thanks for coming. It's nice to see you."

"Thank you. You, too. Wasn't sure you'd survive, or that I would."

"See me? Or survive?" I asked.

"Huh? Oh . . . Yes! I almost forgot, you literally listen," she laughed, "I guess I wasn't sure you OR I would survive, or that I WOULD see you."

"Well, the trip wasn't an easy one; I felt near death more than once, when I feared NO ONE would ever see me again. . . . AND we had major personnel . . . challenges that had us considering turning around."

"You spent a lot of time together on what's certainly a small boat with tight living quarters. You knew Walt; was Rocco the challenge?"

"Either him or me. Walt left in the Bahamas, went home. I had to live with just Rocco for an excruciating length of time."

"I can't wait to hear about it! You look good, a little shaggy, but none the worse for wear. I've never seen that many curls. Could use a little trim, which I'd be glad to do. No doubt you have scissors."

"You know me; I try to be prepared—before it's too late! I have the scissors, but nature doesn't wait. I've wished I'd had more sailing knowledge to begin with; I know what I'm doing now, but I was as useless as a barnacle on a keel when I started, couldn't have even drawn a nautical simile. Nonetheless, here I am and, maybe more remarkable, here you are."

"Well, what can I say?"

"Then I'll say it." I asserted. "I sense something's different; is it?"

"Still have that boldness, don't you?" She smiled.

"After this, it's probably worse."

"What do you think is different?"

"So far, your hug."

"My hug?" she exclaimed, flinching backward, surprised if not offended.
"Yeah."

"What's different about my hug? I always hug you when I see you."

"I know, but you didn't pitty-pat me on the back this time."

"Do I usually? Never noticed . . . is that bad?"

"Not patting is a warmer, more sincere hug; patting shows signs of insincerity, or nervousness, maybe a social hug. It might not always be a bad sign, but I've long wondered if I made you nervous. It's been a concern."

"When did I pat you on the back?"

"Oooohhh, for about four years. Were you nervous all that time?"

"Hmmm . . . maybe being concerned about you for more than two months is making me hold on a little tighter," she laughed. "Think that could be it?"

"It's plausible. . . . You've never talked like that."

"If that's true, hmmmm . . . well, guess I need therapy," she chirped, while doing her endearing pursing and twisting of her lips.

"There may be some on the boat."

"I've been needing this for a while now," she smiled. "Hope it's deep therapy."

"The boat does come well equipped for its size, especially therapy for a vivacious, attractive, needy guest from the mainland."

"Oooh! Is that me?"

"Could be; do you have a reservation?"

"I . . . I think so. At least for a berth on a boat down here somewhere. Got one? I guess I could look arou"—

"No, no, that's not necessary. Here it is, and it's non-cancellable."

We spent a little more time bantering, catching up, and finishing the appetizers. Suddenly, she placed her knife and fork in the middle of her plate, took a last swallow of iced tea, dabbed her full lips with her napkin, then stood up, ready to move on. "Let's go!"

"You're ready?"

"That doesn't begin to describe it!" She headed toward the exit.

Good afternoon, Jim. Your assignment, should you decide to accept, is NOT . . . Mission Impossible. Pfffftt. . . .OH, and Mr. Phelps, just one more thing, it appears deciding NOT to accept your assignment IS Mission Impossible.

"Hey, don't leave without your therapist!" Already getting behind, I quickly dropped payment on the table and tried to keep up. She had her luggage from the hostess and was waiting at the door.

In contrast, *Speedy* was waiting patiently. We placed her luggage in the dinghy, jumped in as carefully as wearing a skirt requires, and headed for the boat. After time to unpack, look around, and relax, we had dinner, then stayed around the table to discuss the last two months. One of my many questions concerned whether she, not one to sit around and forsake a social life, had found a new love.

"Well, I had plenty of time, but I was able to get away to make this trip," she teased. "How about you?"

"Oh, you know, the path from Florida to here is littered with opportunities, mostly professional girls, though. So few passing boats, so many women."

"Bet you had a lot of mermaids jumping into the boat."

"How'd you hear about that? . . . No more than one or two at a time," I confessed.

"Mermaids can't be as rare as unicorns," she assured me.

"Don't tell me you scored with a unicorn!"

"I can't talk about it. They're very secretive and sensitive."

"They are sensitive, and not as fortunate as they might seem. Regardless, here we are. And I did find a phone to call you, which wasn't easy."

"Not easy to call me, or find a phone? . . . When you left, it seemed you were being careful to avoid saying 'see you later,' so I thought that might be the end of it. I was surprised you called."

I passed on answering her questions, thinking this was not the time to work on the fatal flaws in a four-year relationship, based on the sage advice that you shouldn't discuss contentious issues with your spouse in the bedroom. Why take a bullet after a truce has been called? As for the next two weeks, why screw them up when any issues can be revisited later in a larger space and less glamorous environment with an exit strategy.

"Any limitations on what you can do while you're here?" I asked.

"Well, I'm not some Tammy Wynette staying home baking cookies and serving tea. I pursue my own interests."

"That sounds familiar. Should I quote you on that, or someone else?"

She paused, set her jaw in an alluring way with a mischievous smile, put her hand on my thigh and, with her other, unbuttoned two top buttons on her blouse, exposing her firm cleavage and fine lingerie, saying with a grin, "Maybe you should check to see if any damage has been done!"

That settled it. Any time for ambivalence was over. A woman's hand on the inside of your thigh, alone in a boat, is a strong signal, and a woman traveling this far best not be denied, nor scorned, as in "Hell hath no fury like . . . " especially since she is staying, or at least was invited, for two weeks. Such directness, delivered with eye contact, was what I'd been wanting for years, now first coming to me in paradise while feeling betwixt and between. Any further delay on my part would either scorch the next two weeks or set her on fire.

"Well, as a proper host, dedicated to your satisfaction, maybe I should, especially if you insist, get this junket started off right. So you've otherwise been a good girl, huh?"

"With a little torture, I might find something to confess. Or make it up."

"Ah-hah! I'm game; let's play." True to her religion, hoping to expunge a little guilt or ratchet up the stimulation.

After a long kiss, embrace, and partial disrobing, I escorted her to the "lab" and performed a deliciously slow and thorough inspection, then applied appropriate therapy. The confined spaces and the low ceiling of the V-berth encouraged and assisted the wonderful physicality of our reunion. Time apart added to the rigor and excitement. Having no place to go and plenty of time, we exhausted the evening.

After Megan fell asleep, I had time to reflect on how my invitation had been extended thinking she would enjoy the experience, since we had visited St. Thomas two years ago and she liked boats. And, I thought having her company would be better than spending the next two weeks alone, feeling unfulfilled for not sharing such an unprecedented and exceptional opportunity. How I would feel toward Megan after all that had happened during the last ten weeks was uncertain. However, the siren call of love, spiritual or physical, is a beguiling call that engenders all manner of behavior, which led to a great night's sleep.

The next day, after tidying up the boat and doing our first "anchors aweigh" together, we went into Crown Bay marina. When we reached the gas dock, several boats were already there, in essence parallel parked, and one was following me in, putting pressure on my securing the last available space. As a fresh skipper, I was nervous and wanted to keep on going since I was totally new to the required maneuvering of backing up and moving sideways. Going slow is advisable, but with wind and the current at work, the boat is always in motion, and a driving force is a necessity for steering. I didn't know the rotation of the propeller and direction of the rudder required to "walk" the boat to the dock, but guessed correctly, and my maneuvering was successful, increasing my confidence. Soon, I'd be teaching this stuff. We fueled up, dumped the trash, bought ice in memory of Chris, and away we sailed to St. John, one more tour, same general direction as with Chris and Ken but different stops with surely different experiences.

We sailed to Maho Bay, anchored, then rode Speedy back to Cinnamon Bay, where there was a campground with park-provided basic living structures, camp store, and water sports concession, to check general availability of board sailing equipment. While beached, we cleaned the bottom of *Speedy*, then zipped back to the boat for a shower, early dinner, and to watch many schools of fish breaking the surface. Something was going on down there; they were unusually active, perhaps leaping for a look at my new "yacht adornment" on board. They may have been saying, "Hey, the guy is straight after all. Total turnaround. Third time's the charm. Blub, blub." In fish trash-talk, they use a lot of clichés.

Pelicans dive-bombing for fish and an occasional turtle surfacing or swimming by added to the natural beauty of the Maho Bay cove, one of the prettiest bodies of water in the area, the color always appearing to be a brighter, denser aquamarine. It was separated from the deep green foliage of the hills by a ring of golden sand, and topped with a clear blue sky floating only a few cotton balls of silver-white clouds. The natural beauty and the calmer water, with a saddle between the hills through which cooling breezes from the east entered the cove, made this a superb anchorage.

Maho Bay is the site of an ecologically-based tent colony carved out of the hillside by hand on St. John, designed by ecotourism pioneer Stanley Selengut. Recycled materials are used for construction, with solar and wind sources for electricity. The sites overlook the bay and are connected by an elaborate system of many steps and wooden pathways. From the boat anchorage below, there is little evidence of the resort's presence. It is a rustic experience, definitely well located, in great demand and, according to one source, one of the ten best lodgings in the U.S. National Parks. If you want a sample of home life in the U.S. where we depend only on wind and solar for our energy, this is it. Leave the hair dryer, anything electric, at home; bring plenty of sunscreen and deodorant. We use solar and wind for the boat, but it's the fossil fuel-powered generator that makes life certain when the other two cannot handle demand. Only otherwise is the future unknown.

The next day, we lounged until noon, then set out to rent a sail board. When we got to Cinnamon Bay, no wind—not unusual when you want some—so we went back to the boat and suited up for snorkeling to explore the shoreline east of the bay, up to a point that separated Maho from Francis Bay. We saw a small barracuda along the way, and a much larger one at the point. Barracuda don't swim around like most fish, they hang in one place like a badass thug on a street corner in a rough neighborhood. Giving them a wide berth, we witnessed a stunning orchestration of fish at the point, consisting of a large school of bright yellow juvenile blue tang, a school of adults in royal blue, backed up with large jacks and many others, with the 'cuda off to the left—the scene from this side looking like the President's kid and classmates on a school playground with the Secret Service standing guard. When sufficiently mesmerized, we decided to return, again giving the "Secret Service" a wide berth. We took a walk on the beach, rode Speedy back to the boat, had a late lunch, and lounged on the bow, cushioned by a bagged sail until sundown. The setting was awesome—temperature was delightful, water was gorgeous, scenery magnificent, there was no place I'd rather have been. Having a female companion was not so bad, either. This seemed to be a time to be thankful—for the day and the year.

After-dark activities were to prepare and eat dinner, wash dishes, top off and recharge the boat batteries, then make plans for the next several days. Being the last day of the year, I decided that perhaps I should do the customary planning for a greater time horizon! From a reasonable point of view, it was hard to find fault with life, since I was living what I had worked toward. What, then, as a plan for the coming year?

The New Year Top Ten List

1. Have faith in yourself. The proof is in the pudding that I'm enjoying this year.
2. Stay away from any temptation to grab additional "instant" wealth. It is high risk, and unlikely.
3. Take advice only from those demonstrably wiser than yourself. Many talk a good game; look to their personal performance for conviction.
4. Spend less than you earn.
5. Enjoy what you spend, or don't spend!
6. Be skeptical; it's appropriate.
7. Associate only with those who add value to your life. Expect that they will do similarly. If you want to keep them as friends, provide value.
8. Prepare for the rest of your life. Work on self-improvement through reading, travel, language study, random and spontaneous acts of charity and helpfulness, proper diet and exercise. Take a multivitamin and vitamin D, just in case.
9. Set specific financial goals and attain them.
10. Enjoy each day; life is uncertain.

Saturday, January 1, 1994

I started the year like much of last year, my first year of retirement—getting up late (comparatively). A wholesome breakfast in Maho Bay, with a helping of Ken's carrot bread, was deeply satisfying.

The wind was up, so Megan and I went to Cinnamon Bay and rented sailboards—big, safe, floaty boards, perfect for Megan's experience level, and spent most of the first hour getting her started. In the "small swells" conditions we had, after several dunkings and step-offs, she got her counterbalancing for the wind and waves under control, achieved a successful uphaul of the sail, and stayed up long enough to sail out of shouting distance, almost out of sight, on a beeline for St. Thomas. I wasn't sure what approach she was using, since she had yet to turn around, but she was staying on the board. Eager for action, I did a beach start and took off.

Much later, unable to see her on the several occasions when I could briefly glance up, I became concerned, beached my board, walked up on the rise of the shore and more thoroughly scanned the water. Still unable to see her, I dragged the dinghy into the water and motored downwind. Riding slowly by other board sailors, I found none resembling her. Any sails down seemed to have someone floundering nearby. That was positive; a rig without a flounderer would be deeply concerning. Searching back and forth across the water, mimicking a Coast Guard rescue plan, I saw nothing familiar. Oh my! If she drowned, the board should float, but to where? I checked the current and, from what I could tell, the wind would be the determining factor. There was no giving up; dead or alive, she must be somewhere, and there were fewer folks to check out this far downwind from the sailing site. Anyone here had a big job ahead to get back upwind. Soon, there was nothing left to offer any hope.

Not being one who panics—it hurts your performance when you need it most—I was baffled, unsure what to do next. What more should I do, and what would it be, before I alert the real Coast Guard? Is time of the essence? I kept telling myself she's somewhere, but where? There's an answer, I just don't know it. If nothing else, there should be a board; having a foam core, they will not sink. The lee shore was quite distant and, if she reached it, where did she go? I decided if I didn't find her before I got to it, I would sweep by the shore back toward the launch site looking for a board and a sail before heading out into open water, where I would need help.

I again scanned the bay, empty of any sailor downwind (though I kept hoping to see her if I blinked and looked again), the shore still too far away to reveal anything as small as a board. Meanwhile, the bow of a distant speedboat came into view, coming toward me at high speed. I semiconsciously tried to move aside while contemplating my next action. However, with each move, it was correcting its course to coincide with mine. Having alluded to James Bond while snorkeling Johnson Reef, he was now about to run over me, a threat aforementioned only in jest. What the hell was going on?

It was unmistakably a beauty of a classic Chris Craft, only owned and maintained by those with discretionary cash—rich mahogany hull and decking; chrome windshield trim, spotlight and air horns; an enclosed engine; and American flag flying off the rear deck. The pilot could play a leading man in a movie, handsome in his captain's cap and cool shades. An elegant boat, like a restored Duesenberg or Cord car. Why did he continue to bear down on me? When the boat slowed and its bow dropped, leveling out, I discovered—to great relief devolving to a bit of pique—he was carrying someone of recent acquaintance on the port side of the boat, dressed in a swimsuit and a sheepish grin. *OH. Thank. Goddd! . . . Now . . . where have you been?*

I could breathe again.

Megan quickly crawled over the starboard gunwale and into *Speedy*— quite a comedown, from highly varnished mahogany to faded red rubber— we thanked the captain profusely and started toward the board.

"Wow! . . . Well, just wow! You've done unexpected things before but, this one . . . you had me very worried. Glad you came along when you did; I didn't know what to do next." I lightened up. "And here you are, just out running around with another man. If only you'd told me. . . . Are you okay?"

"Yeah, I'm tired, but okay."

"I'd say you're doing okay. Sent you off on a $1,000 sailboard, and you return in a $50,000 speedboat. Just how good was your day, Megan? Anything unusual happen?"

"Oh no, not really, just a little boardsailing. Couldn't get the board to cooperate and turn around, had a mind of its own, so it became a one-way trip. I discovered land waaaay down there . . . though I looked for it all along the way."

"Well, you get high marks for staying on the board all that way."

"I wasn't on the board all the time. When I fell off close enough to shore to stand up, I staggered and crawled out of the surf, drunk from exhaustion."

"So between that and the boat ride, what happened? Was the boat nearby?"

"No . . . I crashed a garden party, ran into Ricky Nelson . . . but he didn't look the same, didn't hear any songs . . . had hors d'oeuvres and refreshment until they could give me a ride back to you . . . the usual."

"This might be funny now, but I was cussing, worrying about what I was gonna tell your mom. Even if she weren't high strung, she'd have had a shitfit, like I did, if I said I was sending her a six-foot box for Christmas, something I wasn't looking forward to."

"Ooh, she'd understand. She knows I live near the edge. Drives her crazy."

"You are pretty adventurous; we've had many good ones, you never turned one down. Wonder if anyone got a movie of your ride . . . or swim?"

"I don't know, but God, I'd love to see it. Sure to be an Oscar winner . . . Best Live Action Short, if they did . . . I was on and off that damn board too many times. It had to be a riot . . . never felt so helpless, said words I hadn't used for a while, a few you've never heard from me . . . triceps will be sore tomorrow . . . everything will."

The hyperbole of anxious relief might have continued, but we soon found the board and sail, balanced them across the dinghy leaving little room for ourselves, and made our way back to the concession site to return the gear.

What happened between her landing and the boat trip? Didn't know at this point but it would've been just like her to enjoy canapés and a drink at a garden party following a harrowing board sailing session, holding court in her bathing suit while telling a story of being shipwrecked after being commandeered by an unrelenting force. She'd had an adventure, a meal, and a social visit. In this, she was emulating my experience in bringing the boat south, where each misfortune or landing led to interesting people and events.

When we returned to *Godspeed* around 1530, our anchorage was getting crowded. Because many of the boat charters start at Tortola on Saturday, nearby anchorages fill up on Saturday afternoon and evening. For me, an après-sail reading of the wind surfing magazines usually follows a struggling day on the water. It's my good intention to read before I go out, so the know-how will be fresh in my mind, but I seldom do it. Megan admittedly would have benefitted, especially regarding how to turn around upwind (tack). She had her technique reversed, and all attempts at an upwind turn took her downwind, requiring a jibe, something she hadn't mastered. Thankfully, her litany of uncompleted jibes eventually arced her back toward land as opposed to the middle of Pillsbury Sound, her initial point of sail.

Megan was a great sport about it, so it must have been quite the party, giving her drama a happy ending, though she seemed to be catching a cold, or showing evidence of having caught one earlier. Her state of exhaustion likely opened the door. Tomorrow, we would see more of the exotic islands, probably Tortola, if she could get out of the berth.

As we were finishing dinner in the cockpit, a young man in a dinghy stopped by. Nathan was 16, living on a boat with his parents, a brother, and a cat, most recently from Maine, a place better to be from if you want to sail year-round. The family had sold everything to be here, so he would be staying at least through March, the future unknown. Their boat was named *Carapace*, good name for a cocoon, as boats sometimes serve. It had belonged to the well-known Dr. Benjamin Spock, who kept it in the British Virgin Islands, frequenting the Peter Island Yacht Club. Nathan was not sure if the doctor had babied the boat, but said it behaved pretty well if properly nurtured and given good instruction. Nathan worked at Coral Bay, but had been board sailing near us this afternoon.

He approached our boat because it hailed from Annapolis, MD, as did Nathan three years ago, a commonality and how friendships start in this world of transients. After spending a lot of time on a boat, you long to talk to others with whom you might have a little in common and, I suspect in Nathan's case, be free from parental coaching (or just talked out). Nathan looked hungry for conversation with anyone new, especially equals, seemed to be an amiable fellow, dressed differently, as most mariners do. Boat dress can be anything you choose, whatever is left after the estate sale and the ravages of the sea. Anyone dressing too nattily is usually here short term. We enjoyed his visit.

The anchor chain groaned most of the night, preventing any quality sleep, unusual for Maho Bay. The rain started and stopped many times during the night, which required closing and opening the hatches and portholes. If it were cooler, we could have left them closed all night, but it became too stuffy and hot. To get the sleep hours, if not the quality, we slept late, then headed for Soper's Hole, also called West End, Tortola, disliked for the little bit of anchorage that's available for an anchor rode of 100–150 feet. I dropped anchor in a spot I thought would work, then got into the dinghy to check its hold using a glass-bottomed bucket. As I was watching, it broke loose and the boat started drifting backward, either out to sea, or sooner into the boat aft of us. I quickly re-boarded, secured *Speedy*, started the engine, weighed anchor, and headed for Road Harbor, deciding to come back by taxi if Soper's Hole as an attraction warranted it.

Road Harbor was an upwind sail through big swells, so I set up the autopilot and hid behind the dodger to avoid the splash. We anchored in Baugher's Bay after cruising the harbor, looking for a calm site where we might later find sleep.

Checking in with Customs, I was enlightened that it was a holiday and we could pay triple the normal rate for the privilege of checking in on a Sunday after New Year's Day, something like a Scrabble triple word score in reverse. The staff would be paid in any case, but those checking in underwrote the holiday salary. No one died, just the cost of education, supporting the cliché that education, costly as it may be, is less expensive than ignorance. We checked out the town, found nothing to buy, then took the dinghy to Village Cay Marina for dinner al fresco, a tasty experience with a million-dollar view from our boardwalk table.

Back in Baugher's Bay, the boat was a-rockin, and not the sensual kind, while I tried to do crossword puzzles, which was tough enough anyway. Wind was bringing us rain; maybe there would be calm after the storm.

The rolling didn't slow much overnight, so I was more than ready to cut my losses and motored out of Road Harbor early in the morning. Outside the harbor and heading east, the waves were still significant. Our trip to Beef Island was short enough, though more memorable than the distance would deserve. Along the way, there was another boat approaching our port side, crossing our path at a right angle on a port tack using a genoa sail (a foresail large enough to overlap the main mast), so their vision was restricted. From a long distance back, I could see them and they could see me, but as we closed, I became obscured by their sail and they had too many happy, chatty people on board to be paying attention to sailing.

Their boat had the right of way, since they were under sail; I was motoring, and thought there was time to pass in front of them. The way sailboats bob and weave at just faster than walking speed, it can long be uncertain where you'll be later. We were fighting oncoming waves and wind, so we didn't have the progress and mobility a boat under power would normally possess. Much of our progress seemed vertical and hard to achieve, so I was reluctant to give any of it up.

Realizing too late I was wrong and now in jeopardy, I got their attention at the last minute and they swerved behind me. They were pissed because they weren't paying attention; they just didn't know that was the reason. I was red-faced with embarrassment. As they passed behind me, now readily visible, I proffered my best mime of a mea culpa, then went around Beef Island and entered Trellis Bay, appropriately chastened with my tail tucked between my legs, everything luckily still intact. I'd come as close to hitting another boat as I would care to, learning a crucial lesson and principle without any expense other than a few frightened moments and a loss of pride. It can be summed up with three words: "Don't risk it." Next time, if there is any doubt whatsoever, I will plan early to pass behind, no matter that it may seem out of the way. There is no way you can go wrong passing behind the other boat, unless, of course, there is a following boat, or one coming from the opposite direction, or you run aground—there may be more.

We anchored in a recommended location, and took Speedy to the beach. I bought groceries, two hand-drawn souvenir maps from a local artist, and checked out the sailboard equipment. Rentals from a location this remote were twice the Red Hook price. After her last experience, Megan wasn't psyched to do it again. We had a lazy lunch on the boat, sunbathed, and got ready for dinner and a show at The Last Resort, built on a small nearby island in the center of Bellamy Cay.

It was tricky getting to The Last Resort after dark; coral barely below the water's surface fought with the propeller. I tried to row, but the wind had picked up to where it was a dissuasive force. Eventually, we found sufficient prop clearance, docked, and enjoyed the evening. The buffet dinner was good, with the restaurant owner providing riotous entertainment—jokes, songs, sound effects. The show contained a lot of deprecating jokes about sailors like us and Brits like him, likened to *Goon Show Goes to Sea*, and he was assisted by a white donkey named "Vanilla," assuaging my recent feelings of being the lone jackass in the area.

Our anchorage was documented as being well protected and having a good holding ground. Before the show, the anchor looked well set when I checked it, though there was grass on the bottom. Afterward, the night deteriorated into wind and rain, keeping us up much of the night, opening and closing the hatches. During one of those closings, I looked out the companionway and saw a much larger boat a few feet behind us, looming over the cockpit like a freighter. Our anchor had broken loose; we were moving backwards, now within inches of another boat!

I started the engine, pulled up the anchor, moved forward, dropped the anchor and tied it off in the pitch black of night, then got in the dinghy with another anchor. While positioning the second anchor, the night turned into a gray, rainy dawn. Hopefully, the anchors would hold; we were desperate for sleep.

We went to bed later in the morning as the rain continued, which meant hatches closed, and slept on and off until noon. While checking out the set of the anchors by snorkeling over each, the skies cleared, so I took *Speedy* to Marina Cay, a small and pretty island to the north, to look around.

Megan was sleeping off her flu-like malady, so it was a good day for roaming in the dinghy, for yacht maintenance, and reading. I was making good progress on the massive Pulitzer prize-winning book, *The Prize*, by Daniel Yergin, about the 150-year history of the global oil industry, its money, power, and impact on the world. Part of my daily exercise routine was restraining the book, the 800-page gorilla in the room.

With two anchors, more scope on the anchor rodes, and no rain, I awoke the next morning with a renewed feeling of joy and appreciation of this adventure. It was easy to forget all the repairs and nighttime showers when in paradise with a good night's sleep.

After a leisurely breakfast, we motored out of Trellis Bay, heading for Gorda Sound. A perfect day to sail, we hung out the jenny (nickname for a genoa, a large form of a jib, both foresails), and sailed close to Great Dog Island trying to gain upwind ground. Approaching Great Dog, we tried a tack (change in direction by swinging the bow through the eye of the wind), our first as a sailing team. As the bow swung around, the sheet knots at the clew of the jenny hung up on the inner forestay and we missed the tack, going into irons, getting back winded, then blown sideways, losing much of any upwind gain. We eventually sailed out of it, but it pushed us back severely, requiring an extra couple of tacks, obviously not our forte. All tacks were a problem with the inner forestay in place. Once underway, a powerful gust came up and severely rolled the boat on its side. We both cussed and decided to furl the sail and motor on, reducing further panic.

We anchored in Gorda Sound off of Prickly Pear Island, my usual place, and explored the sound in the dinghy. We were back at the boat before dark for dinner, then stargazing. It would be hard to overstate the fascination of the night sky. The sailing manual had sky charts to help identify constellations, which were easier to see absent the light pollution of the larger islands.

Megan was eager to exchange the unsteady platform of the boat for a solid day on the beach at the Bitter End, where sailors could rent a towel, beach chaise, and the pool. The setting was paradise-perfect cover material for a travel magazine. Palm trees, flowered landscaping, blue skies, clear blue-green water, everything you could ask for. Picking a double chaise with a hood, and thick, padded cushions, we settled into our reading, taking an occasional bracing dip in the palm tree-shaded pool. It was a fabulous day, possibly the ultimate paradigm for couples' paradise time.

Megan was getting rid of her ailment, offloading it to me—sore throat, motion-sensitive stomach, general overall malaise. Nonetheless, after breakfast the next day, we rented a Jeep at Leverick Bay, my first time to drive since Florida. The roads were scary, no wider than one and a half lanes, seldom any shoulder, edges were sharp and fell off into nowhere, surface was bumpy—ski-slope steep—and the drive wheels slipped on the steeper grades; good four-by-four terrain. The drive from Leverick Bay took us close to the top of Gorda Peak, providing panoramic views of the bays and sounds of the east and south side, the Bitter End, Necker Island to the north and northwest, and more distant islands we had passed getting there; stunningly gorgeous. Upon descending, we arrived in Spanish Town, where we fueled up before going to Little Dix Bay, a five-star resort.

The resort was precision-manicured-with-scissors elegant. While walking around, enjoying the incomparable panoramic views from the restaurant patio, we found an open-air reading room where I made myself at home, kicked back, and checked out the news, stocks, and mutual funds in USA Today.

We then headed for the Baths, which were quite extensive, and explored all the way to Devil's Bay. Glad I finally went the distance, it required climbing of rocks and ladders, as well as a hike, to access this portion of the area, but was worth the effort to see the combinations of pools, rocks, and scenery. Nothing I've seen equals this creation of boulders bigger than most houses, the shaded grottoes and pools created by the rocks leaning on one another, and the white sand beaches bathed by crystal clear water. I had to tell myself the stones had been here for ages and probably would not shift in the next two hours. Bring a camera, the family or a model, and the photo composition opportunities using curved and straight lines, shadows and shafts of streaming sunlight, pools of water, sand and rocks are a photographer's dream.

Near the car park, we enjoyed a fruit punch at the Mad Dog Bar before continuing to the end of the island, over an unpaved road with steep inclines, where we discovered the ruins of a Spanish copper mine, appropriately on Copper Mine Point. Signs claimed it was being restored, since 1987. If true, it will take a while at the pace things are going. The place was so remote, you would not want to get in trouble of any kind here. Not a place to meet to settle an argument, better to build a luxury resort.

Back at the boat, we were alone. Charter boats have to be closer to their check-in port for a timely return on Saturday. We had all of Gorda Sound to ourselves, feeling like kids who didn't want to go inside at dark.

For the next day and a half, I recharged the boat's and my personal batteries, trying to forestall energy problems. Late Sunday morning, we motored through Gorda Sound into Leverick Bay for potable water. Our approach to the dock was perfect, being able to hand ropes to the attendants without bumping. At my skill level, the wind had to cooperate. The attendant pumped in sixteen gallons, which I thought was too few, but the tank was full and, because the water was salty, I only inquired once to verify they pumped so little. Maybe they weren't charging for the salt.

We were reluctant to leave the luxury of the Bitter End Resort and the beautiful, protected waters of Gorda Sound, but decided to move on to see other sites. I was making my eighth and last trip through the shallow channel on the easterly end of the sound, a shortcut off-limits to chartered boats: they require more draft than our boat and have to navigate around Colquhoun

Reef, the graveyard of many bare boats (boats chartered without paid crew). Midway through, I saw the depth finder reading 4.5 feet. Knowing we needed 3.5 from the sounder's location in the hull, my heart skipped a beat. A large power boat was coming alongside, and I thought it possible the swells and troughs of his wake might nail me to the bottom. However, we cleared the shoal area before his wake caught up to us, motoring without incident through the narrows, and passed Anguilla Point. We put up the foresail, catching a brisk wind for a spirited sail west on the Sir Francis Drake Channel to an anchorage on the southwest corner of Salt Island, where the RMS Rhone sank during a hurricane in 1867, killing 123.

After tying up to a mooring, we took time to bolster our courage, double- and triple-checking that we had everything, then rode *Speedy* closer to the dive site of the RMS Rhone and tied up on a mooring line. The sea was kicking up, concerning me about Megan and her disposition to disappear. There was zero possibility of another garden party downwind without drowning first: next stop—St. Croix, 35 miles. Confident my snorkeling skills were adequate, I was no lifeguard if she panicked.

We practiced snorkeling for a few minutes, made adjustments and, if her squinched up look through the face mask was a look of terror, she would never admit to it, so I led the way in search of the wreck. Each time I looked back for Megan, she was headed elsewhere, her flippers splashing like a paddlewheel river boat powered by the Energizer bunny. Finally together at the site, we could see only a ghost-like outline of the wreckage, due to its 45-foot depth and the whipped up waters carrying sediment. This was a challenging scuba dive, not a snorkeling experience.

We looked around for a while, then headed back to *Speedy*, almost getting run over by a motorboat on the way. Taking a few moments to regain our composure and remove our gear, we then climbed on *Godspeed* and set sail for Leinster Bay, skirting several rain showers. Not wanting a repeat of Trellis Bay, we set two anchors so only rain could interrupt our sleep. Megan was up most of the night and, knowing that she was on watch, I slept well.

She took a nap after breakfast, likely the exercise, fear, and lack of sleep were quite stressful. Around 1200, we decided to cross the channel to Soper's Hole for a late lunch after we snorkeled around Waterlemon Cay, finding bountiful starfish, sea urchins, rays, a diverse assortment of colorful tropical fish, plus the occasional sinister-looking sharp-toothed barracuda.

Soper's Hole:
Catching the plague at West End

The ride to Soper's Hole in *Speedy* was an anxious 1–2 mile crossing—rough, open water, waves as high as the dinghy was long. We crossed the channel in good shape by handling each wave carefully, then went behind Frenchman's Cay into an idyllic cove surrounded by lush green hills, coconut palms, and many sailboats at anchor. We tied up and enjoyed pizza al fresco at a charming Pusser's Landing, with white tables and umbrellas on the boardwalk, buildings painted in coral and teal with cupolas, latticework, and second floor open-air dining—an icon of paradise.

After a great lunch and being within eyesight of a Customs office, we thought it'd be prudent to clear out of Customs. Standing in line there, I noticed one particularly gruff agent and hoped to avoid him, though Rocco had tirelessly prepared me for strange encounters of the gruff kind. The line inched forward until I arrived at the front.

"Who's next!"

I looked up to see "Agent Gruff" glaring at me. I walked over and presented my documents for inspection.

"Where's your boat?"

Dammit! It had dawned on me standing in line that it needed to be in BVI waters. It was in U.S. waters, and now was too late to turn and run. "Out there," I said, pointing to a window overlooking the cove and the channel. I was telling the truth, willing to swear I had not brought the boat inside.

"Where is it?"

He persisted, not at all impressed with my vague generalities but, if not outside, where would it be—in the hall, tied to the elevator? Customs officers are trained to read body language, and my body must have been screaming "Oh hell!" in red neon.

"Right out there," I said, hoping one more word would be consoling and fill his every need. Technically, it was to my left, but it was to his right, which I thought would be instructive. Did he suspect it was in the basement? We were on a large pier, so it could be, if I'd scuttled it. But it wasn't mine to scuttle. When he's done with me, it may be his to scuttle if he chooses.

Able to see my "lying eyes," probably dilated to the size of nickels, he confidently strode toward the window and asked, "Which one is it?"

I looked out the window from my side of the counter, and realized out loud, "Oh, I guess you can't . . . can't see it from here." I should have exclaimed, *Well damn, someone stole it, or it drug anchor. It's not there. I gotta go,* then grabbed my papers and ran out. Maybe it drug anchor all the way back to Leinster Bay, or to Jost Van Dyke, which would put it in BVI territory, where it belonged at this crucial moment.

"So, where is it?"

Almost certainly having heard this scenario before, I bet he could taste the money. This must be his favorite flavor of sadism. *I don't really have a boat. I'm doing an undercover story on the abrasiveness, discourtesy, and corruption of customs officers,* I wished. "Well, it's just across the channel, in Leinster Bay. I thought it was visible, but it's hidden by that piece of land jutting out there, that, that 'stick out!'"

That was pretty lame, but I was feeling like my ass was on the carpet all of a sudden, in a stickup.

"You're not supposed to leave the area until you check out of Customs. I could seize your boat and put you in jail, don't you know that?" the gruff beast said rather angrily.

"Sir, had I known you felt that way, I wouldn't be here. Obviously, I haven't left the area, and obviously I had to get here in a boat." I felt like I'd checked all the boxes.

I took a deep breath to slow things down, not wanting to go rapidly to jail. No one ahead of me had been asked where their boat was and, had I dared to look behind me, I might have noticed attrition of the waiting line. But I had to keep my eyes on him to show proper deference.

I, then Megan, told him of our problems trying to anchor in Soper's Hole—only having 100 feet of anchor line, no room in shallow water, anchor dragging—all leading to our decision to anchor in Leinster Bay.

(They probably dredge the Hole just for this reason.) Megan was obviously incensed; when she gets excited, her voice goes way up, up there with Mariah Carey. Philosophically, in a dispute it was good to have her on my side for a change, not looking forward to jail time with any more gusto than I.

"Good sounding excuses, but I can't accept them. You could have docked temporarily outside."

I appreciated his recognition and praise for the effort. But "docked temporarily outside," where signs say you should not even think of tying up there? What a prince of a guy; the contrast between him and us scofflaws was so great, he should cuff me without further ado, and my accomplice can speak for herself. "But, it says no docking there."

Glancing around, I could see the other agents looking at mine like he'd lost it, or lied as usual, thinking *there he goes again*. They know you can't dock there; they make easy money from those who do. A sign saying, "Please dock here so our Customs agents can experience the joy of meeting your immigration needs" has not even been thought about, much less painted and hung. They'll hang me first. If I could assemble a jury, I might go free, but didn't have that option. At least it had not been brought to my attention quite as clearly as had my errors in what was a kangaroo court, dignified by calling it a bench trial.

"You can dock there long enough to clear Customs," he informed me.

"I'm only in Leinster Bay long enough to clear Customs. What's the difference . . . and how am I supposed to know which law I can ignore?"

To which his answer would always be, "Not this one." For a moment, I thought I had a "Stay-Out-of-Jail for two" argument. Were it a level playing field, I might have.

"Don't make it any worse. I'm just going to fine you, and let you go. . . . Fifty dollars!"

In other words, he's saying *don't challenge me on the contradictions in my statements, just gimme money willingly, under government coercion, so I don't have to pull my gun on you and risk it going off. It gets messy, a whole nother matter.*

That's when I knew the difference between Leinster Bay and Soper's Hole—obviously, anchoring over there to pass Customs is against the law;

whereas you ostensibly *can* tie up here to pass Customs . . . at this given minute on this given day, otherwise, it, too, is against the law. A distinction without a difference. Being saved from jail and seizure of the boat by paying a fine was the better of two bad options, and cheaper than hiring a lawyer to explain it. The way this guy works, the jail may have been full anyway.

He slammed down his gavel of injustice. Guilty! Fifty bucks! I wanted to counteroffer at seventeen-fifty, hoping to settle near twenty-five, but thought better of it. I had no leverage, and he might counter my counter at $75, or more. Tortola could use the money, I supposed, or maybe he got a commission—anything over the statutory seventy-one cents—so he didn't offer jail as a choice, nothing in it for him, and I didn't object. You may have to buy these jobs, like a McDonald's franchise. He'll probably give to his pastor and finance minister for the Christian Mariners Outreach Ministries, having outreached another mariner to his wallet, and keep the rest. Law enforcement, or law enrichment?

When he finished reading us the riot act (which took another two minutes, time he could have used to shanghai the next sap) and preparing us for the eventuality of jail time, then gracing us with his mercy by stamping our passports, holding what had been my money in his fist, he invited us to return: "Come back and see us," he said, in a disinterested tone of voice.

My, what a charming, hospitable man. Such emotion from a magnetic personality with a contagious sense of humor; how could I not return? "Yeah, well, my schedule's full, for about ten years," after which I encouraged Megan to pick up the pace walking out, hoping to turn a corner before he reneged on our agreement. I had an urge to share a sign language reflecting my feelings but I was nowhere near enough to the asylum of the U.S., and freedom of speech, even sign language, can be a finicky concept in a foreign country. It was prickly enough across the channel. Some passions are better left unexpressed. So I kept everything in check and got the heck out of there, not wanting to risk jail time where they may not revere such free speech.

The ride back to the boat was amusing. We were now partners in crime—a common enemy making us more together—thankful not to be in jail with other lawless yachters, and I was reliving it using self-deprecating humor. Was this similar to the runner's high, or state of relief that people get from the absolution derived through confession or other forms of guilt-mitigation, like fines? Cheaper than parking in a handicapped spot, my debt was paid to society. I must confess to not knowing the more esoteric rules: Sure, I could have docked where it said "No Docking." Uh-huh, maybe for a hundred bucks. Or they might have impounded the boat, which they didn't do because it was inconvenient; easier to collect money than boats.

On the other hand, fines are levied to dissuade undesirable, and encourage preferred, behavior. It just didn't seem there was universal thought on the import by all the staff. As recently as two years ago, Tortola reportedly still had the gallows, so I was glad I'd kept my head and didn't offend Agent Gruff.

If you think education is expensive, consider the cost of ignorance.

Back at the boat, a too-late-to-be-helpful glance at our sailing guides warned us the BVI laws are enforced zealously, and to "Check in at Jost Van Dyke with Fat Albert, or at the Virgin Gorda Marina at Spanish Town. Never check in at Roadtown, and avoid West End Customs like the Plague." Soper's Hole is the West End. Obviously, other folks had issues. That one sentence is worth the price of the book, but . . . what good are the books you don't read? And many times the words stand out only after you have a relevant experience. The two recommended sites were not convenient to us, though now I had more respect for the Plague.

I was reminded of a quote from Baltasar Gracian: "The wise do sooner what fools do later. Both do the same, the difference is when." As another reflection, I didn't remember Walt checking in with BVI customs at all.

Dinner in the refuge of the boat was as light as my wallet, and my book was almost finished with me. A book this size, like the 800-pound gorilla or a Customs officer, does exert influence. Feeling a little beat up, I tried twice to get to sleep, so my day was comprised of two days. Blood pressure and heart rate may still have been elevated.

In the morning, we sailed from Leinster Bay to Hawksnest Bay, usually a good anchorage. However, my hopes of anchoring where we had in the past were dashed. There were several boats in that area, one of which was *True Love*, a day charter my brother and I had taken when we were first here in 1974. How different the landscape looks when you know it well. Hawksnest was then a mystical, exotic island bay, an otherworldly destination for snorkeling, reached only by chartering a boat. Now it was a beautiful venue in a familiar context, among several, for a repeat overnight anchorage.

The overheating alarm of the engine sounded while I was idling into position. Deciding it was more important to not overheat the engine than continue maneuvering, I dropped anchor even though we were in 25–30 feet of water, more depth than I preferred when I had to lift the anchor by hand, which was every time. The proper scope of no less than 5:1 required letting out over 100 feet of anchor rode, more than we had. The wind and currents were turning the boats in different directions to each other, so I was more comfortable re-anchoring when one of the boats left. It worked for a while, but we were still dragging anchor, and I had to re-anchor, eventually tying up to a National Park Service mooring when it became available.

Megan felt it was too far to take *Speedy* to Cruz Bay, so we stayed on the boat. A surge coming in from the north kept us rocking and rolling all evening and night, but we had no anchor worries while on the mooring.

We were happy to leave Hawksnest Bay for Cruz Bay the next morning, finding a place to anchor along the ferry and barge shipping lanes in shallow water, probably 7–8 feet, so the anchor line would be short, and the swing would be minimal, keeping us from swinging into the ferry lanes.

Megan was drawn to Mongoose Junction for shopping and looking at stuff I would not buy, but someone must! Perhaps travelers on guilt trips: *I went to unbelievably gorgeous Paradise for two weeks, and bought you this leprechaun sitting on a toadstool. Made by the millions. Now we're even.* Not feeling too chipper due to long-term lack of sleep, hoping to find my own toadstool of refuge, we decided on lunch at Grumpy's, an apt fit, on the second floor with a covered deck overhanging the street, providing island ambience and interesting views of tourists ambling about, going in and out of shops. Feeling the need for an iron-rich protein boost, I ordered the Grumpy's burger, a big eight-ouncer for big bucks. Surely this would be the big cheese of burgers. So certain was I of getting everything I could ever want on a burger at that price, which carries the establishment's imprimatur and reputation on its back, that I gave the waitress a rare break and didn't grill her on what came with it. Surely the accoutrements would be resplendent and delicious. A horn of plenty came to mind: fresh tomatoes and lettuce, sliced hamburger dills or a pickle spear, French fries or potato salad or onion rings, or all three. Surprise me!

Surprise! Ask for nothing, you'll likely get it. When she placed the unappetizing monstrous lube job in front of me, sitting in isolation on its drip plate, I muttered in disbelief to the waitress about whether it came with French fries, or maybe potato chips, conceding that the cornucopia of accoutrements was yet to follow, if only more grease that would ensure triple bypass surgery before dark! She counter-muttered something about having no deep fryer and no chips, and in no time we were about even on the mutterings. I surmised why they call it Grumpy's burger; people who order it feel that way when they've had their fill. It may be a matter of corporate pride that no one ordering it ever goes away feeling anything but empathy for the eponym. "We are Grumpy! Grumpy! Grumpy! Grumpy!" The clue was there; I just didn't buy it.

Another shop or two, another mall, a yogurt cone, and I was able to entice Megan back onto *Godspeed* with the prospect of tying up at Sapphire Beach, a marina/resort I spotted in the sailing guide. The rolling of the boat would definitely be less. If not, we could step off. Otherwise, she was ready to rent a condo, which would suit me just fine. We radioed the marina, reserved slip S29, then went after it. We were on St. John, and the marina was across Pillsbury Sound near Red Hook, on St. Thomas, a sail of less than two hours, barring any unforeseen disasters.

Going into the slip was flawless. It took me a little time to get the lines right to allow for the change in tide. I'd done no marina docking, contrary to most sailors who've done nothing but. However, I could stop the boat on a submerged dime. Eventually, we had the spring lines and bumpers/fenders in place and could look to other things, like tennis. I knew a little about the resort from prior trips, but never from the venue of the marina. After touring the facilities, we had our first game of tennis on this trip. Salt spray had corroded my game.

Sapphire Beach became our small and stable corner of paradise, from which to shop locally for food and venture into Charlotte Amalie for exotic gifts such as lace tablecloths, perfume, and jewelry. Time on the beach was heavenly, and we signed up to take clinics from the resort's tennis technician, Ivan.

Ivan looked Spanish, but spoke no Spanish at all to Jose, a Spanish-speaking-only student. We hit balls back and forth for a half hour, then Ivan picked up the balls, told each of us what we were doing wrong (just one of surely many things) and headed for the gate. That approach caught me by surprise. Most of my teachers did not expect students to be a shining star with just one clue of what not to do, which would be endless. Ivan let us groove our bad strokes under his watchful eye, then told us to forget them, with no time remaining to try another wrong way to hit a ball, a unique approach to tennis instruction. He obviously wasn't positioning himself to sell private lessons, and used the same barking approach as the Customs officer. At least he didn't fine us.

Megan had a couple days remaining, with no appetite for more sailing, so we enjoyed a good meal and terrific ambience at Piccolo's on the pier in Red Hook. I later encountered a former co-worker and tennis partner, Homer, and his wife who had seen my name on the tennis clinic log and asked where to find me. I'd walked up to the desk just as they were walking away, was informed of their inquiry, and caught up to them, one of those "small world" events in a large world. They were staying in a condominium and were astonished I was there by boat, wanting to see it. We invited them over, then had lunch together the next day after a tennis match.

It seemed like in no time, Megan and I were in the shuttle van on the way to the airport, then saying goodbyes with a solid hug and not much emotion, knowing we would see each other in a few days after Walt returned with Felicity. I had no luggage, so my return trip in the shuttle van was an observation of commerce between driver and tourist, and the variability of charges. I said nothing, just helped with the baggage when appropriate, but noticed, when the math was bad, it was always in favor of the driver. Imagine that.

Time after Megan's departure had a sedated feel to it. Everybody had come and gone; things seemed anticlimactic, the gyroscope stopped spinning. I had the boat to myself and had finally achieved my pre-trip vision of resort-living, however brief. I'd been to a lot of places, done a lot of things, met many people, made several good friends, had been near or scared to death, had an abundant taste of Heaven, and learned a lot. I knew life and I would never be the same, and wondered how things would change when I got back home.

The next day was mostly cloudy with intermittent rain, so I spent the day cleaning and waxing the dinghy, then preparing the boat to turn over to the owner—cleaning, sorting, cooking muffins, and getting rid of leftovers, especially the "augh-rotten" potatoes, then scheduled a tennis game with Jose for the next day at 0900.

At 0715, it was raining so hard, I thought the tennis game was a washout. By 0900, most of the water had dispersed, a benefit of the tropics and sand courts. Jose played well, and we exchanged names and addresses afterwards, as well as "mi casa es su casa's." I now had a place to stay in Buenos Aires, but I had better learn Spanish.

It took forty-five minutes to finish cleaning the boat, leaving time for a last swim. When I arrived at the pool, Jose and his family spotted me and invited me to their table at the poolside grill, where milk shakes and hamburgers were recommended. His two daughters, Silvina (14) and Valerie (10) were charming and knew English. Silvina did a great job of translating; Valerie spoke English, but was shy. Jose, 54, was in the printing business, and also worked in an optical association. His wife, Hajdee, must have been close to 43, as well as I could understand. Women often couch their age in something algebraic, a sonnet, or perhaps Haiku. If they tell you a number straight out, you ask again, unsure whether to trust your ears. They had a third daughter, 28, who had married within the last year, and was a popular singer, likened to Whitney Houston. An "Ooo, la, la!" made the parents beam. A lovely family. I answered a few questions they had for me, mostly over their amazement that I was so untethered and free to roam at my age, which seemed most intriguing and had started the discussion about ages. Jose would sign us up for the 0830 clinic tomorrow. I could hardly wait for another of those special tennis lessons, which should net me a berth at Wimbledon with a bye until the quarter finals.

After the clinic, Jose and I played our last tennis match, said our goodbyes, including my inviting him to D.C. again, and him returning the gesture, suggesting we continue the tennis in Buenos Aires. Or so I thought. When I saw him again at the pool, he insisted we have pictures taken. That should constitute closing ceremonies for this friendship. I then finished packing my three months of stuff, retrieving it from cubbyholes and lockers, shelves and refrigerator. Ninety days gives you time to thoroughly spread out and, with poor recall, certainly leave something behind. I went to a pay phone to call the airline to ensure my plane would be leaving on time.

When I returned, Walt and Felicity had arrived. My first message for the, until then, happy vacationing couple was that I couldn't leave the next day; my plane was canceled. USAIR tried to put me on a Continental flight leaving at 1500, going to Newark, New Jersey, because it was snowing too hard at my destination of Baltimore. I called Megan to get a read on the weather—impassible! After more research, I decided to stay in place two more days, until Megan could pick me up. Better to be stuck a few days wearing sandals and shorts in a sunny paradise resort than at Newark in a blizzard. Even flippers and a snorkel mask there would not adequately improve traction or vision.

Walt and I took a dinghy ride, shared experiences, and rejoined Felicity for dinner at Pizza Hut in the center of the island before shopping at Pueblo to replenish empty food lockers. Then back to Jose's condo to schedule more tennis. Walt wanted to play, and surely Hajdee and Jose would also. They were surprised to see me at their door, thinking tomorrow was my departure day.

The tennis was a great match. They won, 1–6, 6–2, 7–5, winning one more game than we did. Walt and I had not played doubles together for many years, in a company tournament decades ago. We made enhancements to the boat after spending time at the seaside pool—eating cheeseburger, fries, and banana daiquiri; life was good. When would it end? Still too soon to tell, but the end was near. The signs are out there; it's coming! Though Jose and Hajdee may have been skeptics by now.

I was hesitant to leave paradise and head into the complexity of the mainland—snow, ice, earthquakes, sitting in traffic jams—who needed it? Life was simple here; worst thing was the sameness. The prices seemed high, but didn't much matter, and no worse than Washington D.C. But the die had been cast; unless I rented a condo for a month or two, I would return to sub-zero temperatures and put a period on the end of this 90-day epic adventure. Or maybe an exclamation mark! Brrrrr!!

Mike Eakins, a lawyer from Atlanta here for ten days, tied up on our port side. He showed us around his 51' CYV charter boat which looked roomy, naturally, but not as homey and warm as Walt's boat, especially since we installed a new light over the kitchen sink that lights up the place nicely, and it was *my* home. Learning of my plans to leave tomorrow, he asked to share a cab with me to go into town.

Felicity needed my easy-access berth, so I slept in the quarter berth, otherwise called the coffin. I better understood why Rocco seemed disgruntled, to put it mildly. (When I die, I hope to afford a full-size coffin. It'd be hell to be cramped forever.) I was almost packed, and flexible to the max. I could sleep on the dock if I had to, but gave the coffin another try.

Sleeping was better on my last night, though I literally still didn't fit: too tall. In the morning, Walt ran around trying to get his laundry washed. I had packed and was ready to leave, since most planes were flying, but caught up with him long enough to say goodbye.

"Hey, Walt, I'm about to move on, but I think you're all set, and in a good spot. Boat's in good shape."

"Yeah, this is a nice place, real nice; how'd you find out about it?"

"Ad in the guidebook. Megan couldn't take any more nights at anchor, had to do something or she was going to mutiny, me with her."

"Well, this is excellent. I think we'll use this as a base for the time we're here."

"How long are you staying?"

"Until it warms up at home, maybe another two months. I'm going to leave the boat here for a few winters, get to know the place, nothing like this at home."

"That's a great idea, especially after what it took to get here. You put a lot of work into it."

"Well, so did you, B-Byrd. I don't know where we'd be if you hadn't been aboard when I had to leave. I was about to turn around. Rocco wouldn't have stayed by himself, didn't want to come in the first place. This didn't go as I expected, but by damn, here we are, with a lot of thanks to you. You're always welcome aboard whenever you can come down. We'd love your company. Felicity is just not able to do much since her surgery, has little use of her arm. Nice to have someone to play tennis and snorkel with. Did you have any trouble sailing?"

"Nope. You took me from a passenger to a pretty good sailor; thank you. I've learned and done a lot. The last four weeks have been a real treasure."

"Do you realize you've spent more contiguous nights on the boat than I have? I was figuring about 94 nights."

"Everything else does seem like an eternity ago. . . . Here comes Mike, looks like he's rented a car, gonna give me a ride to the airport. Thanks for the adventure. I hope you enjoy yourself." Walt's a big guy, but I got my arms around him for a big bear hug, then went for my luggage.

Mike and I left Sapphire Beach at 1230, and had lunch near the airport at Emerald Bay Resort—where I'd put Rocco ashore—sharing an interesting conversation of unusual depth, dealing with careers, the quality of life, and how one impacts the other. Mike was my age and felt a lot of the same stressors, even though he was a partner in a firm. Being an owner/boss was supposed to give you control; lack of control is reputedly one of the major stressors in life, something I was learning once again, in a 94-day 24/7 lesson. It was interesting to reflect that I'd known of Mike one day, and within hours we were talking significant feelings and facts over lunch, exchanging contact information, unlike anything possible with Rocco. How different might have been the sail with this man—judicious, learned, confident, considerate, and communicative? Oh my! There's a lesson—*if* you have a choice.

It was time to go home—I'd seen it all. Mike called the airport for my departure time on his cellular phone. This could catch on, for the few who can afford it. The airline was further delayed by two hours, which suited me well. I was in no hurry, enjoying good conversation over cheeseburgers in paradise.

Mike dropped me at the airport with an invitation to call him, if I was ever in Atlanta, to get together for a sail on Lake Lanier. While walking around the airport burning up time, I discovered the Pirraglia's (Jose & family). They were surprised at how I kept showing up one more time. Wait until they learn I'm their captain, then their chauffeur, maybe their gardener or chef. It was an emotional departure. Jose smiled broadly, though his lack of English seemed to be a source of self-consciousness, the way I would feel in Argentina. I shook the hands of the daughters, then Hajdee's, and gave her a buss on the proffered cheek. All of a sudden the daughters were lined up: they each wanted to be bussed, too. Heartwarming and cute. They waved while walking backward all the way to their plane's ramp. I was in love with the whole family; would have liked to join them. Don't cry for me. Maybe later, in Argentina.

My flight had a short segment to San Juan, Puerto Rico, a major hub for the Caribbean, where many passengers deplaned. After the door was closed, a bearded gent, Ransom, left his seat and sat in the aisle seat of my row, which had been vacant but for me, vaporizing my dream of a little sleep on a stable platform. While waiting for takeoff, I finished the book I was reading, *Maybe, Maybe Not* (Robert Fulghum), a collection of essays about life that I could appreciate, and began to read a sailing magazine from Walt which Ransom noticed: "So, are you a sailor?"

The question at first seemed out of left field and I had to wonder—was it because I was growing scale and barnacles, or based on *old sailors never die, they just smell that way*? To my relief, I realized the *Sailing* magazine was the stimulus, so maybe it's *you become what you read*? If so, I might have asked the stewardess for a copy of *Playboy* or *Golf Magazine*.

"That's never crossed my mind . . . I doubt it, but then . . . let's just say after a fashion and thirteen weeks." I could have shown the book title to him, and had a succinct, reasonable answer.

While being told by the stewardess how to surely die like a man with your seat cushion clutched to your chest in case of an unlikely ocean landing (collision), I drifted off into thought. Am I a sailor? What defines a sailor? In discussions about the definition of boat versus ship and yacht, it usually ends with "size matters" but what of the qualifications of a sailor? You may need to do more than ride along, but must you steer? Must you know how to tie the basic knots? Suppose you call a line a rope; is that a disqualifier? Would a little experience and a proper hat suffice? I was more than a hat, though still felt "all hat and no cattle" as far as sailing skill. Must one own a boat and read the magazines? One magazine alone didn't do it; that just raised the question.

Surviving a hellish night in the Devil's Triangle and being left alone on a boat for a month might both be qualifiers, or the latter might qualify one for captain, the former might add a purple heart. I couldn't think of anything I was faced with that I didn't handle successfully, though not always by myself, and the list was long.

The dire pre-flight announcements over, and the oxygen masks put away, I turned to Ransom, "If I don't admit to being a sailor, then many who think they are, aren't. Rather than denying them, I'd like to join them, so I'll say, darn right I'm a sailor, I am."

Epilogue

In late spring, I took the opportunity to witness the reality of my theory of abundance and dearth. Much had been said about the soft belly of the U.S. which, of course, speaks to its citizens and their comfortable life of relative affluence and abundance (for the more fortunate ones).

Conversely, 94 days of sailing without most creature comforts other than swimming, while sleeping in crowded, non-private quarters, washing clothes and bathing using buckets and rain water, enduring weather and the ocean in its various moods, and eating modestly from a thin menu, to be charitable, had me feeling near-invincible. After spending so long doing so much with so little, I was confident of my ability to quickly accomplish the difficult or impossible without breaking a sweat. I'd never felt more capable and self-sufficient, so I decided to rid myself of the feelings of confinement and lack of self-control during those 94 days in such a small space by taking as much time as it took to wander through and explore the U.S. in a motor vehicle, the ultimate expression of freedom and self-determination. We love our motorized wheels.

A part of my itinerary came immediately in my brother's usual invitation to join the annual bicycle trek across his state of Kansas in early June. As a corporate employee with limited vacation, I couldn't imagine spending a precious week of vacation sleeping on a gymnasium floor, showering with hundreds of strangers so I could enjoy biking 500 miles through wide-open, wind-swept, tornado-prone hot prairie. Up to 1,000 bikers, many from Kansas looking for something to do while the crops grow, ride across the surprisingly beautiful state known to most outsiders as Interstate 70 between Missouri and Colorado, flyover/drive-straight-through country, with a sprinkling of grain elevators, several head of cattle, and billboards announcing the biggest this and historic that.

Since I'd hardly been home, and my local acquaintances were not used to my presence, I decided to accept the invitation. Following my drive to, and bike through Kansas, would be an opportune time to explore the vast part of the country lying west of the Kansas border. I prepared to bike across Kansas and explore the U.S. and Canada coast to coast. With a sleeping bag, a few clothes, a tennis racket, two bicycles (road and mountain), a couple of credit cards, and a lot of maps packed into my customized-for-living van, I would be ready to set off on another open-ended adventure.

Not so fast. When leaving on the sailing trip, I was sure my relationship with Megan was dead. Later on, it arose from its grave (at least peeked out of the coffin) when she came to St. Thomas. When I needed a ride home from the airport, she was there, loyal and resilient. I thought the relationship, barely breathing, might deserve one more check of the pulse, something less permanent than the "diamond ring" test, but another probe to see if it had signs of life.

She had long expressed a desire to see more of Colorado, so I proposed she meet me at an airport somewhere out West after I did the boring, mind-numbing drive, and we'd spend two weeks exploring places in which she had a deep interest. Then she could return home from another airport. I assumed she would not want to be away from her business for much longer than two weeks.

"How does that sound to you?" I asked. "Would you want to fit it into your schedule?"

"Sounds great, but I need to take a stand somewhere."

"Take a stand? What does that mean? Like at the airport? . . . Or like

Custer's Last Stand, Little Bighorn, where he gives it all up? . . . I'm confused."

"I mean we cannot just keep on having great times together!"

" . . . We can't? Do you hear what you're saying? Have many friends with the problem of unabating, indefatigable great times?"

"We need to work on our relationship," she assured me.

"Well . . . we tried that, a waste of money, our differences apparently irreconcilable."

"You need to be involved."

"Why, what do you think is wrong with our relationship?"

"It's not going anywhere!"

"That's all?"

"Yeah."

"It's more than that. But I'm offering you a chance to take it out West, a dream of yours. That's where I'll be."

Her airline ticket would have been an "open jaw," an airline industry idiom for using different arriving and departing airports that now described my face. Had she mentioned she gets sick when we have such fun, as she recently did for the better part of two weeks, I would have better understood her negativity toward positive experiences.

Still, being one who doesn't give up easily, even when I should, I hoped to be absolutely sure I wasn't kicking the relationship to the curb prematurely. So I asked Megan a values/agenda question that had long been ruminating in the back of my mind: "Which of your friends do you admire and respect the most?"

After some mental rumination of her own: "I would say Vanessa."

"Why?"

"I guess because she married well."

"Both times!"

"Yeah, I think so."

Blaaahhht! Unsure whether to be relieved or frustrated, that couldn't possibly be the right answer. Marriage is not a multi-level career path for me. Maybe she and Vanessa were devoted viewers of *The Jefferson's* TV show: "Well, we're moving on up . . ."

It wasn't necessary to ask how Vanessa's first marriage could have been such a good marriage if there had been another to follow, and God only knows how many more great ones are to come; it was early yet. I was hoping for more substance and evidence of a similar mind. Not the time to coach her to a better answer, I had to take what I was given. Asked an off-the-cuff values question, she gave what was for me a revealing off-the-hook values answer—to so many questions. I understood better (peer pressure?) why Megan had asked on each anniversary of our initial meeting, 'Where is this relationship headed?' I should have asked, 'Is it as good as you can make it?' Or would have liked to hear 'What can we or I do to make our relationship better?' Anytime I offered such information uninvited, I got it back like a letter stamped: Return to Sender; No Such Person. She wanted to be married; when I settle down, I want it to be for love. Knowing the former, I might always wonder about the latter.

Megan's perverse party prescription of "Do More Work to Reduce Great Times" caught me in a free-spirited, unreceptive mood and I RSVP'd my regrets prior to taking flight due to conflicting priorities and values. Apparently, Peter Pan was alive and well, his spirit coursing through my veins. *Really, really wish I could fly, Tinkerbell! Because it looks like time to take off. 'I don't want to grow up; I don't want to wear a tie' with a bad knot.*

I had Megan's Little Bighorn-style rejection and her values test results before Elle came home from Caicos, so I was free to fulfill my promise to contact her. We had a few delightful tennis-match get-togethers in the time I was packing for my May-August road trip. As wonderful as they were, and as she was, it was inescapable that Elle was training as a marine biologist with a bright and passionate future ahead of her; I was winding down a career with a desire to go wherever the winds blew, leaving openings for unexpected adventure, so our paths would surely diverge. If we were ever on the same boat, it would be against all odds, and I doubted we could do it a second time. We vowed to stay in touch. I suspected our out-of-phase issue would be resolved by summer's end: I'd still be available—who was I going to meet, wandering around in the wilderness of the far west—probably not as true for her. But few things are certain.

Having verified Megan was in the business of marriage marketing and sales rather than relationship construction, and bid Elle adios, I closed my mental portals and had a liquidation sail. Looking through the windshield toward the vast horizon, I put Willie Nelson's "On the Road Again" in the tape deck, hung out the spinnaker of my mind to catch a freshening breeze, took a firm grip on the helm and, without reservations, set a course for the western horizon without much looking back. Okay, maybe I did shout out an answer Megan had been seeking other than the annual "I have no visibility." Where is it headed? *It's headed west, toward a continental divide.* Having been in the company of others for so long, could I survive such a trip alone? *Oh, yeah!*

Weeks later, as I drove alone across eastern Colorado flatland, nothing certain but that Earth is somewhat round, I mourned the loss of my relationship with Megan and our investing so many years, but through the tears accompanying a deep, numbing emptiness, it had become clear that we valued different behaviors with no ability to resolve our differences. Few things hurt like a heartbreak, even though it set me free. Not the conclusion I wanted, but one I had to accept.

I'd rather be alone than wishing I were.

Feeling the last couple of months had been open season on my heart, I decided to give Nikki a shot at it, curious to know the totality of the carnage. After Julie called her to the phone, I asked, "How would you like to join me on a cross country ramble of the national and state parks of the U.S. and Canada for the next two months?"

"Oh my, there you go again. That's my dream trip. . . . . I'll just sell the business, rent a jet, and meet you at general aviation in what airport? Give me a date and time—and six months."

"Yeah, that's the truth of it, isn't it?"

"Yep, sorry to say no again, but I want to manage this situation to a reasonable conclusion, then I will have play time."

"I gotta ask, do you really rent jets?"

"Would if I had to. Not yet."

"Wow! Do you pick up the dinner check, too?"

"I do my share."

"Wow. I'm liking what I'm hearing."

"Don't want to be unfair or treated like chattel."

"Admirable. Shame that the proverbial greener grass is behind an electric fence with concertina wire on top. . . . How about something to make you smile?"

"I'm doing okay, but . . . alright, try me."

"How do you make a handkerchief dance?"

"Oh, my gosh . . . I don't know."

"Put a little boogie in it. . . . Are you smiling yet?"

"That's a riot. Okay, I have a question for you, Bryan . . . Have any interest in traveling in Europe?"

"Sure. Been several times, last trip was '89; I'd love to go back. Would need to review my language tapes. Got plans?"

"Would you want to go with me?"

"Are you kidding? Of course, Nikki. I'd love it. Speak any foreign languages?"

"French, German, some Spanish."

"Really! Fluently?"

"Good enough."

"There's more to you than you've let me know."

"I'm not hiding anything; we haven't had time to discuss the past, just barely the current stuff. . . . I keep having to get off the phone. Wish I could curl up in bed with a bunch of pillows and talk to you when you call. Or in-person, someday? . . . Reminds me of when we first met, I asked if you made late night calls. Maybe I can ask again, more seriously this time."

"I remember. . . . I have two beginner calling plans—a Six-Pack, for the party-goers, and the Still Single, which is one call, automatically renews until you cancel. The Infinity package is unlimited, by invitation only, and only one is available."

"Oh, how accommodating. I'll try the sex-pack. What's the charge, and can you start tonight?"

"I can if you can. Your satisfaction is my reward."

"Then you'd be well paid. . . . Uh-oh, it has to be a tomorrow date because Julie is ready to take me home. My car's in the shop. I'm very glad you called. Have a great adventure, and call when you can, okay? I love . . . hearing from you. Please be careful."

By the time I returned home from my once-in-a-lifetime 10,500-mile road trip, biking through Kansas and the flower-filled upper meadows and ski trails of Vail and Banff; golfing, rollerblading, playing tennis, and enjoying outdoor concerts at Sandpoint and Sun Valley, Idaho, and visiting many state and national parks, I had lived 84 days as master of my fate, captain of my soul, another experience few have had and not everyone would want. A lot of time was spent alone, but since it was time with my thoughts and of my choosing, I made the best of it and loved it. By driving, I witnessed our vast, gorgeous, and diverse country. From sea to shining sea, the amber waves of (Midwest) grain and purple (Teton's) mountain's majesty were on grand display, an epic journey through America the beautiful and northwest Canada.

The sailing experience had been empowering. On the boat, I was forced to redraw the proverbial fine line between a "want" and a "need." What was essential became apparent, and the ability to do without had been refined. On land, whether I slept in a deluxe hotel, a Bed and Breakfast, friends' homes, a gymnasium, or the van in a national/state park, a rest stop, or restaurant parking lot out in the wild west of the U.S. or Canada where there were no accommodations, I was comfortable. The bed in the van was far superior to the boat and all sofa beds, and I didn't have the unease of being a guest when I awoke, perhaps having to praise food not to my taste. I could go when and where I wanted to go without checking with a captain or host. Mosquitoes were controllable, and the heat was conquered occasionally with air conditioning, or endured with the help of abundant, fresh, cool water. Food in the U.S. was much more available than it was at sea or in the islands. Restaurants and Laundromats were in abundance.

Spartan or luxurious, I had full control, and nothing to complain about. Ironically, on a jet boat tour of Hell's Canyon, we crashed on the rocks and were stranded seventy miles upriver in the wilderness, where the walls were straight up, and the banjo sounds of *Deliverance* wafted over the canyon of my mind, ten miles out-of-reach of our lunch. We were eventually rescued in stages—me being the last since I was conditioned to live without anything, relayed back to Lewiston, Idaho, unfed and barely before day's end. So, maybe not total "full" control, eh?

When I returned home, the fall season was near at hand. Standing at the curbside mailbox, I wondered which neighbors had moved, married, given birth, maybe died. I was feeling akin to being born again, spiritually if not entirely religious, having so many new and different experiences behind and now a part of me, with few current ties to my hometown. I felt younger, wiser, mentally stimulated, untethered, and totally invigorated.

In-depth scientific studies identify that travel stimulates creativity and innovation. The longer you are away, the stronger the effect. Overseas travel enhances it further. Being immersed in other cultures leads to open-mindedness as a result of experiencing ambiguity and many differences. By leaving "your place," you must accommodate your needs creatively while being reminded of all we do not know. This changes the mind, which changes everything. Instead of being so close to a problem that the solution is obstructed, being so removed brings clarity to many issues. Mark Twain adds, "Travel is fatal to prejudice, bigotry, and narrow-mindedness, and many of our people need it sorely on these accounts."

The feeling was empowering. But there was an emotional cupboard, empty of romantic relationships but for Nikki. We shared several calls at first, but with the complexity of multiple time zones and being across the border in western Canada, finding a phone to make a call at the right time was difficult. Should I pursue Nikki, and to what effect, or start anew?

There was a mountain of mail to process, after which I'd develop plans for the future. The mail did offer valuable information. A letter from Nikki was postmarked Stuart, Florida, with no return address. Apparently, she didn't want it returned if it could not be delivered.

My dear Bryan,

We're at almost one year, and yet it seems recent in some ways, forever, in others. You are frequently on my mind, maybe because it was the last affection I've shared. Your phone calls have helped a lot, though I always dreaded hanging up knowing

I might not hear from you for a long time. Our last call was after you got stuck in a massive cattle drive in Rock City, Utah, when the rancher offered to get you a horse so you could give him a hand. Hope you are doing okay, no long-term agony. I've called but left no messages, though it was emotionally calming to hear your voice on the recording.

I wanted to tell you about a recent dive trip when Raul came up behind me, cutting off my oxygen flow, scaring the living crap out of me. I fought him off, got in a lucky kick of my heel that broke his hold, restored my oxygen, and when we surfaced I asked him what the hell he thought he was doing. He said he was making sure I could get myself out of a jam if trouble should occur, that trouble is never planned, so it had to be a surprise. There was a menacing look in his eyes, as though he was forewarning me. I will choose different diving partners on future dives, but I wanted you to have this in writing in case anything happens to me. You know he and I are just business partners now. Maybe he wants the whole business to himself. With less luck, I might be on the ocean floor.

I will keep this short. Just wanted to "talk" to you and leave a note for you to come home to. Miss you. Hoping to hear from you soon, when you get back home if not sooner?

Enjoying our memories, longing for your touch.
Nikki

That was chilling. What to do—drive there and do nothing, or stay here and do nothing? What else was there? Being alone when your life is not in danger gives one time to think, and seeing such grandeur made me wish I could nudge a travel partner and say, "Hey, let's check out this path/road," or "Let's sit here and watch the sunset," sharing something so beautiful you feel selfish if kept to yourself. Many of the friendships formed in that 10,600-mile, three-month venture would almost certainly have been enhanced by her presence, like when a couple I met on a trail invited me to their elegant home for a long, multi-stage dinner overlooking the Wood River near Sun Valley. How many days were spent thinking about tomorrow—an even better "next time," possibly with her? She had been a companion of sorts.

Continuing to sift the mail into piles of "junk," "open later," and "open now," I discovered a second letter.

My long lost Friend,

Missing you. I could sure use a hug, even if a tele-hug, since it has been a while, though I can imagine it is costing a fortune, especially calling from Canada. I really do appreciate it. I'm feeling insecure, a little shaky, and unattractive on my darkest, despondent nights. Could we arrange a get-acquainted-again rendezvous, at a minimum? That may not sound very compelling, considering the risk, brevity, and distance. Dammit! I think it's a good idea, though. I'll sleep on it.

Jerry is telling me Raul has met with two "south of the border" looking guys when I'm not at the store. They talk in the car. Very strange. I'm thinking a dive boat moving freely between the Bahamas and Ft. Pierce could carry more "parcels" into the states than they left with. Is Raul mixed up in the drug trade? I have no evidence. Thinking the boat should be observed on nights following its return, I have put in a call to the Feds to have them call me at Julie's.

I hope you haven't met a troublesome female or, even worse, fallen asleep at the wheel. It's good you have a bed to take a nap, if you pull over in time to use it. After you described the boredom of driving long distances alone, I've been a little concerned. *The security I felt in your arms, even under risky circumstances, was something I have never felt before, and I long for more. So I want you to be careful, and safe. Obviously, if you get this letter, you survived the tedium.*

Business is good, keeping me busy, so really, things are okay. I am doing what has to be done, insofar as I am able to do anything. That may require explaining in person. It's interesting here, that's all I had better say, except I dream of hearing from you soon. I enjoy writing to you because it feels like I am talking to you. When I stop, it feels like we have hung up. I have written many letters I did not mail. Might make a good book. Do you want to be my editor? Do you write? (How would I know?) We'll make a fortune so we can sail away together. Okay, time to hang up, it's getting silly. I'll read this a few times, then send it.

Don't forget you can call about dive tours on a Monday morning between 7 and 8:30, before we open and I am in the store alone. Not a time when folks typically book a tour, but I usually take any calls. If you really would book a dive, I'd go down with you. Meanwhile, you'll have to settle for biking, rollerblading, and golfing in Steamboat Springs, and wherever else you have gone, Mr. Lucky.

Don't worry about me. I've got this, just don't want to go back and re-scribble the ramble I just wrote. I'm good.

Looking forward to hearing from you.
Until then,
Nikki

Guess I don't write often enough. I wouldn't have minded writing her, knowing the enduring value of a letter in the right hands. And words—in letters and in books—have the power to make us feel less lonely. But I didn't have an address. Would surely love to visit but for what? An hour? I'd do it for her. Vulnerable can be sexy, it's psychologically smart, and men respond lovingly to damsels in distress. It's what we do. But suppose she was followed? One thing I have observed about takedowns in motel rooms is there is no way out but the front door, so someone is always captured or killed. Imagine how the local newspaper reportage might go down: "Local diver diva and her unidentified paramour are caught surfing the curves during an assignation in their box-canyon motel room by her ragingly jealous ex-boyfriend and his drug lord partners eager to take over her business to launder money and import contraband." It gets messy. One thing I don't expect to do well is shootouts with drug lords. It's embarrassing to have even had such sordid thoughts and observations.

Who knew sailing would lead to this? This should clarify by tomorrow with a call to the office, if it hasn't already. Cannot do nothing. Maybe a dive is in order.

What's in the rest of this mail? Maybe it gets better. Or worse.

About the Future

I was able to reach Nikki on Monday morning as prescribed. She wouldn't say anything about her situation other than business was good, her mood was not, and she had someone in her office. A letter would be forthcoming with greater detail of what she was reluctant to discuss on the telephone. When Nikki's letter arrived a few days later, I had to read it several times:

Dear Bryan,

I miss you. I don't know how much of it is because I am in a bind and you are my confidant, because I don't know you well, I do know you well, or if it is based on lust (all four could be true), but I do long emotionally and viscerally for a second date. Or would it be our fourth? Your voice on the phone, your physical presence, our embrace, my thoughts and dreams of your touch and smell bring a much needed calm to my uneasy spirit. I wonder what we could experience if we had time and a safe haven.

That possibility may be closer than either of us imagined a week ago. Plans are being made for me to take time off from work. Two people are being "hired" to take my place. My "doctor" says I need total rest. The truth is I just have to make myself scarce until Raul's situation can be determined. The officials believe Raul's group is one they have been interested in for a while.

Europe is my planned destination. I was there in the '80s as a law school student doing a comparative analysis of the laws of many nations, one of many projects that were precursors to the recently contrived European Union (Maastricht Treaty), and I've maintained friends I can stay with until I find a discreet place I can base out of as I travel the continent, maybe two— Morocco is an interesting place and my friends' relatives there have given me an open invitation. I can speak German fluently, bits and pieces of others, so I can exist okay, though it is not where I really want to be. But I love travel, can live on almost nothing (not that I want to, but may need to), law school teaches you that, so that is my plan. There will be work for me, I am almost sure. This time it needs to be low profile, which means I may only find typing jobs. Whatever. The time has come.

We've talked about how we might get together, so it would be wonderful to see you (where I really want to be) before I leave, although it might make me miss you more, if that is possible (entirely). My wish would be to take a plane to your place, stay a few days—longer if we get along and depending on your commitments—then take a train, bus, or car from Baltimore to New York for a flight to Frankfurt, Germany, making me harder to trace, should anyone try.

That's as far as I can describe it. I get that far, and it must be all that I want. My brain stops at the point where I imagine myself safe in your "halfway house," in your arms. If our schedules are incompatible, I could stay awhile with friends in the city until they coincide. This is my dream—to finally be able to spend time together, before going to a distant redoubt. Please call and let's see if this crazy plan would work. I'll understand (accept/be crushed/just die) if you can't (or don't want to), and be anxious until I hear from you. Monday morning would be excellent. I finished up at Julie's.

This must be a shocker of a letter, since you knew so little of my background. But in a week's time, we can talk more about you, me, and this situation, if you are game to take that dive.

In the dark, wishing for dawn,
Nikki

An unexpected development, but a possibly fortuitous one—she obviously was moving forward. I had fleeting thoughts about whether I wanted this complexity in my life, but promised I would be there for her. This was the time. I seldom turned down adventure, which this surely was, and this would easily be rewarding though a good result was not guaranteed.

If she was relocating, the heat had been turned up on what was, at one time, just a suspicion, so I responded promptly. She answered the phone on Monday morning with a simple, "Hello."

"Good morning. I didn't know if this was too early to discuss a dive trip but, well, are you open?"

"We don't open the store until nine and I've someone here with me, but I'd be happy to help you. May I ask who's calling?"

"Oh . . . this is Bryan; uhhh, we've spoken a couple times about, like Andros diving."

"Well, how are you?" She couldn't hide the warmth of recognition in her voice.

"I'm fine; I've been traveling a lot, on a three-month road trip, but I've read all my mail and now have a somewhat empty calendar for a while, felt it might be a good time to take that dive trip we spoke of."

"Oh wow . . . that's great, but . . . I, personally, will be away for a while. We have other dive leaders if you'd like."

"Can we do it before you leave? I'm available just about any time. You'd insisted I take a dive only with you. Maybe you were just—"

"I may have, but only have time to train my replacements now, then I must be in DC next Monday by noon to take part in a project with my alma mater, Georgetown University, so time is short."

"Oh really! . . . Can you call me when you're available? You may still have my contact information from the last tank servicing."

"Oh. Yes, we do. You were interested in the Andros or Abacos trips, right? "Uh-huh."

"I should be back before too long. I'll call you as soon as I'm available if that's what you'd prefer."

"Sure, no rush. I'll wait for your call and keep my calendar open . . . oh, I almost forgot, how did the wedding go? I guess congratulations are in order? Do I remember that right?"

"Oh . . . no. We had to defer it and haven't set a new date."

"Sorry to hear that. Hope everyone is okay. Well, good luck with the project. I'll let you get back to work and await your call. Nice to talk to you."

"You, too. And you WILL hear from me . . . goodbye!"

That went pretty well, except her having company was a surprise and inconvenience. I had made notes, just to stay on course. She caught on right away, but what if she didn't? She could call me, otherwise I'd know in a week and a few hours, and was curious as hell how she was making this happen without arousing suspicion and, now, if the alma mater project was real or part of a ruse. She surprised me with an in-town alma mater. Really? And if I had been her confidant, it was part-time and she must be sitting on a storehouse of untold secrets. I had a lot of questions, but had to wait for answers. Pillow talk, I hoped. A week with her could be divine. Until then, it was going to be a long seven days.

In the interim, there was much catching up to do to ready the house and show appreciation for neighbors who had done princely work for many months. It takes several days to process three months of mail, plus I had to think about how to ensure the airport connection was without flaws. Furtive behavior was not my forte, but until I knew she was safely out of public view, it was essential.

My costume had to be planned. I'd go to the Student Union and buy a Georgetown shirt or sweatshirt, wear the Breckenridge, Colorado, cap that has a ponytail attached, and keep my hair long to blend in, trying to look like a school representative, print her name on cardboard to hold up at the gate, and not show any affection until we were in seclusion. I'd case the airport when I knew which one; there are three. I'd have to wait, breathe deeply, and go with the flow.

It had been a long week. She would arrive before noon, so I wouldn't have to wait all day. Julie called after Nikki's departure to give me the flight, ETA, and airport. I immediately headed to the airport and watched the remote-long-term-parking shuttle bus to determine the last stop before it headed back to the terminal, then parked there. If we were the last familiar faces on the bus coming from the terminal, we'd get off. Otherwise, we'd return to the airport and take other evasive action. Not a foolproof plan, but I may also have been overthinking it. I keyed up a cassette tape of Simon and Garfunkel in the car player, jumped on a bus, went to the gate, and waited.

She arrived wearing a soft, flowing, blue silk dress with an orchid pattern, slits up the leg on both sides, a thin gold metal belt and a white jacket. Shoes were slip-ins, small heel, easy on, easy off. I was spellbound, wearing my costume, holding a cardboard sign. The urge to embrace was magnetic, but we had to wait, enjoying only the long and warm handshake and deep look into the eyes, all something to talk and laugh about later—unless the wheels fell off.

We picked up her luggage, caught the shuttle bus to the parking lot, and watched the riders get off as they reached their stop. Several men on the bus were looking at Nikki, some more serious than others, and any of them could be trouble we were hoping to avoid. At the last stop, there was still an

FBI-type who had been on her plane and seemed to be surveilling us. Unsure whether to get off or return to the terminal, we sat for a moment, fumbling with Nikki's luggage and looking out the windows as if I couldn't find the car. Seconds seemed like minutes.

"This is the last stop!" said the impatient driver.

We shuffled again with the luggage, hoping for something from FBI-guy, who was now standing, looking around, walking toward us then turning to the driver.

"I left a couple bags at the terminal. Can I drop these off and return with you?"

"Where's your car?"

"That blue pickup on the left."

"Hey! There it is! I see our car. This *is* our stop, sir. . . . Thank you!" I said, relieved. We hustled off the bus and headed for who knows what.

When we arrived at the house, I carried her luggage in and closed the door. She stood in the foyer and looked around. "Wow, this is nice," then turned back to me. "Now, where did we leave off?" She put her arms around my neck and instantly the passion was rekindled.

This time was different. The same hunger and emotion were there, but we knew we had time we didn't have before, time to linger, stimulate, discover. "Do you live here all by yourself?"

"When I'm here, I do. Haven't been home much this year, maybe a month or two. How are you feeling? Do you feel safe, as you hoped for in your letter?"

"My head is spinning, but yes. Your arms around me feel wonderful."

"Good. I hope you'll be comfortable. Let me take these suitcases to your bedroom and you can decide what's next."

"My bedroom? Where's yours?"

"Same place."

"Oh, okay." She smiled.

I took both cases and started up the stairs, looking back only to see her slide her back down the door, until she was sitting on the floor. *Damn, that's movie-star sexy, but may be serious!* I hurried to sit beside her as tears rolled down her cheeks. "You okay? You've been through a lot, haven't you?"

"Yeah, I'm sorry to be like this. I . . . it's just such a relief to . . ."

"'I'm sorry' is about where we began, isn't it?"

"It . . . it is, isn't it? And both times you've given me what I needed. The first time, love, affection, and hope. Then you promised me a halfway house, or something like that. I forget what you called it, but here I am, wondering why you are doing this for me, just a random shopkeeper selling compressed air."

"*Just*? Best purchase I ever made! Sometimes we don't know why we do things. There could be several reasons, starting with, I find you compelling. And precious. We have a lot to discuss."

"We do; I need to unwind my mind, and . . ." whispering, while looking down, "jump your bones 'til you put me in a coma—I've written down my next of kin." She sniffed, looked up, apprehensively awaiting my response.

"Again, I love your candor! And daring. . . . Would you next like to look around, get something to eat, find a pillow to cry on, change into something comfortable, hang up this beautiful dress, talk, or as you so delicately put—"

"Uhhh . . . let's change the order of all that. I first need . . . something to relax me."

Her look made it clear no more need be said.

"Well, darling, I'll need to know your next of kin."

Can't do much about the past, whether wrong or right.
Though 'til today did it last, when tomorrow starts tonight.

Fit To Be Tied

Sailing involves the use of many lines to effectuate the voyage, or to just remain at rest; knowing how to tie, splice, and knot them is a critical skill. A line unattached to something is in the way, waiting to be put to use. Even if you haven't developed a burning passion to take to the water, there are knots in this section known to sailors that you can use quite successfully to secure your future.

Two good sources for knots, from which some of this material is borrowed, are Roger C. Taylor's *Knowing the Ropes*, Second Edition, and *Sailing and Seamanship* U.S. Coast Guard Auxiliary. If you want more information about knots, Taylor's book is excellent. If you want a more complete sailing manual, the Coast Guard Auxiliary is one way to go. If you can access the Internet, rev up a search engine and research knots there. Here we go. Let's tie one on!

Figure 1:
The Rolling Hitch

This knot does one thing no other common knot will do, which is pull on another line (or itself when looped) in one direction, and will slide for adjustment when moved in the other direction. It can be used to hold a jib sheet while riding turns are removed from a winch, or a block is relocated. I found it extremely useful to pull the halyard away from the mast while in port, to keep the halyard and hardware from banging on the mast all night. Tie a line to the halyard (use the bowline!), loop the line around the shroud, and tie a rolling hitch to itself, and it can be adjusted to take the slack out of the halyard, by pushing the knot up the line toward the mast. A miracle! The captain will love you, at least for a few hours until your next misdeed. A true miracle worker is not a one-trick pony, though. So you can use this to put a spring on the cable, tying a stern line to the anchor rode, to change the position of the boat under unconscionable wind/wave conditions. It can also be used when tying things on the car top, pulling trees and bushes out of the way temporarily, any time you want to use a line to exert an adjustable pull on an object. Very handy! If you got nothing else out of this book (of course you did, or you wouldn't be back here) get this, and rest easy.

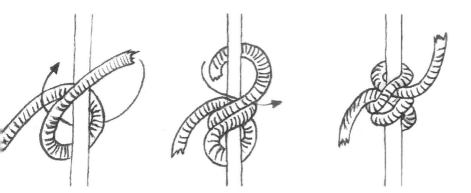

Figure 2:
The Bowline

Often called the "King of Knots" for its many everyday uses on a boat. The bowline provides a loop at the end of a line, to tie lines to anchors, sails, fittings, and other lines. If I was going to tie a rope to a post, and use the rope to keep me from falling off the roof, this is the knot I would use. Your family could also use it to secure a rope to, and pull, the casket to the cemetery plot if you thoughtlessly tie it to the family car bumper before going on the roof. The FAA recommends it as a tie down knot for your light aircraft if you choose to go that way.

No matter how much strain is put on this knot, it is easily untied. It is also known as the Rescue Knot, because it can be tied around a person and the loop will not collapse under strain, getting folks out of a tight situation.

To make the knot, first make a small loop in the line, with the end of the line overlaying what we will call the standing part of the line. Then bring the end (the bitter end) up through the hole (small loop), behind the standing part of the line, and back through the hole. Or, as the age-old saying goes, the rabbit (end of the rope) is in the hole, he comes up out of the hole, goes around the "tree" and goes back into his hole. Is that knot cute? When tying this knot, make sure the "rabbit" goes around the tree, or stay off of the roof. There are quicker ways to tie this knot, which you may want to discover on your own.

Step 1. Create the small loop, which will be the "rabbit hole."

Step 2. Put the end up through the "rabbit hole, and behind the standing part (the "tree") of the line.

Step 3. Insert the end down through the "rabbit hole." Pull the knot tight and you have a bowline. Leave six inches on the end to ensure the end does not pull back through the knot.

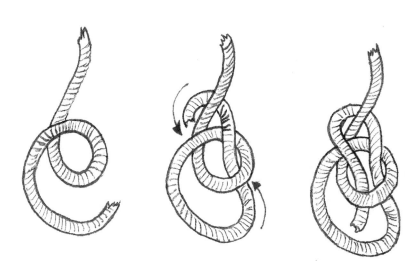

Figure 3:
The Square Knot, or Reef Knot

This knot's name originates from its use to reef sails, where its easy-spilling behavior is very handy. A sailor could collapse it with a pull of one hand; the sail's weight would make the collapsed knot come apart. When I reefed the sails, I usually included one slip loop (half bow) in the knot to make sure they came out quickly when I wanted them out. They always held under tons of pressure.

Some knotting guides claim misused reef knots cause more deaths and injuries than all other knots combined. So be warned. The prior knots are more secure for most things. This knot is mentioned for its simplicity and the difference it can make, especially in the *tying of shoes*: Once, not many times. Tie it wrong, and they come loose, using what is typically called a granny knot. Tie it square, and they stay there.

Try tying your shoelace, then shake your shoe a bit and look at how your bow sits. If it's sitting crooked, it's probable your shoelaces are always coming undone! When tied using the square knot, it will sit flat, left to right, and won't be coming undone. It only takes one simple change.

To tie this knot, make your first crossover as usual (step 1). Then make the "bunny ears" loop in A that will comprise half of the bow, the slip knot loops. Before you loop B around A, make sure the end of lace A and the loop you make with it lies on the same side of opposing lace B as lace A was coming into the first crossover. Bend loop A over and parallel to A, and wrap lace B around the loop of A in step 3, forming loop B as you pull it partially through with the fingers holding loop A. If you've done it right, A parallel to A, B parallel to B, the knot will be square, flat, and secure. Pull the bunny's ears tight, as usual, and bingo! You have a secure square knot with slip loops. Now you determine when it comes untied; just pull on the "bitter ends." In other applications, you may not want the slip knot loops, or may want just one.

Step 1.   Step 2.   Step 3.

Index to Satellite Imagery

If your interest in this story extends to wanting to see the intriguing territory covered, you may be able to do so using computer-based satellite imagery and the connections as listed below. I could not provide you with a better visual treat any other way. This feature enhances the story by adding participation and visual details to context, and you can wander until satisfied, experiencing and verifying your favorite and most curious passages, within limits! It is easy to become enthralled with the aerial view. If this encourages a non-user of computers to "travel" using this innovative feature, it possibly will open up a whole new world, and change the way you read books.

At the time of publication, Google had software (Google Earth; G.E.) available for free download to your computer. Many readers may already have and be quite familiar with it. The coordinates of many prominent locations mentioned in the story are listed below. As you navigate using the coordinates, trying to get them to match Google's as closely as possible, you will gain a sense of how GPS works in a marine application, different only in appearance to a land application, where you never see the underlying coordinates. Once you get the hang of G.E., you may be hard to stop.

There are two ways to make the journey using Google Earth (or any evolution/migration of the software (now found at www.earth.Google.com)). From within Google Earth:

1. Locate the islands of the Bahamas or the Caribbean between Florida, USA, and South America. Click on and spin the Earth to get the desired location centered, then double left-click to zoom in, double right-click to zoom out, or roll the scroll wheel if you have one. You can drag and relocate Earth with the left button pressed. As the land formation gets closer (Eye Alt is in feet), features and icons may appear. In some locations, blue dots appear as you zoom closer in, which may turn into camera icons, representing pictures. Hover the curser over the dots, and detail

will appear. Click on one, and a picture may pop up, showing the view from that location. Click the picture to enlarge it.

2. There is an easier way, though it doesn't let you appreciate where you are in relation to the rest of the world. You are getting the "destination" without the "journey." Copy the coordinates from the following list and paste in the search box in the upper left corner, click on the magnifying glass icon, and watch it all appear before your eyes. Almost too easy, but may be the only way you will find some of them.

3. Click and browse among the pictures (blue dots) to your delight, as mentioned in method 1. You might also want to visit unlisted destinations. Use the round circle navigator to change elevation view (top slider bar) and the direction of the view. You can view from satellite, helicopter, to deck level, nearly simulating our topographical view. It is a gorgeous and interesting world. Have fun, be careful, keep your arms in the window, enjoy the voyage. Or take the kids.

Island Site - Book One	Coordinates
Bahamas, Nassau, Paradise Is	.25° 05' 13" N, 77° 21' 14" W
Musha Cay	23° 53' 37" N, 76° 15' 44" W
Bahamas; Warderick Wells	24° 23' 34" N, 76° 38' 01" W
Great Exumas, George Town	23° 30' 18" N, 75° 46' 06" W
Caicos; Providenciales (Provo), Sapodilla Bay	21° 44' 39" N, 72° 17' 14" W
South Caicos; Cockburn Harbor	21° 29' 41" N, 71° 32' 08" W
Turks; Cockburn Town	21° 27' 50" N, 71° 08' 17" W
Dominican Rep.; Luperon	19° 53' 48" N, 70° 57' 22" W
Dominican Rep.; Samana	19° 12' 04" N, 69° 19' 54" W
Puerto Rico; Boquerón	18° 01' 28" N, 67° 10' 27" W
Puerto Rico; Ponce	17° 58' 20" N, 66° 37' 16" W
Puerto Rico; Palmas Del Mar	18° 04' 45" N, 65° 47' 48" W
U.S. Virgin Islands; St. Thomas, Honeymoon Bay	18° 19' 26" N, 64° 57' 11" W
USVI; Sapphire Beach	18° 20' 10" N, 64° 51' 02" W
USVI; St. John, Cruz Bay	18° 19' 53" N, 64° 47' 48" W
USVI; Hawksnest Bay, St. John	18° 20' 59" N, 64° 46'48" W
British Virgin Islands (BVI); Tortola, Road Harbor	18° 25' 04" N, 64° 36' 56" W
BVI; Soper's Hole, West End	18° 23' 17" N, 64° 42' 07" W
BVI; Virgin Gorda, The Baths	18° 25' 56" N, 64° 26' 41" W

Bibliography

Caldwell, John. *Desperate Voyage*. New York: Sheridan House Inc., 1991

Coast Guard Auxiliary, U.S. *Sailing and Seamanship*. 5th ed. Wash. D.C., 1985

Dugard, Martin. *The Last Voyage of Columbus*. New York: Little, Brown and Co., 2005

Fields, Meredith Helleberg., ed. *Yachtsman's Guide to the Bahamas*. Atlantic Highlands, NJ: Tropic Isle Publishers, Inc., 1989

Gilder, George. *Life after Capitalism*. Washington, D.C.: Regnery Gateway, 2023

Jones, Tristan. *Encounters of a Wayward Sailor*. New York: Sheridan House Inc., 1995

Maloney, Elbert S. *Chapman Piloting, Seamanship and Small Boat Handling*. 57th ed. New York: Hearst Marine Books, 1985

Peterson, Jordan B. *12 Rules for Life: an Antidote to Chaos*. Toronto: Random House Canada, 2018

Rogers, John G. *Origins of Sea Terms*. Boston, Mass: Nimrod Press, 1985

Schultz, Patricia. *1,000 Places To See Before You Die*. New York: Workman Publishing Co., Inc. 2003

Sleightholme, J.D. *This is Basic Sailboat Cruising*. Boston, Mass: Sail Books, Inc./ W.W, Norton & Co. 1976

Street, Donald M. Jr. *Street's Cruising Guide to the Eastern Caribbean.* 5 vols. New York: W.W. Norton & Co. 1980 – 1995

Taylor, Roger C. *Knowing the Ropes: Selecting, Rigging, and Handling Lines Aboard.* 2nd ed. Camden, Maine: International Marine/McGraw-Hill, 1993

Van Sant, Bruce. *The Gentleman's Guide to Passages South.* Florida: Cruising Guide Publications, Inc., 1989

About the Author

Bryan M. Byrd, a native of Washington, D.C., absorbed his love for words, meaning, and rhythm from his mother, a distinguished violinist and writer. His professional trajectory in telecom, hi-tech, and psychology encompassed diverse writing endeavors, but a twist of fate led him to break free from the confines of a conventional job at an early age.

Authorship initially played second fiddle to Byrd's adventurous lifestyle, epitomized by a life-changing voyage. When a friend enlisted his help in sailing a boat from the U.S. to the Virgin Islands, Byrd embarked on a coming-of-age journey that extended to Trinidad and back. The wide-ranging nature of this experience compelled him to pen his debut work, *Surviving Paradise: the Perils and Pleasures of the Caribbean*, an auto-fiction novel that encapsulates the unimaginable moments he encountered and was encouraged to share.

Future publications will include the continuation of the Caribbean sailing to Trinidad and return to the U.S. and his adventures as a two-time cyclist in the Tour de Thailand.

www.bryanmbyrd.com